J

S0-BRG-460

David Lichtman

MODERN ATOMIC
AND NUCLEAR PHYSICS

UNIVERSITY PHYSICS SERIES

A Group of Text Books for Intermediate and
Advanced Courses

WALTER C. MICHELS, Ph.D.
CONSULTING EDITOR

Introduction to Optics. FOURTH EDITION. *By* John K. Robertson, F.R.S.C., *Professor of Physics, Queen's University.*

Principles of Electricity. THIRD EDITION. *By* Leigh Page, Ph.D., *Late Professor of Mathematical Physics, Yale University;* and Norman Ilsley Adams, Jr., Ph.D., *Professor of Physics, Yale University.*

Physical Mechanics. THIRD EDITION. *By* R. Bruce Lindsay, Ph.D., *Hazard Professor of Physics, Brown University.*

Introduction to Mathematical Physics. *By* William Band, *Professor of Physics, Washington State University.*

Modern Atomic and Nuclear Physics. *By* C. Sharp Cook, *U. S. Naval Radiological Defense Laboratory, California.*

MODERN ATOMIC
AND NUCLEAR PHYSICS

BY

C. SHARP COOK

*Head of Nucleonics Division,
U. S. Naval Radiological
Defense Laboratory, California*

D. VAN NOSTRAND COMPANY, INC.

PRINCETON, NEW JERSEY

TORONTO   LONDON

NEW YORK

D. VAN NOSTRAND COMPANY, INC.
120 Alexander St., Princeton, New Jersey (*Principal office*)
24 West 40 Street, New York 18, New York

D. VAN NOSTRAND COMPANY, LTD.
358, Kensington High Street, London, W.14, England

D. VAN NOSTRAND COMPANY (Canada), LTD.
25 Hollinger Road, Toronto 16, Canada

Copyright, ©, 1961 by
D. VAN NOSTRAND COMPANY, INC.

———

Published simultaneously in Canada by
D. VAN NOSTRAND COMPANY (Canada), LTD.

———

No reproduction in any form of this book, in whole or in part (except for brief quotation in critical articles or reviews), may be made without written authorization from the publishers.

PRINTED IN THE UNITED STATES OF AMERICA

PREFACE

This book is intended for the college or university student who has completed at least one year of classical physics and mathematics through calculus. It has evolved from two courses, one a course called modern physics that I taught at Washington University (St. Louis) between 1948 and 1952 and the other a course called atomic physics that I have been teaching since 1956 as a part of the University of California Engineering and Sciences Extension. Because of the wide coverage of topics required in a book written for a course of this type, there can be only a limited depth to the subject matter in each chapter. It is my belief that the general coverage of the subject of atomic and nuclear physics, as is done in this book, serves either of two purposes. In the first place it provides the student who is planning to continue his studies of physics a reasonable base for a more meaningful understanding of many of the advanced texts and courses that he encounters later. On the other hand, those students who do not plan to continue their study of physics beyond the level of this text have acquired at least a speaking acquaintance with the atom and are better prepared to become a more knowledgeable citizen in our current atomic age.

It is with a great deal of gratitude that I acknowledge the assistance of Professor W. C. Michels in making this text what it is. I feel that Professor Michels went far beyond his duties as editor of the University Physics Series in providing a thorough review of the manuscript as it was being prepared for the publisher. I know that his review and commentary have been extremely beneficial in producing a much improved text. In addition to Professor Michels I also want to thank Mr. R. S. Alger and Dr. James Ferguson for their review and many helpful suggestions regarding Chapter 9 and Chapters 13 and 14, respectively. Typing of the manuscript consumed many hours of the time of Jeanne Hennecke, Carole Abbott, and Marian Cook.

C. Sharp Cook

San Mateo, California
January, 1961

CONTENTS

CHAPTER I

THE ATOMIC NATURE OF MATTER

CHAPTER II

THE ELECTRON

CHAPTER III

RELATIVISTIC MECHANICS

CHAPTER IV

THE WAVE PARTICLE DILEMMA

CHAPTER V

The Bohr Model of the Hydrogen Atom

CHAPTER VI

Quantum Mechanics

CHAPTER VII

Atomic Structure and Atomic Spectra

CHAPTER VIII

Molecular Structure

CHAPTER XIII

NUCLEAR STRUCTURE

CHAPTER XIV

ELEMENTARY PARTICLES

APPENDICES

Chapter I

THE ATOMIC NATURE OF MATTER

1.1 Atoms and Molecules. A great number of the macroscopic properties of matter and of electromagnetic radiation have been satisfactorily explained using the assumption that any single type of material or radiation field is continuous throughout its volume. Carrying such an assumption to its limits, a volume of water, for example, should, even after division into as many parts as desired, still retain properties characteristic of water.

Practical experience using the five senses seems to verify that matter is continuous, but experience using special tools for probing into the submicroscopic world has long ago shown that no object can be subdivided indefinitely and still retain the character of the matter of which it is composed. Continued division ultimately ends either with an atom, the smallest subdivision of matter which retains any chemical characteristics of its own, or with a molecule, a combination of atoms appropriately put together to form some compound. The evidence of the special tools had been anticipated historically through reasoning that showed that the behavior of matter in bulk is consistent with the existence of molecules and of atoms and that some macroscopic observations are, in fact, explained more readily on the assumption of atomicity than they are otherwise. The chemical laws for the combining of masses and for the combining of volumes, the laws of electrolysis, and the occurrence of plane faces at fixed angles to each other in a given type of crystal were among the early pieces of macroscopic evidence that led to a belief in atoms. Both microscopic and macroscopic evidence for the existence of atoms will be encountered in this and later chapters. Before coming to it, however, it seems worth while to state the principal conclusions about atoms and molecules that are held by present-day scientists.

According to the best picture that can be drawn from the evidence now available about the structure of matter, a drop of water, for example, consists of myriads of water molecules, each of which is composed of two atoms of hydrogen and one atom of oxygen. Each molecule in the drop is water; however, if there is any further subdivision, the matter loses any

1

possible identity as water, but the atoms into which the water molecule divides retain their characteristics as hydrogen and oxygen.

Most atoms may combine with others to form molecules, the exact nature of the combination depending on the structure of the atom. Sometimes the same types of atoms combine in a variety of ways to form different molecules. For example, atoms of carbon and hydrogen combine in a large number of ways; a molecule of methane has one carbon atom and four hydrogen atoms, whereas a molecule of propane has three carbon atoms and eight hydrogen atoms. On the other hand, sodium and chlorine combine into only a single type of molecule, which consists of a single atom of sodium and a single atom of chlorine.

1.2 Avogadro's Number. It is difficult to comprehend a physical dimension as small as either the distance across an atom or the mass of an individual atom. Because of these extremely small physical dimensions, it is not convenient to measure atomic masses in any of the commonly accepted fundamental units. Therefore their masses have been determined on a relative scale, adjusted to a mass of 16.000 units for an oxygen atom. These units of mass are called *atomic mass units* (AMU). Appropriate masses using the same scale can then be assigned to all other types of atoms. The seemingly arbitrary selection of an atomic mass (often called an *atomic weight*) for oxygen was initially made because it resulted in nearly integral values for the atomic mass of many other, but not all, elements.

Atomic masses were determined during the nineteenth and early twentieth centuries, largely by chemical means. The various experiments performed by the chemists of that time were explained by assuming that chemical compounds are formed only by the union of atoms of different elements in simple numerical proportions. For example, it was experimentally determined that 11.19 percent by weight of hydrogen combines with 88.81 percent by weight of oxygen to form water. If the mass of an oxygen atom is 16.0000 AMU and there is only one oxygen atom per water molecule, the mass of the hydrogen in each water molecule is 2.0016 AMU, which would be the mass of the hydrogen atom if the ratio of hydrogen and oxygen in the water molecule were 1:1; but, since by various means it can be shown that there are two atoms of hydrogen in each water molecule, the mass of the hydrogen atom is 1.0080 AMU. Similarly to form calcium oxide requires 71.47 percent calcium and 28.53 percent oxygen. In this particular molecule the atom ratio between the number of calcium and oxygen atoms is 1:1, so the mass of the calcium atom is 40.08 AMU. Since atomic masses were generally determined by weighing, it has been customary to call the mass of the atom the atomic weight. The chemical atomic weights are listed in Appendix 1.2.

Because the AMU is simply another unit of mass, it is possible to determine a factor of proportionality between the AMU and the units of mass in any of the other more customary systems of measurement. The ratio between the AMU and the gram, for example, is usually expressed as the number of atoms, or molecules, in one gram atomic mass (weight), or one gram molecular mass (weight), which, for any pure substance, is a mass in grams numerically equal to the mass in AMU's of the individual atom or molecule. The currently accepted value for this ratio, known as *Avogadro's number*, is $N_0 = 6.0247 \times 10^{23}$ atoms (or molecules) per gram atomic (or molecular) mass. This ratio must also be numerically the same for all types of atoms and molecules. The gram atomic mass of oxygen, for example, is 16.0000 grams, in which there are 6.0247×10^{23} oxygen atoms. Because there are two hydrogen atoms and one oxygen atom in a molecule of water, the gram molecular mass of water is 18.0160 grams and must be the same whether the water is solid, liquid, or gas. Experimental determination of Avogadro's number is most easily made through the use of other results which are discussed in later chapters; for example, see Problem 2, Chapter 2, and Problem 13, Chapter 4.

1.3 Kinetic Theory of Gases. Experience shows that under appropriate circumstances, molecules form either gases, liquids, or solids. In solids and liquids individual molecules are quite closely packed and rather strongly influenced by their neighbors. But the molecules composing a gas are for all practical purposes individually free particles, moving in space. They are influenced only by the general force fields in the region through which they move and by their collisions with other molecules. In liquids the molecules are packed much more tightly and therefore are influenced much more by neighboring molecules. But they are still essentially free to move relative to each other so that any volume of liquid forms itself into a shape conforming to the shape of the container in which it is held. In solids the molecules are relatively rigidly fixed with respect to their positions one to another and have extremely limited mobility within this structure.

It is the purpose of this section to present some simple concepts about the behavior of the molecules in a gas and the interactions among them. For this purpose a gas is pictured as an almost unlimited number of individual tiny molecules which, on an average, are separated by distances very large compared to the diameter of a molecule. At room temperatures each molecule moves with high speed, and scatters from other molecules at irregular intervals, whenever it comes close enough for a collision. The effect can be simulated in two dimensions by placing a few inflated basketballs on a basketball court and rolling another basketball through this group. The moving basketball may hit another ball and impart some of its kinetic energy to that ball. The incident ball then moves away from the collision with a new direction and a new speed both of which depend on how closely the line of approach of the two balls prior to the impact coincided with a head-on-collision. If the moving ball hits a wall it simply bounces off the wall. For a gas, imagine a similar process occurring in three dimensions but with the additional requirement that all balls are moving. Furthermore, suppose no loss of energy because of frictional forces such as occur between the basketball and the floor or other objects with which it comes into contact. In a gas individual molecules move randomly, making collisions in a random manner with other individual molecules. Therefore it is impossible to say exactly what will happen to a single individual molecule as it moves through a region containing other similar molecules. It is possible, though, to use the laws of probability to develop mathematical expressions which express the relative numbers of molecules moving with specific speeds and directions.

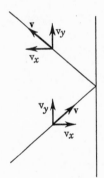

From the macroscopic derivation of the equation of state of an ideal gas, it is known that $PV = nRT$, where P is the pressure exerted by the gas on the walls of the container in which it is held, V is the volume of the container, n is the number of moles of gas in the container, R is the universal *gas constant* (8.31×10^7 erg/mole-degree), and T is the temperature of the gas in degrees Kelvin. To determine the cause of the pressure on the container walls, the motion of individual gas molecules is considered. A gas consists of myriads of molecules moving randomly within the space defined by the walls of the container. The density of molecules within the container determines how often each molecule makes an elastic collision with another molecule. When a molecule comes to the wall of the container, it bounces elastically as illustrated in Fig. 1.1. The x-component of its velocity, v_x, is reversed. Thus, its

FIG. 1.1. Illustration of the change in the x-component of velocity when a molecule bounces elastically off a wall.

momentum is changed by an amount $\Delta p = 2Mv_x$, where M is the mass of the molecule. If the molecule under observation is confined to a box of length x, it moves back and forth between the walls, alternately striking the two sides of the container. The time between successive impulses on any one wall is $\Delta t = 2x/v_x$. Since force is defined as time rate of change of momentum ($\Delta p/\Delta t$), the force exerted by a single molecule on one wall of the container is

$$\Delta p /\Delta t = (2Mv_x)(v_x/2x) = Mv_x{}^2/x. \tag{1.1}$$

If the total area of this wall is A, the pressure P (force per unit area) exerted by the individual molecule on the wall is $Mv_x{}^2/Ax$.

The total pressure exerted on the wall is the sum of the pressures exerted by the individual molecules. To determine this summation requires a knowledge of the distribution of velocities of individual molecules in the gas. These molecules have a possible range of kinetic energies from zero to infinity. If it is assumed that there exists for the molecules in the container a mean square velocity $\overline{v_x{}^2}$ defined by the equation:

$$N\overline{v_x{}^2} = \Sigma\, N_v v_x{}^2,$$

where N is the total number of molecules and N_v is the number with component velocity v_x, the total pressure applied to a wall by all the molecules is $MN\overline{v_x{}^2}/Ax$. Because it is impossible to distinguish between the different directions in the box, the mean square velocity $\overline{v^2}$ for all three dimensions of the box is $\overline{v^2} = \overline{v_x{}^2} + \overline{v_y{}^2} + \overline{v_z{}^2} = 3\overline{v_x{}^2}$. To distinguish between directions would be to say that the pressure exerted by a gas in a balloon at one point on the surface may be different from the pressure at some other point. Thus, the pressure on the single container wall is $P = \frac{1}{3}NM\overline{v^2}/Ax$. Since the volume of the box is Ax, the empirical ideal gas law, discussed earlier in this section, becomes $\frac{1}{3}NM\overline{v^2} = nRT$. If N_0, Avogadro's number, is the number of molecules per gram molecular weight, $N_0 = N/n$, and the gas law becomes

$$\tfrac{1}{3}N_0 M\overline{v^2} = RT. \tag{1.2}$$

Suppose a gas constant per molecule, known as *Boltzmann's constant*, is introduced. Mathematically this is $k = R/N_0$ such that $\frac{1}{3}M\overline{v^2} = kT$. In terms of the mean kinetic energy of the molecules, $W_K = \frac{1}{2}M\overline{v^2}$, the gas law becomes

$$W_K = \tfrac{1}{2}M\overline{v^2} = \tfrac{3}{2}kT. \tag{1.3}$$

The mean kinetic energy associated with any single dimension, say for example the x-dimension, is

$$W_{Kx} = \tfrac{1}{2}M\overline{v_x{}^2} = \tfrac{1}{2}kT. \tag{1.4}$$

The molecules of the particular type of gas considered in this discussion have translational motion only; the particles simply move through space with component velocities in the x-, y-, and z-directions, the three independent coordinates of the Cartesian system. The momentum of a system of particles must be independently conserved in each of these three coordinate directions. Because of this independent conservation of the momentum component in each coordinate direction, a particle having translational motion only is said to have three *degrees of freedom*. But other degrees of freedom may also be present. For example, a basketball can rotate while it moves through space. So can an atom or molecule. The angular velocity of the rotation is independent of the translational motion of the basketball or molecule; hence the rotational motion represents another degree of freedom. Another type of molecular motion cannot be simulated by a single basketball. This is the vibrational motion. For this purpose it is best to consider basketballs as individual atoms. Thus it is possible to represent a two-atom molecule by two basketballs rigidly connected to the ends of a spring. The system can rotate or it can vibrate as the spring expands and contracts. In this system there are two rotational degrees of freedom and one vibrational degree of freedom. Similarly, in simple diatomic types of molecules there are six degrees of freedom; three translational, two rotational, and one vibrational. There must be an equipartition of energy among all degrees of freedom, not simply among the three translational degrees of freedom. The gas law must then be generalized to say that the average energy of a particle of atomic dimensions is $\frac{1}{2}kT$ per degree of freedom. Thus for the dipole type of molecule the average thermal energy of the molecular system is $3kT$.

1.4 Maxwell-Boltzmann Distribution of Energy.

Suppose we now consider the distribution of kinetic energy among the molecules of a gas. Since any one molecule cannot be distinguished from any other of the same type, it is impossible to determine the energy of an individual molecule. It is possible, though, to determine the distribution of energies among the molecules. In deriving this distribution the general assumption is made that individual molecules are completely independent of each other except at the instant of collision. Thus any molecule at any arbitrary time can have any energy.

Before going to the more general energy distribution, consider first a relatively simple problem involving molecules in a planetary atmosphere. In this problem the force, $F = -Mg$, exerted on each molecule by the gravitational field of the planet is introduced. The pressure on any layer of the atmosphere is dependent on the total force exerted by the molecules in a column of air of unit cross sectional area extending upward from the layer at which the measurement is made. Thus the differential between the pressure P_2 exerted on the lower surface of a small volume of gas of depth dh and the pressure P_1 on the upper surface of the same volume is (see Fig. 1.2)

$$dP = -NMgdh/V, \qquad (1.5)$$

where N is the number of molecules in the volume V, M is the mass of

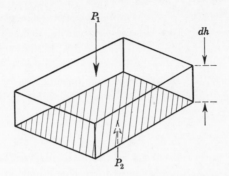

FIG. 1.2.   An incremental volume of air of height dh on the top of which the pressure is P_1 and the bottom of which the pressure is P_2.

one molecule, and g is the acceleration produced by the gravitational attraction of the earth. Since $PV = nN_0kT$:

$$dP = -NMgPdh/nN_0kT \quad \text{and} \quad dP/P = -Mgdh/kT. \qquad (1.6)$$

If all molecules are of the same type, such that the mass M remains constant, and if the temperature T is constant, integration of Eq. 1.6 to determine the pressure as a function of height above the surface of the earth gives the result $\ln P = -Mgh/kT +$ a constant. Under the same conditions of constant M and T, the number of molecules per unit volume is directly proportional to the pressure, since $N/V = P/kT$. Hence the number of molecules in some predetermined volume at a height $h = a$ above the planetary surface relative to the number in the same volume at another height $h = b$ is found from the equation:

$$\ln N_b - \ln N_a = -(Mg/kT)(b - a), \qquad (1.7)$$

and is

$$N_b \doteq N_a \exp\left[-(Mg/kT)(b - a)\right]. \qquad (1.8)$$

The quantity $Mg(b - a)$ is the potential energy required to raise one molecule from a point a to a point b against the acceleration of gravity, g, such that

$$N_b = N_a \exp\left[-(W_b - W_a)/kT\right], \qquad (1.9)$$

where W_a and W_b are the potential energies of the molecule at a and b, respectively.

The only part of the molecular velocity having any significance in determining the height to which a molecule can rise is that component perpendicular to the earth's surface. When a molecule reaches its maximum height above the earth's surface, all its translational motion in the vertical direction has been transformed into potential energy. But part of this potential energy again becomes kinetic energy as the molecule falls toward the earth. Just before striking the surface of the earth the molecule reaches its maximum kinetic energy. If the vertical component of its kinetic energy is zero at the surface, the molecule remains there. If the number of molecules at the surface having this zero vertical component of kinetic energy is N_{sh}, the number N_a of molecules that just reach some height a is

$$N_a = N_{sh} \exp\left[-(W_a - W_s)/kT\right], \qquad (1.10)$$

where W_s is the potential energy of the molecules at the surface of the earth. In a somewhat more general form this equation is applicable to any system of particles to which a force is applied, and in this more general form it is known as the *Boltzmann distribution*.

For a molecule to reverse its vertical direction of motion at a height a, the vertical component of its kinetic energy must be $W_a - W_s = \frac{1}{2}mv_a^2$ when it is at the surface. Thus, with a slight modification, the Boltzmann distribution becomes a valid expression for the numerical distribution of the vertical components of molecular kinetic energies at the earth's surface. In this form, the distribution of the number of molecules with a vertical velocity component v_a at the earth's surface is $N_a = N_{sh}$ exp $(-mv_a^2/2kT)$. This is the one-dimensional Maxwell distribution of velocities and is plotted in Fig. 1.3.

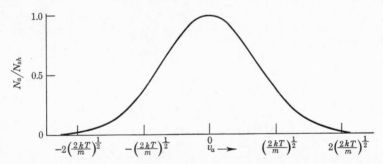

Fig. 1.3.   The one-dimensional Maxwellian distribution of velocity components.

From what is known as the principle of the equipartition of energy, the conclusion is reached that the energy of a system must be divided equally among all the degrees of freedom. Some of the ideas governing this principle were expounded in Section 1.3, where it was concluded that the single dimensional mean square velocity of a gas molecule is one-third of the total mean square velocity: $\overline{v_x^2} = \overline{v^2}/3$. Although momentum, a vector quantity, must be dimensionally conserved, energy, a scalar quantity, must be conserved only *in toto*. For example, after the collision with a molecule at rest of a molecule moving in the *x*-direction, each molecule will most probably be moving with velocity components in all three coordinate directions, the primary requirement being that both momentum and energy be conserved in the interaction. After many such collisions among the almost countless numbers of molecules of a gas, the kinetic energy of the system is divided equally among all degrees of freedom, obeying the principle of the equipartition of energy.

Because of the equipartition of energy, there must be in each of the other two translational directions a distribution of particle velocities similar to that in the vertical direction for the air molecule problem. To derive an expression for the distribution of particle kinetic energies, the combined motion in all three directions must be considered. If the distribution of particles as a function of velocity component v_x is as expressed above, the number $dN(v_x)$ in some incremental interval of component velocity between v_x and $v_x + dv_x$ is

$$dN(v_x) = N_{sx} \exp\left(-mv_x^2/2kT\right)dv_x. \tag{1.11}$$

All real particles have components of velocity in the y- and z-directions as well as the x-direction, so the total number of particles having velocities in the interval dv_x, dv_y, and dv_z is

$$dN(v) = C \exp\left(\frac{-mv_x^2}{2kT}\right)\exp\left(\frac{-mv_y^2}{2kT}\right)\exp\left(\frac{-mv_z^2}{2kT}\right)dv_x dv_y dv_z, \tag{1.12}$$

where C is a constant for any given temperature T, related to the total number of particles N in the system. The probability of finding a single particle in all of velocity space must be unity, so

$$C\int_{-\infty}^{\infty} \exp\left(\frac{-mv_x^2}{2kT}\right)dv_x \int_{-\infty}^{\infty} \exp\left(\frac{-mv_y^2}{2kT}\right)dv_y \int_{-\infty}^{\infty} \exp\left(\frac{-mv_z^2}{2kT}\right)dv_z = 1. \tag{1.13}$$

Since it is impossible to distinguish between components, each must individually be unity, with the result that

$$C^{1/3}\int_{-\infty}^{\infty} \exp\left(\frac{-mv_x^2}{2kT}\right)dv_x = 1,$$

and

$$C = (m/2\pi kT)^{3/2}. \tag{1.14}$$

If there are N particles the probability of finding a single particle is N rather than unity, and C is increased by a multiplicative factor N.

A molecule may be traveling in any direction. Thus, to include all particles having speeds (a scalar of the total velocity without considering direction) in the range between v and $v + dv$, all possible directions of travel must be considered. With this type of problem it is best to transform the velocities into the spherical coordinate system. Then it is necessary only to integrate over all θ and ϕ to determine the number of particles in the spherical shell of thickness dv in velocity coordinates. In velocity space the differential volume of velocities is $dv_x dv_y dv_z$ in Cartesian coordinates, but it is $v^2 \sin \theta \, d\theta \, d\phi \, dv$ in spherical coordinates. Since $v_x^2 + v_y^2 + v_z^2 = v^2$,

$$dN(v) = C \exp\left(-mv^2/2kT\right)v^2 \sin \theta dv d\theta d\phi \qquad (1.15)$$

in the differential volume of velocity space in spherical coordinates. In the spherical shell of velocity space between v and $v + dv$, the number of particles is

$$dN(v) = C \exp\left(-mv^2/2kT\right)v^2 dv \int_0^\pi \sin \theta \, d\theta \int_0^{2\pi} d\phi$$

$$= 4\pi C \exp\left(-mv^2/2kT\right)v^2 dv, \qquad (1.16)$$

and the distribution of particles as a function of their speeds, known as the *Maxwell distribution* of speeds, and plotted in Fig. 1.4, is

$$\frac{dN(v)}{dv} = \frac{4\pi m^{3/2} v^2 N}{(2\pi kT)^{3/2}} \exp\left(\frac{-mv^2}{2kT}\right). \qquad (1.17)$$

This function is a form of the *Maxwell-Boltzmann distribution law*.

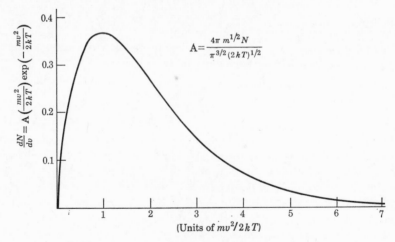

$$A = \frac{4\pi \, m^{1/2} N}{\pi^{3/2}(2kT)^{1/2}}$$

(Units of $mv^2/2kT$)

FIG. 1.4. The Maxwellian distribution of speeds.

Equations 1.10, 1.11, and 1.17 may be used to express a physical picture in mathematical terms whenever like particles act completely independently of one another. Further use of these equations will be made in appropriate physical situations later in the text.

The distribution of molecular speeds in a gas was not experimentally verified until many years after it had been derived theoretically, although such experimental verification can be made in principle in a relatively simple manner by sampling the distribution of speeds of the molecules that escape through a small aperture in one wall of the container in which they are enclosed. In a time Δt the number of molecules that escape through the aperture with a velocity component v_1 normal to the plane of the aperture are distributed in the exterior region in a column with a diameter equal to the diameter of the aperture and a length $v_1\Delta t$. The number of molecules with velocity v_2 which pass through the aperture during the same interval of time are contained in a cylinder having the same diameter but of length $v_2\Delta t$. Thus, if measurements are made of the distribution of speeds of all the molecules that escape from the aperture, the observed distribution is not the same as the distribution of speeds within a unit volume of gas inside the enclosure, but the number in each speed interval between v and $v + dv$ is further proportional to the speed v. Thus the integrated distribution that is observed to emerge through a small aperture is

$$\frac{dN(v)}{dv} = \frac{4\pi m^{3/2}v^3 N}{(2\pi kT)^{3/2}} \exp\left(\frac{-mv^2}{2kT}\right) \tag{1.17a}$$

rather than the distribution of Eq. 1.17. Note, though, that the distribution of Eq. 1.17 is valid if the sampling outside the enclosure comes from a unit volume rather than the integrated sampling.

Miller and Kusch* verified the theoretically derived distribution of speeds using the experimental arrangement illustrated in Fig. 1.5(a).

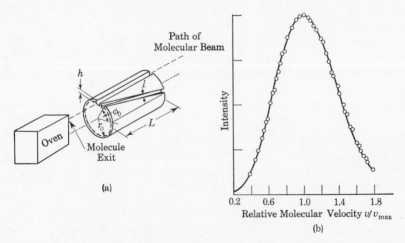

Path of
Molecular Beam

Intensity

Relative Molecular Velocity v/v_{max}

(a)

(b)

FIG. 1.5.   (a) Schematic diagram of the experimental apparatus used by Miller and Kusch to determine the Maxwellian distribution of speeds, and (b) their results for thallium. [*Phys. Rev.* **99**, 1314 (1955)]

Phys. Rev. **99**, 1314 (1955).

They placed a solid, such as thallium, into the oven which was heated to a sufficiently high temperature for some of the molecules to boil off as a vapor. In this arrangement many of the vapor molecules find their way through the molecule exit in the oven and some pass through the straight slot, as shown in Fig. 1.5(a), if the cylinder is not moving. If the cylinder is rotating with an angular velocity ω, a molecule traveling with a speed $v = \omega L / \phi_0$ that enters the oven end of the helical slot passes through this slot without changing its position relative to the sides of the slot. Molecules with low speeds require longer time to make the transit through the helical slot than those with higher speeds. By appropriate selection of angular velocities for the cylinder, molecules with different speeds pass through the slot and are received by the detector. The distribution of molecular speeds as found by such an experimental system, with the theoretically expected distribution, is shown in Fig. 1.5(b). The expected distribution of speeds is therefore verified.

1.5 Rutherford Scattering — The Structure of the Atom. The preceding paragraphs treat atoms as the basic component particles from which matter is built. Perhaps from the discussion therein it might even be concluded that atoms are some sort of tiny spherical balls, each of which possesses some magical property that enables it to combine with selected other atoms to form various types of molecules. But is there further structure to the atom? Why not probe deeper into its interior to find whether it is composed of other more fundamental particles, assuming, of course, that a suitable probe can be found with which to investigate a region as tiny as the interior of an atom?

The best probe to investigate any region of space is an object of smaller dimensions than the region to be investigated. Rutherford found (1911) such a probe in the alpha particle, a positively charged particle that results from the radioactive decay of some of the heaviest known atoms, such as uranium, thorium, or radium. In such decay the radioactive atom splits into two parts, one part only slightly less massive than the original atom and a second part, the alpha particle, with a mass almost four times the mass of the hydrogen atom and carrying a positive charge.

To understand the physical characteristics of an alpha particle, consider first how a positive charge can be placed on an atom. In its most stable state an individual atom or molecule is electrically neutral, but with the expenditure of a relatively small amount of energy, a tiny negatively charged particle known as the electron can be removed, leaving the atom or molecule with a positive electrical charge. This electron removal process is known as ionization, and from it results an ionized atom, or ion. It is now known that the alpha particle is identical with a twice-ionized helium atom. No more than two electrons can be removed from a helium atom, so the alpha particle is a fully ionized helium atom.

Alpha particles are emitted by the radioactive nucleus with kinetic energies very large compared to the energy required to ionize an atom. When emitted they are traveling at very high speeds; therefore they make excellent bullets to shoot at the atoms the structure of which is being investigated. This is precisely what Rutherford did. He sent the alpha particles incident upon thin foils of gold and of silver.

Perhaps the most important discovery made by Rutherford was that most of the alpha particles incident upon a silver or gold foil penetrate without being deviated from their original path, even though the foil is several hundred, or even a thousand, atomic layers thick. However, a few alpha particles are observed to scatter through various angles, some even through very large angles. These results indicate that most of the volume of the foil contains nothing with which the alpha particle interacts; otherwise there would be no possible explanation for so many particles going through the foil undeflected. Even though the foil visually appears solid, the alpha particle apparently sees something which is mostly empty space. Such results are consistent with the idea that each atom consists of a tiny, positively charged, massive nucleus surrounded by electrons in a space very much greater than the space occupied by the nucleus. Almost all the mass of the atom is concentrated in this nucleus. The reason the alpha particle can so easily penetrate the space in the foil is because it, too, is a tiny nucleus, that of the helium atom.

That the atom has this structure may be verified by calculating the distribution of angles through which the alpha particles are expected to be scattered by the electrostatic repulsion of the heavy nuclei of a foil, and comparing this distribution with the distribution experimentally observed. If the alpha particle with a mass m is incident toward a much more massive nucleus, such as gold or silver, as indicated in Fig. 1.6, the electrostatic repulsive force between the two particles is $F = 2Ze^2/\epsilon r^2$, where the charge of the target nucleus is Ze and the distance between the two nuclei is r.* As the alpha particle approaches the target nucleus, the

*In this equation ϵ is the electric permittivity. In the unrationalized cgs and the Gaussian systems of units its magnitude in vacuum is unity and it is customarily considered to be dimensionless (see Appendix 1.3). For this reason this equation is usually written in texts using the cgs system of units simply as $F = 2Ze^2/r^2$. In recent years, though, there has been a considerable increase in the use of the rationalized MKS system of units, in which ϵ is no longer of unit magnitude in vacuum and this equation is $F = 2Ze^2/4\pi\epsilon r^2$. Even though the equations in this text are written in an unrationalized system and are thus directly applicable to the customary cgs units, ϵ will nevertheless be retained in its appropriate position in equations throughout this text in order to assist students who want to transform the equations to the rationalized MKS system.

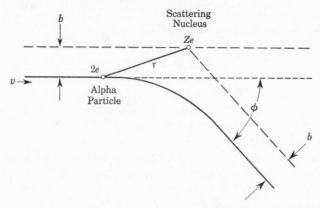

FIG. 1.6.   Illustration of the scattering of an alpha particle by the Coulomb repulsion from a nucleus with charge Ze.

magnitude of the electrostatic repulsive force increases. This force causes the alpha particle to change its direction of motion such that after the interaction it moves at an angle ϕ with respect to its initial direction of motion. Using the conservation laws for energy, momentum, and angular momentum, a calculation can be made which shows that the angle of deflection ϕ is related to other known quantities by the equation (see Appendix 1.4)

$$\cot \phi/2 = \epsilon m v^2 b / 2Ze^2, \qquad (1.18)$$

where v is the velocity of the incident alpha particle as it approaches from a large distance and b is a distance that would be the distance of closest approach of the two particles if the alpha particle continued without deflection.

Experimental measurements determine the relative number of alpha particles scattered at any angle ϕ, but there is no way experimentally to track an individual particle; hence it is not possible to determine the magnitude of the parameter b for a single particle. It is therefore necessary to transform this equation into a form that will give the relative number of alpha particles scattered at an angle ϕ independent of b.

If n alpha particles per unit area are incident normally on a thin foil of thickness t having a density of N atoms per unit volume, the number of particles n_b which pass within a distance b of a nucleus can be calculated. If a volume of radius b is drawn around each nucleus in the foil, from a position outside the foil a cross sectional area πb^2 is observed, as in Fig. 1.7, to surround each nucleus. In a unit cubical volume of material the total cross sectional area which appears from outside to surround the target foil nuclei is $\pi b^2 N$. If the foil has a thickness t, the total observed area within the shaded circles is $\pi b^2 N t$ for each unit cross sectional area.

If t is sufficiently small that essentially no shaded areas overlap, the relative number of alpha particles that pass within a distance b of any nucleus, n_b/n, is the ratio of the shaded area to the total area. Since the total area is unity, this ratio is $\pi b^2 Nt$. Thus, the number of alpha particles scattered through an angle greater than ϕ is

$$n_b = \pi b^2 n Nt. \qquad (1.19)$$

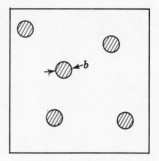

FIG. 1.7. Illustration of the effective area presented to an alpha particle entering a thin silver foil for scattering at angle greater than ϕ.

The number scattered within an increment of angle between ϕ and $\phi + d\phi$ is the difference between the number incident within the circle of radius b and the number incident within the circle of radius $b + db$. This number, $dn_b = 2\pi n Nt b\, db$, is, since $b = (2Ze^2/\epsilon mv^2) \cot \phi/2$,

$$dn_b = 2(Ze^2/\epsilon W_K)^2\, nNt \cot (\phi/2) \csc^2 (\phi/2)\, d\phi, \qquad (1.20)$$

where W_K is the kinetic energy of the particle, $mv^2/2$.

An alpha particle scattered in an incremental angle between ϕ and $\phi + d\phi$ may be scattered anywhere within a region between two cones, as illustrated in Fig. 1.8. The axis of each cone is the direction of the

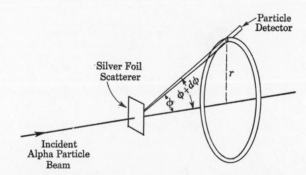

FIG. 1.8. Schematic diagram of an experimental arrangement used to observe the scattering of alpha particles by a silver foil.

incident beam of particles and the apex of each is the scattering foil. The alpha particles scattered in the region between ϕ and $\phi + d\phi$ are thus scattered into an annular ring the area of which is $(2\pi r \sin \phi)(r\, d\phi)$; and, if the area of an alpha particle detector is A, the ratio of the number of alpha particles that are counted by the detector to those scattered into the region defined by the incremental angle $d\phi$ is $A/2\pi r^2 \sin \phi\, d\phi$.

Since $\sin \phi = 2 \sin (\phi/2) \cos (\phi/2)$, the number of alpha particles scattered into the solid angle defined by the increment $d\phi$ of scattering angle is

$$dn_b/d\phi = [4\pi r^2 (Ze^2/\epsilon W_K)^2 nNt/A] \csc^4 (\phi/2) = \text{const}/\sin^4 (\phi/2). \quad (1.21)$$

A comparison of the experimental results using a silver scatterer to the expected theoretical values are shown in Fig. 1.9. The agreement is

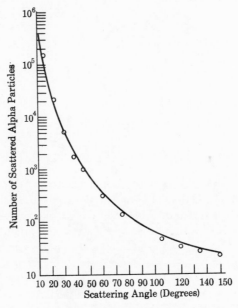

FIG. 1.9. Experimental results observed by Geiger and Marsden for the scattering of alpha particles by a silver foil and the predicted Rutherford distribution. [Based upon results quoted in *Philosophical Magazine* 25, 604 (1913)]

excellent considering that measurements had to be made over four orders of magnitude. Thus, the assumption that an atom consists of a small positively charged nucleus surrounded by electrons at considerable distance, as compared to the size of the nucleus, appears quite valid.

1.6 Cross Sections for Atomic Interactions. The equation:

$$n_b = \pi b^2 nNt, \quad (1.22)$$

used here for a specific type of interaction, is given somewhat more general usage to describe almost any process in which a beam of atomic particles (n incident particles per unit cross sectional area) impinge upon and interact with the atoms of a target material (N particles per unit volume). In the more general case, πb^2 is usually replaced by the Greek letter σ and is called the cross section for the process.

The cross section for an interaction often is not related directly to the physical size of the scattering particle. It may be related to some other physical property as, for example, the repulsive electrostatic force field of the Rutherford scattering interaction. In later parts of this book numerous examples will be found in which an effective cross section is the best quantity for describing the strength of an interaction.

The concept of interaction cross section has been applied quite generally, not only for interactions between atoms, but also for interactions between all types of individual atomic size particles.

1.7 Reduced Mass. A simplifying assumption made in the description of the scattering of alpha particles by silver nuclei is that the alpha particle is scattered by the electrostatic field of a particle which does not recoil from the interaction. Only a scatterer having infinite mass is not affected by the force field produced by the approach and retreat of the scattered alpha particle. In reality, though, every nucleus has finite mass and therefore must be given some momentum by any interaction with another particle. However, a silver nucleus is so much more massive than an alpha particle that it can be approximated as having infinite mass, as illustrated in Fig. 1.6. If the mass of the scatterer is more nearly equal to the mass of the incident particle, no such simplifying assumption can be made, but it is possible to calculate an effective mass for the incoming particle, such that one can assume an infinite mass for the scatterer and still get the same result as in the real observed situation. The mass so calculated is called the *reduced mass*.

Under real conditions the target nucleus, as well as the incident particle, moves. Thus all motion must be considered around some point that can be fixed in space relative to the two particles but which may nevertheless move relative to the laboratory coordinates. This fixed point is the center of mass of the system, a point which is located between the two particles in such a manner that $mr' = Mr''$, as illustrated in Fig. 1.10. Around this point the angular momentum of any set of particles is constant. If use is made of center of mass coordinates, in which the center of mass remains fixed as the origin of the system, the

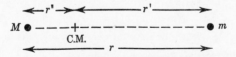

FIG. 1.10. Two particles with finite masses m and M having a center of mass (C.M.) between them.

two particles in a scattering interaction appear first to move toward the center of mass and then to move away, as in Fig. 1.11. A line connecting the two particles always passes through the center of mass. Since $r' + r''$ $= r, r'' = rm/(M + m)$ and $r' = rM/(M + m)$. No matter what point on the straight line connecting the two nuclei is fixed, the apparent angular velocity ω for both particles is the same at any instant of time.

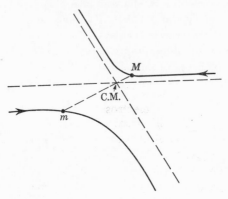

FIG. 1.11. An interaction between two particles with finite mass can most easily be illustrated in a fixed center of mass system of coordinates.

Thus, the total angular momentum around the fixed center of mass is

$$mr'^2\omega + Mr''^2\omega = [mM^2/(m + M)^2 + Mm^2/(m + M)^2]r^2\omega$$
$$= [mM/(m + M)]r^2\omega. \tag{1.23}$$

It is the quantity $mM/(m + M)$ which is the reduced mass. This is the effective mass which must be placed in the position of one of the particles to be able to consider the other particle as having infinite mass and being fixed in space throughout the reaction process. If one particle has very large mass compared to the other, the heavier particle is located so close to the center of mass that it shows no apparent motion as a result of the effect of the smaller particle and hence it can be considered to be at the center of mass of the system.

1.8 Mean Free Path. Whenever a particle passes through a region occupied by a random distribution of other particles with which it may interact, it occasionally collides with one of these particles. Such is the case of the molecule passing through a gas composed of similar molecules, discussed in Section 1.4, or the case of the alpha particle passing through a foil consisting of a random distribution of silver atoms, the nuclei of which act as scattering centers for the alpha particle, as discussed in Section 1.5. The distance traveled between collisions may have a wide range of magnitudes depending on the instantaneous physical conditions.

As in the case of the determination of the number of alpha particles scattered by silver nuclei, no single incident particle may be experimentally followed, but the relative probability that an incident particle moves a predetermined distance between collisions can be calculated. From this probability distribution certain physical characteristics related to the motion of the particles, such as the mean distance of travel between collisions, called the mean free path, may be determined. In the next few paragraphs there will be developed a mathematical expression for the mean free path that is based upon an experimental situation involving an incident hard sphere and a myriad of randomly spaced target spheres each of which has a fixed location in space. In principle this experiment is very closely related to the scattering of alpha particles by the nuclei of a silver foil. For the hard spheres, though, there is a sharp boundary from which scattering occurs.

As an incident particle with radius r_1 moves through space, it encompasses a cylindrical region having a radius r_1, as in Fig. 1.12(a). If the center of any target particle with radius r_2 is less than a distance r_2 from the edge of this cylinder, there must be a collision; see Fig. 1.12(b). Since target particles are randomly distributed in space, the

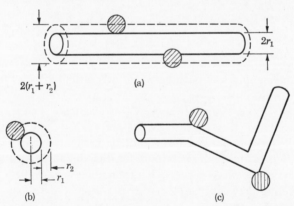

FIG. 1.12. An incident sphere, radius r_1, moving through a region of target spheres (shaded), radius r_2, (a) encompasses a cylindrical region having a radius r_1; (b) collides with a target sphere whenever the centers of the two spheres approach within a distance $r_1 + r_2$ from each other; and (c) changes its direction of motion after each collision with a target sphere.

number of target particles with which an incident particle collides does not remain constant in each unit length of path. However, when a large number of randomly oriented cylindrical paths of unit length and radius r_1 are considered, the number of target particles overlapping each cylinder is distributed around some mean number μ. What then is the probability that there is a path length x between successive collisions?

To determine this probability, divide the length x into a large number n of small intervals Δx. Then the probability that a target sphere of influence is in a given interval Δx is $\mu \Delta x$, and the probability that such is not the case is $1 - \mu \Delta x$. The probability Δp that no collision occurs in n successive intervals, but that there is a collision in the $(n + 1)$st interval is

$$(1 - \mu \Delta x)^n \mu \Delta x = \Delta p. \tag{1.24}$$

Since $x = n \Delta x$, this equation may be rewritten:

$$\Delta p / \Delta x = \mu (1 - \mu x / n)^n. \tag{1.25}$$

As the size of the interval Δx is decreased, $\Delta x \to 0$, $n \to \infty$, and the equation takes on a differential form

$$dp / dx = \mu [\lim_{n \to \infty} (1 - \mu x / n)^n] = \mu e^{-\mu x} \tag{1.26}$$

(see, for example, Woods, *Advanced Calculus*, Ginn and Co., 1934, p. 19). Therefore the distance x between successive interactions has a probability distribution given by $dp = \mu e^{-\mu x} dx$.

Since, if the incident particle travels far enough it must eventually interact with a target particle, the probability of interaction over an infinite path must be unity, so that

$$\int_0^\infty \mu e^{-\mu x} \, dx = 1.$$

Hence the mean length of path between interactions is (see Problem 10)

$$\int_0^\infty x \mu e^{-\mu x} dx \bigg/ \int_0^\infty \mu e^{-\mu x} dx = \int_0^\infty x \mu e^{-\mu x} dx = 1 / \mu. \tag{1.27}$$

This is called the *mean free path* and, if designated by the letter L, results in a probability distribution for the distance traveled by an incident particle between successive interactions such that the probability of scattering between x and $x + dx$ is

$$dp = e^{-x/L} dx / L. \tag{1.28}$$

To determine the magnitude of L, it is necessary to find the required density of target particles to have μ of their spheres of influence fall at least partially in the cylindrical volume of unit length encompassed by the moving particle. For some part of a particle to occupy this region, its center must be within a distance r_2 of the edge of the volume. This radius is assumed to differ from the radius of the moving particle to give the most general condition in which the incident particle is different from the target particles. Then, to have μ particles occupy some part of the cylinder of radius r_1, there must be μ target particles in a cylinder having radius $r_1 + r_2$ and the particle density must be $\mu / \pi (r_1 + r_2)^2$.

Thus the mean free path is $L = [\pi N(r_1 + r_2)^2]^{-1}$, where the density of target particles is N particles per unit volume. It must be noted that the mean free path has been derived using an idealized situation. In reality the incident particle changes its direction of motion after each interaction; hence the cylindrical path of Fig. 1.12(a) should more properly be represented by a diagram similar to Fig. 1.12(c). It should also be noted that the mean free path is related to the cross section for the interaction, $\sigma = \pi(r_1 + r_2)^2$, through the density of target particles, N.

In most gases the incident and target particles are the same, so, assuming the treatment just given is a true representation for a gas,

$$L = [\pi N(2r)^2]^{-1} = [\pi N d^2]^{-1}. \qquad (1.29)$$

However, in a gas all molecules are moving, target as well as incident. A more correct treatment, considering the relative motions of all the molecules, leads to a mean free path $L = [\sqrt{2}\pi N d^2]^{-1}$. An indication of why a correction must be made to the mean free path derived for stationary target particles can be shown relatively simply. A word of caution must be introduced, however, that even though the numerical answer derived from this physical reasoning is correct, the treatment is very much oversimplified and must not be considered as a rigorous proof of the results. To show the logic behind the factor $\sqrt{2}$, it is necessary first to calculate the mean time between collisions, which for stationary target particles is $t = [\pi N \bar{v} d^2]^{-1}$, where $\bar{v}$ is the mean speed of the incident particles. If, as in a gas, all molecules are in random motion, there are just as many target molecules moving away from as toward the incident molecule. Hence the mean velocity component of the target molecules parallel to the direction of motion of the incident molecule is zero, the mean time between collisions is infinite, and one must conclude that the mean free path is infinite for unidirectional motion of the molecules. Physically this simply means that, if there is a collision between two identical particles of a gas, the momentum of each is transferred to the other and, to an outside observer, it is just the same as if each particle passed right through the other and continued on its way. In the direction perpendicular to the direction of motion of the incident molecule the story is different. There is an apparent finite mean speed of the other gas molecules at right angles to the direction of motion of the incident molecule. The mean speed of the target molecules in the perpendicular direction must also be $\bar{v}$, and the mean relative speed of the incident molecule to any target molecule is $v = (\bar{v}^2 + \bar{v}^2)^{1/2} = \bar{v}\sqrt{2}$, which results in a mean time between collisions of $t = [\pi N \bar{v}\sqrt{2}\ d^2]^{-1}$, and a mean free path

$$L = [\pi N \sqrt{2} d^2]^{-1}. \qquad (1.30)$$

References

F. S. Woods, *Advanced Calculus* (Ginn and Co., Boston, 1934).

D. C. Peaslee and H. Mueller, *Elements of Atomic Physics* (Prentice-Hall, Inc., Englewood Cliffs, N. J., 1955).

M. Born, *Atomic Physics* (Blackie and Son, London, 6th Ed., 1957).

A. P. French, *Principles of Modern Physics* (John Wiley and Sons, Inc., New York, 1958)

G. Joos and I. M. Freeman, *Theoretical Physics* (Blackie and Son, London, 1951).

E. H. Kennard, *Kinetic Theory of Gases* (McGraw-Hill Book Co., Inc., New York 1938).

E. N. Andrade, "The Birth of the Nuclear Atom," *Scientific American*, **195**, No. 5, 93 (1956).

W. Band, *Introduction to Mathematical Physics* (D. Van Nostrand Co., Inc., Princeton, N. J., 1959).

E. Rutherford, J. Chadwick, and C. D. Ellis, *Radiations from Radioactive Substances* (Cambridge University Press, Cambridge, 1930).

L. B. Loeb, *The Kinetic Theory of Gases* (McGraw-Hill Book Co., Inc., New York 2nd Ed., 1934).

C. G. Paradine and B. H. Rivett, *Statistical Methods for Technologists* (D. Van Nostrand Co., Inc., Princeton, N. J., 1953)

Problems

1. It is difficult to imagine a number as large as 10^{23}. To assist in understanding the size of Avogadro's number, assume that the aluminum atom can be represented by a ping pong ball (approximately 1 inch in diameter). If you were to place ping pong balls side by side, how far west from New York City must these ping pong balls be placed before there is a number equal to the number of aluminum atoms along one edge of a cube of aluminum having a volume of one cubic inch? If a manufacturer can produce 100,000 ping pong balls a day, how much of the cube would be filled if all the balls manufactured since the first day of 1900 had gone into filling the cube? Suppose it had been possible to have begun the manufacturing of ping pong balls on the first day of the year Columbus discovered America, and the process had continued every day since then. How much of the cube could have been filled?

2. To form the chemical compound hydrogen chloride requires 2.76 percent hydrogen by weight and 97.23 percent chlorine by weight. For magnesium chloride 25.53 percent magnesium and 74.47 percent chlorine are required, and for magnesium oxide 60.32 percent magnesium and 39.68 percent oxygen are required. Assuming the smallest possible number of atoms in each molecule, what is the chemical atomic weight of chlorine and of magnesium? Use only the information given in Section 1.2.

3. Assume that the atmosphere is composed entirely of nitrogen. Starting with normal pressure, a temperature of 20° C at sea level, and assuming that the temperature remains constant throughout the atmosphere, calculate the pressure at 20,000 feet elevation, and at 40,000 feet elevation. Make the same calculation at −20° C. Compare these calculations with the observed air pressures at these elevations. Is it reasonable to assume that the air is composed of nitrogen when making a calculation involving the atmosphere? Remember that the nitrogen molecule consists of two nitrogen atoms.

4. Make the same calculations as in Problem 3 but with helium as the gas What is the factor of proportionality between the number of helium atoms and

the number of nitrogen atoms that would be required in the earth's atmosphere to create the same pressure at the surface?

5. If a large number of very tiny particles of uniform size are suspended in a liquid, each particle undergoes random successive displacements because of the interactions these particles make with the molecules of the liquid, and as a result the particles do not all sink to the bottom of the liquid but are agitated into an equilibrium distribution similar to the distribution of the molecules in a gas that is under the influence of a gravitational force. The rapid series of successive displacements by the particles is called Brownian motion, after its discoverer. During the first decade of the twentieth century Perrin used a suspension of uniform particles of mastic in water to determine Avogadro's Number. He found these particles to have a radius of 0.52 micron and a density of 1.063 gm/cm³. At room temperature the number of particles actually counted in successive layers six microns apart were 305, 530, 940, and 1880. With appropriate substitution for the Boltzmann constant k in Eq. 1.6, calculate Avogadro's number from this information. Remember that the mass m is an effective mass, not the real mass. Because of the buoyancy of the liquid, the effective mass of the particle is the difference in the mass of the particle and of the liquid it displaces.

6. From the Maxwell distribution of speeds, Eq. 1.17, determine the most probable molecular speed, that is, the speed for which the maximum of the distribution occurs. At what kinetic energy, in units of kT, does the most probable speed occur?

7. Derive from Eq. 1.17 the distribution of molecular kinetic energies, this being $dN/dW_K = 2\pi N(\pi kT)^{-3/2}W_K^{1/2} \exp(-W_K/kT)$. What then is the most probable molecular kinetic energy, in units of kT? Why is this different from the most probable speed?

8. In momentum space the distribution of molecular momenta is $dN/dp = 4\pi N(2\pi mkT)^{-3/2}p^2 \exp(-p^2/2mkT)$, in which p is the momentum. Derive this equation from Eq. 1.17.

9. Some of the earliest balloons were lifted by using a fire under the balloon to heat the air inside. Suppose the air inside a balloon is heated to a temperature of 130° F, and the balloon sealed at that time. If the inside of the balloon remains at 130° F and the exterior of the balloon is at 70° F, to what altitude will the balloon ascend? Assume that the interior volume of the balloon remains constant and that the shell of the balloon is weightless.

10. Present day balloons use helium as an interior gas. Assume that the balloon of Problem 9 is filled at sea level and sealed. To what height will the balloon rise? Assume an equilibrium of temperature between the outside and inside of the balloon (70° F).

11. The mean value $\bar{x}$ of some quantity x, the independent variable of the differential distribution dN, is defined by the equation $\bar{x} = \int_0^\infty x\,dN / \int_0^\infty dN$. What then is the mean speed $\bar{v}$ for the distribution of molecular speeds of a gas confined within an enclosure at temperature T? What is the mean speed of a beam of molecules escaping through a tiny aperture in the wall of the enclosure?

12. Calculate the mean square velocity $\overline{v^2}$ for both conditions of Problem 11.

13. Plot on the same piece of graph paper the distribution of gas molecular speeds within an enclosure at temperature T, and within a molecular beam that is escaping from a tiny aperture in the wall of the container. Indicate on the graph the value of the mean speed, mean square velocity, and most probable speed in each case.

14. In the experiments of Miller and Kusch, $L = 20.40$ cm and $\phi = 2\pi/74.7$ radians. If the oven is heated to 900° K, at what speed must the cylinder rotate to transmit molecules which in the interior of the oven had a speed corresponding to the peak of the Maxwellian distribution of molecular speeds? To the mean speed? To the mean square velocity? Assume in one case that the beam consists of potassium atoms and in another of thallium atoms.

15. Estermann has studied [*Phys. Rev.* **71**, 238 (1947)] the distribution of molecular speeds using an experimental arrangement that makes use of the force of gravity on the molecules. If, in Fig. 1.13, cesium molecules are boiled from an

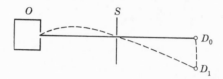

FIG. 1.13.   Illustration for Problem 14.

oven O through a slit S to a detector D, they follow a series of trajectories such as the dashed line ending at D_1. If $OS = SD_0 = 100$ cm, and the temperature of the oven is 450° K, what is the distance of fall D_0D_1 for a cesium molecule with a kinetic energy such that $mv^2/2kT = 2$? For a molecule with the most probable emergent beam kinetic energy? Plot the distribution of beam intensities expected in the D_0D_1 plane.

16. Assume that the radius of a gold nucleus is 10.5×10^{-13} cm, and that the radius of the alpha particle is 1.6×10^{-13} cm. If it is assumed that there is only a mechanical interaction between these two particles, what is the mean free path of an alpha particle when it traverses a gold foil? The density of gold is 19.3 grams/cm³, and its molecular weight is 197.2 AMU. What fraction of the number of alpha particles incident vertically upon a gold foil 100 atomic layers in thickness would be expected to make a collision with a gold nucleus?

17. What fraction of the alpha particles going through the gold foil of Problem 16 would be expected to be scattered by Rutherford scattering through an angle larger than 20°? Why is this number different from the number of collisions calculated in Problem 16? Assume $v = 10^9$ cm/sec.

18. Assume the velocity of an alpha particle from a radioactive nucleus to be 10^9 cm/sec. What fraction of the incident alpha particles are scattered by a silver foil 100 atomic layers in thickness at an angle of 90° into a detector having 0.01π steradian of solid angle? Assume initially that the silver nucleus has infinite mass, and next that the silver nucleus has finite mass. To get 90° scattering the foil is tilted at an angle of 45° with respect to the direction of the incident beam. Make the same two calculations for an aluminum foil and for a beryllium foil. Why then were silver and gold foils used for the experimental verification of Rutherford scattering?

19. How many of those alpha particles scattered at 90° from the silver foil in Problem 18 are removed from the scattered beam because they undergo a second collision with a silver nucleus before they escape from the foil? Define a collision as an interaction in which the alpha particle is scattered through an angle of 10° or more. Assume that alpha particles are initially scattered so that, on the average, they come from the middle of the foil.

Chapter II

THE ELECTRON

2.1 The Electrical Structure of Matter. Chapter 1 was concerned primarily with the division of matter into its component parts. Only once, in connection with Rutherford scattering, was there need to indicate that some parts of the atom carry an electric charge. Charge, though, plays a very important role in atomic structure. For example, the attractive force between the negative charge on the electron and the positive charge on the nucleus holds the atom together. It will also be found in later chapters that the force holding molecules and solids together results from the appropriate distribution of charged particles.

The existence of electric charge in atomic processes has been known for many years. Beginning in the latter part of the nineteenth century, experimenters observed the effects of a small charged particle in a number of experiments, but they did not always recognize it as the same particle nor even necessarily as an integral part of the structure of matter. It was observed initially as cathode rays, later as thermionically emitted charged particles, as the charged particles emitted from a surface as a result of incident ultraviolet radiation and x-rays (photoelectrons), and as the charged beta radiation from radioactive substances. Many years of research were required to show that the negatively charged particles from all these processes were what are now called electrons and to determine the detailed physical characteristics of the electron.

Outlined in the following sections are experiments which describe the physical nature of the electron. The descriptions of these experiments have generally been simplified from their actual forms — only the basic principles are presented. In addition there were usually many variations of the experiments, some of which were more successful than others in obtaining the desired results.

2.2 Quantized Charge — The Millikan Oil Drop Experiment. Two basic quantities which must be determined for any fundamental particle, such as the electron, are its electric charge and its mass. The ratio of electron charge to electron mass, as discussed in the next section,

25

was in principle a relatively simple measurement, but the determination of the absolute magnitude of the electronic charge was quite elusive. Once an absolute value for the charge was determined, though, the mass of the electron could also be determined.

The first really precise measurement of the absolute magnitude of the electronic charge e was made by observing the motions of a tiny charged droplet in the electrostatic field created between two parallel charged plates. This measurement was performed by Millikan, and hence known as the Millikan Oil Drop Experiment. Although there were earlier experiments which pointed in this direction, it was the Millikan Oil Drop Experiment which conclusively showed the quantized nature of charge and measured the magnitude of this smallest unit of charge. This experiment utilized the fundamental physical knowledge that a particle carrying a charge q in an electric field E is acted upon, in the direction of the field, by a force $F = Eq$. For a negative charge in the field the magnitude of the force is the same as for the equivalent positive charge, but the direction of the force is reversed.

A schematic diagram of the experimental apparatus used by Millikan for performing these measurements is shown in Fig. 2.1. An atomizer A

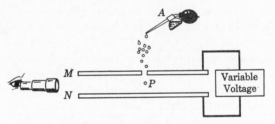

FIG. 2.1.   Schematic illustration of Millikan Oil Drop Experiment.

was used to spray tiny droplets of some nonvolatile liquid into the region above the parallel plates. Some earlier experiments had been attempted using water droplets, but, because of evaporation, the mass of the droplet could not be kept sufficiently constant for precise measurements. As the droplets fell under the influence of gravity, a few passed through a tiny opening at the center of the electrode M into the region between the two parallel electrodes M and N. A particular droplet P was selected to be observed telescopically from a direction in a horizontal plane between the parallel electrodes. An arc source of light illuminated the droplet. Because of frictional forces, many of the droplets produced in the atomizer carried a residual charge. Therefore application of a sufficiently large voltage between M and N produced an electric field that caused the charged particle P to rise against gravity. For a successful experiment the droplet that was selected had to have a sufficiently small mass that, for any applied voltage of reasonable magnitude between the plates M and N, a change of charge on the droplet equal to a single electronic charge e could produce a measurable change in velocity. Should inadequate charge exist on the droplet under observation, or should a change of charge be desired, radiations from an x-ray tube could produce sufficient charge on the droplet for the desired effect. On the other hand, if a droplet having too large a mass were selected, there was nothing that could be done except choose another droplet.

If a particle, such as the droplet in the Millikan Oil Drop Experiment, falls under the influence of gravity through a viscous medium, such as the air, an equilibrium condition is reached in which the resistive force of the viscous medium just equals the force of gravity. Under these equilibrium conditions, the droplet falls with a constant velocity v_1, and the two forces balance; that is, $mg = kv_1$, where k is a constant. If the electric field E is then applied to the region between the electrodes and an equilibrium condition again attained, the force equation becomes $mg - Eq = kv_2$, where q is the charge upon the droplet and v_2 is the velocity of the droplet under these new equilibrium conditions. In these equations the forces and velocities are vector quantities and must be assigned direction as well as magnitude. The force of gravity (down) has been arbitrarily called the positive direction. Hence v_1 is always positive. On the other hand, since the force produced by the field E, which is used to cause the particle to rise, is in the negative direction, the velocity v_2 may be either positive (down) if $mg > Eq$ or negative (up) if $mg < Eq$. If the force of the electric field just balances the gravitational force, the velocity v_2 is zero and the charge q on the droplet is mg/E. However, in general the charge q is

$$q = \frac{k}{E}(v_1 - v_2) = \frac{mg}{v_1 E}(v_1 - v_2). \tag{2.1}$$

In either case the problem becomes that of determining the mass m of the droplet on which the charge is located, since g is known and E, v_1, and v_2 are measurable quantities.

If the droplet of radius R is composed of a material having a density ρ, its mass is $\frac{4}{3}\pi R^3 \rho$. Since the density can be independently determined, the problem reduces to the determination of the radius of the droplet. This can be done through use of *Stoke's law*, which states that the force on a droplet of material falling through a viscous medium with coefficient of viscosity η is $F = 6\pi\eta Rv$. The coefficient of viscosity can be measured independently of the experiment under observation. The force equation $mg = kv_1$ can now be rewritten as

$$\tfrac{4}{3}\pi R^3 \rho g = 6\pi\eta Rv_1, \tag{2.2}$$

from which it is seen that

$$R = (9\eta v_1/2\rho g)^{1/2}, \tag{2.3}$$

and the charge on the droplet can now be found in terms of measurable quantities:

$$q = 9\sqrt{2}\pi\eta^{3/2}v_1^{1/2}(v_1 - v_2)/E\rho^{1/2}g^{1/2}. \tag{2.4}$$

During the course of the years, Millikan and his co-workers made many series of observations of numerous droplets. The results always yielded the answer that the charge existing on each droplet that they observed was an integral multiple of a given charge e, which is now known to be $e = 4.8029 \times 10^{-10}$ esu of charge ($= 1.6021 \times 10^{-20}$ emu of charge $= 1.6021 \times 10^{-19}$ coulomb). This smallest incremental charge observed by Millikan is the charge on the electron, the lightest particle found in nature possessing both mass and charge.

2.3 Charged Particle in a Magnetic Field. If a wire exists in a region of magnetic flux density B, the force on any small length dl of that wire is $dF = IB \sin \alpha \, dl$, where I is the current flowing in the wire and α is the angle between the direction of the magnetic flux density (magnetic induction) and the direction of current flow. The current I is the rate dq/dt at which a charge q flows through a cross sectional area of wire. Thus, if the increment of charge dq moves in a magnetic flux density B with a velocity $v = dl/dt$, the force exerted on it is $dF = vB \sin \alpha \, dq$. Integrating over all the charge q, moving in a wire with a velocity v, the total force exerted upon the length of wire through which the charge moves is

$$F = qvB \sin \alpha. \tag{2.5}$$

If the direction of the magnetic flux density is perpendicular to the direction of motion of the charge q, $\sin \alpha = 1$. Then $F = qvB$, and the force is directed perpendicular to the plane formed by the direction of the magnetic flux density and the direction of motion of the charge q.

The moving charge need not necessarily be confined to a wire but may be on a small droplet, such as was observed in the Millikan Oil Drop Experiment, or it may even be a naturally occurring particle from which the charge cannot be separated, such as the electron.

If a charged particle moves in a uniform magnetic field, the force exerted upon the particle always is perpendicular to the plane common to the direction of motion of the particle and to the direction of the magnetic field. Therefore, the force always is exerted toward the center of a circular trajectory through which the particle moves. The force produced by the interaction between the magnetic flux density and the moving charged particle is thus the centripetal force necessary to maintain the particle in uniform circular motion, $F = mv^2/r$, in which r is the radius of curvature of the particle. The force equation is then

$$qvB = mv^2/r. \tag{2.6}$$

2.4 The Mass of the Electron. After the absolute magnitude of the electronic charge had been determined by the Millikan Oil Drop Experiment, simple substitution of the appropriate value of the charge e into the already experimentally determined ratio e/m, of the charge to mass for the electron, provided a value for the mass of the electron.

Many variations of the combined use of electric and magnetic fields have been devised for the determination of the ratio e/m of the electron, but the basic principles of all are encompassed in the simple experimental arrangement shown in Fig. 2.2. An electron, obtained from any one of

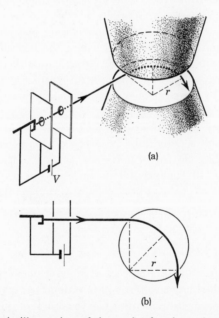

FIG. 2.2. Schematic illustration of the path of a charged particle, accelerated by a potential V, after it enters a uniform magnetic field between two circular poles. (a) Perspective view. (b) Cross sectional view.

a variety of sources, such as thermionic emission from the cathode shown in the diagram, is accelerated to a kinetic energy $W_K = fx = Eex = eV = mv^2/2$ by a set of electrodes between which there is an applied voltage V.

If there is a small aperture in the positively charged electrode, some of the electrons escape into the region of magnetic flux density B. The electron is forced to move in a circular path of radius $r = mv/qB$ by the effects of the magnetic field. The equations expressing the motion of the electron in the two types of fields have in them two unknown quantities, m and v. By eliminating the velocity v, it is found that the mass of the electron is

$$m = er^2B/2V. \tag{2.7}$$

With the introduction of the magnitude of e from the results of the Millikan Oil Drop Experiment, all quantities on the right side of the equation are experimentally determinable.

Results of this and other similar, but more precise, experiments give a value of $m = 9.1086 \times 10^{-28}$ gram for the mass of the electron.

2.5 The Electron Volt. Because atomic dimensions are so small, utilization of the cgs, MKS, or other of the more common systems of units leads to dimensional quantities which are many orders of magnitude different from unity. This has led to the introduction in atomic physics of new units of more appropriate size, such as a unit of energy known as the *electron volt* (ev). An electron volt is the amount of energy gained (or lost) by an electron when it is accelerated (or decelerated) through a potential of one volt.

Since the energy W acquired by a particle carrying a charge q, when accelerated through a potential V, is $W = qV$, one electron volt in the MKS (or practical) system of units is 1 ev = $(1.60 \times 10^{-19}$ coulomb) (1 volt) = 1.60×10^{-19} joule. In the cgs-esu system of units, in which the charge on the electron is 4.80×10^{-10} statcoulomb, and one volt is $1/300$ statvolt,

$$1 \text{ ev} = (4.80 \times 10^{-10} \text{ statcoulomb})(1/300 \text{ statvolt})$$
$$= 1.60 \times 10^{-12} \text{ erg.} \tag{2.8}$$

An electron volt is an extremely small amount of energy in comparison to the energies which are encountered in ordinary everyday experiences. For example, mass measurements to an accuracy of one microgram are beyond the limits of most advanced undergraduate laboratory chemical balances, and dimensional measurements to 0.01 millimeters are about the limit of accuracy in most machine shops; yet to lift a one-microgram mass a distance of 0.01 millimeter against the force of gravity requires the expenditure of almost a million electron volts (1 Mev) of energy. However, the electron has so little mass that, when it is given an energy of one electron volt, it is moving with a speed of more than 10^8 cm/sec, about one percent the velocity of light.

The kinetic energies of the alpha particles used by Rutherford and others for his coulomb scattering experiments, quoted in Chapter 1 simply as being large, were several Mev.

2.6 Electron Spin. Later in the text it will be found that a number of experimentally observed phenomena can be explained only if it is assumed that certain atomic particles, including the electron, are spinning on an axis, perhaps much as the earth spins on its axis. This produces what is known as a magnetic dipole. The methods for direct experimental observation of electron spin are not as simple in principle as most experimental methods used to observe the other physical properties of the electron. If an electron passes through an electric or magnetic field, a force is exerted upon the electron as a result of the direct interaction between the field and the charge on the electron, as discussed in Sections 2.2 and 2.3. If a complete atom, containing electrons, but neutral in charge, is sent through a *uniform* electric or magnetic field, there is no resulting force on it, because there is no net charge with which the field may interact. On the other hand, if selected atoms move through an *inhomogeneous* magnetic field, there is a force exerted upon these atoms as a result of an interaction between the field and the magnetic dipole properties of the spinning electron. The electron spin can be experimentally determined from the magnitude of the displacement of these atoms after they pass through the inhomogeneous magnetic field.

Before discussing the experimental determination of electron spin it is perhaps best to introduce an explanation of the way a force is exerted on a dipole by an inhomogeneous field. To do this it is easiest to start with an electric dipole, illustrated in Fig. 2.3(a), which consists of a positive and a negative charge of equal magnitude q, displaced from each other by some small dis-

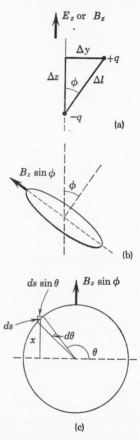

FIG. 2.3. (a) An electric dipole consisting of two charges, $+q$ and $-q$, separated by a distance Δl, in an electric field, the z-component of which is E_z; (b) a charge carrying loop of wire as a magnetic dipole; (c) illustration to assist in the calculation of the torque on a charge carrying loop of wire.

tance Δl. Its dipole moment is $q\Delta l$, which, in the arrangement shown, has two components: one, $\mu_y = q\Delta y$, in the y-direction, and the other, $\mu_z = q\Delta z$, in the z-direction. If the dipole is situated in an electric field which is non-uniform in the yz-plane, the magnitude of the y- and z-components of the field at some point (y',z') is related to the magnitude of these components at some other point (y,z) by the equations:

$$E_{y'} = E_y + (\partial E_y/\partial z)\Delta z + (\partial E_y/\partial y)\Delta y \qquad (2.9a)$$

and

$$E_{z'} = E_z + (\partial E_z/\partial z)\Delta z + (\partial E_z/\partial y)\Delta y. \qquad (2.9b)$$

Because the force on a charge q produced by a field E is $F = qE$, the force in the z-direction on the charge $-q$ at z is $-qE_z$, and the force on the charge $+q$ at z' is

$$qE_{z'} = q[E_z + (\partial E_z/\partial z)\Delta z + (\partial E_z/\partial y)\Delta y]$$
$$= qE_z + \mu_z\partial E_z/\partial z + \mu_y\partial E_z/\partial y. \qquad (2.10)$$

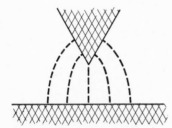

FIG. 2.4. Cross sectional view of a set of electrodes or magnetic poles capable of producing an inhomogeneous magnetic field.

The net force in the z-direction on the dipole is $qE_{z'} - qE_z$. There exists a similar set of force components in the y-direction. If the dipole is located directly below the apex of the upper electrode of a set of electrodes shown in cross section in Fig. 2.4, the inhomogeneity in the field exists only in the z-direction, and the resulting force components are $F_z = \mu_z\partial E_z/\partial z$ and $F_y = 0$. This is the simplified physical condition that will be used here to explain the measurements of electron spin.

If free magnetic poles existed, a magnetic dipole exactly analogous to the electric dipole could be constructed, except that a magnetic pole m would be substituted for the charge q, and the magnetic flux density B would be substituted for the electric field E. The result would be a net force, $F_z = \mu_z\partial B_z/\partial z$, on the dipole for the simplified conditions derived above. Should the dipole make an angle ϕ with respect to the direction of the field, as in Fig. 2.3(a), the force could be written in terms of the total dipole moment as

$$F = \mu \cos \phi(\partial B_z/\partial z). \qquad (2.11)$$

The torque produced around the center of the dipole as a result of the magnetic field would be

$$T = +mB_z(\Delta l \sin \phi)/2 + m[B_z + (\partial B_z/\partial z)\Delta z](\Delta l \sin \phi)/2$$
$$\approx mB_z(\Delta l \sin \phi) = \mu B_z \sin \phi. \qquad (2.12)$$

The magnetic dipole postulated above is fictitious because there are no free magnetic poles. On the other hand, a magnetic dipole can be calculated for a current flowing in a closed loop, which is perhaps an appropriate picture for a spinning electron. When the loop is located in a magnetic flux density B, a torque is applied to the loop as a result of the interaction between the current flowing in it and the component of the magnetic flux density parallel to the plane of the loop. If the loop is oriented as in Fig. 2.3(b), with its plane perpendicular to the dipole of Fig. 2.3(a), the component of B_z parallel to the plane of the loop is $B_z \sin \phi$. The torque is then the sum of the products of the force perpendicular to the plane of the page on each incremental length of wire ds and the lever arm x of Fig. 2.3(c). In the geometry shown, because it interacts with B_z, only the component of the current perpendicular to x is influential in producing the force responsible for the torque.

For a small increment of wire ds through which a current i is flowing, the force perpendicular to the plane of the page is

$$dF = (ids \sin \theta)(B_z \sin \phi) = (ird\theta \sin \theta)(B_z \sin \phi), \qquad (2.13)$$

and the torque exerted on this increment of wire is

$$dT = xdF = r \sin \theta \, dF = ir^2 \sin^2 \theta \, d\theta \, B_z \sin \phi. \qquad (2.14)$$

Thus for the entire loop the torque is

$$T = ir^2 B_z \sin \phi \int_0^{2\pi} \sin^2 \theta d\theta = i\pi r^2 B_z \sin \phi = iAB_z \sin \phi, \quad (2.15)$$

where A is the area of the loop.

This equation is similar to that for the dipole (Eq. 2.12) if, for the loop of wire in which there is a current i, the magnetic moment is iA. This conclusion can also be shown to be valid for all other shapes of wire loops as well as the circular loop. For an electron with charge e the magnetic moment then is $\mu = iA = \pi r^2 ev$, where $v = \omega/2\pi$ is the rotational frequency of the electron.* The angular momentum of the electron is $L = m\omega r^2 = 2\pi v m r^2$, so the ratio of magnetic moment to angular momentum, known as the gyromagnetic ratio, is $\mu/L = G = e/2m$. Since the current is derived from magnetic quantities, the charge e in this equation is in electromagnetic units or in MKS units. If e is to be expressed in the more customary electrostatic units, the gyromagnetic ratio must become

$$G = \mu/L = e/2mc, \qquad (2.16)$$

which is the form in which the equation is usually seen.

*The use of the symbol μ for magnetic moment is in accordance with standard practice. It must not be confused with the magnetic permeability for which the symbol μ is also used.

It will be learned later that the magnitudes of all atomic angular momenta are approximately the same, differing usually by not more than one order of magnitude. If there is a very large difference in the mass of two atomic particles, the one with the smaller mass would thus be expected to have the larger magnetic moment resulting from its axial spin. The proton, for example, with a mass almost 2000 times the mass of the electron, has a magnetic moment very much smaller than that of the electron, and thus is influenced much less than an electron by an inhomogeneous magnetic field.

Thus if a neutral atom of hydrogen, consisting of a single electron and a single proton, moves through an inhomogeneous magnetic field, the force on the dipole formed by the spinning proton is extremely small compared to the force on the dipole formed by the spinning electron. Such a physical situation occurs if a hydrogen atom moves along a path perpendicular to the plane of the page directly below the apex of a magnetic pole face shaped as shown in cross section in Fig. 2.4. It is moving in a magnetic flux density that is inhomogeneous in the z-direction, and a resultant force, $F_z = \mu_z \partial B_z / \partial z$, is exerted individually upon the electron and upon the proton, with μ_z being the z-component of the magnetic moment appropriate to each individual particle. The magnetic moment of the proton is so much smaller than that of the electron that the force exerted upon the proton by the inhomogeneous magnetic field is negligible in comparison to the force on the electron.

As the neutrally charged hydrogen atom moves through an inhomogeneous field produced by the magnetic poles illustrated in Fig. 2.5, the

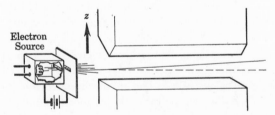

Fig. 2.5. An atom containing a single electron is deflected in the direction of an inhomogeneous magnetic field as a result of the force on the magnetic moment of the electron.

atom is accelerated in the z-direction by an amount $a_z = F/M$, where F is the force exerted on the magnetic moment of the *electron* and M is the mass of the *atom*. Thus at any time t the velocity in the z-direction is

$$v_z = a_z \int_{t_0}^{t} dt = (F/M)(t - t_0), \qquad (2.17)$$

where t_0 is the time at which the atom enters the inhomogeneous magnetic field. The displacement at time t is

$$z = \int_{t_0}^{t} v_z dt = (F/M) \int_{t_0}^{t} (t - t_0) dt = F(t - t_0)^2 / 2M. \quad (2.18)$$

If the horizontal velocity of the atom is v_x and the length of the shaped pole face is l, the atom leaves the magnet gap at a time $t - t_0 = l/v_x$, at which time the displacement in the z-direction is $z = Fl/2Mv_x$.

The force on the atom is $F = \mu \cos \phi$, where ϕ is the angle the axis of the spinning electron makes with respect to the z-direction. If the electron can be oriented in any direction and the orientation of the electron does not change during passage through the inhomogeneous magnetic field, displacements of any magnitude between $z = +\mu l/2Mv_x$ and $z = -\mu l/2Mv_x$ are expected. Displacements in the z-direction of hydrogen and other appropriate atoms after passage through an inhomogeneous magnetic field have been observed. However, only a limited number of displacement magnitudes have been observed, indicating that the electron spin can be oriented only in certain directions with respect to the direction of a magnetic field. The significance of this quantized orientation of electron spin is discussed in Chapter 7. The fact that there is displacement gives positive indication of the existence of a spinning electron.

2.7 Electron Dimensions. How big and of what shape is the electron? For some experiments, such as those in which a moving electron interacts with uniform electric or magnetic fields, it can be considered most easily as a point in space. On the other hand, it is difficult to give the electron a magnetic moment without considering something of finite size spinning on its axis in which least some of the charge is located at a finite, even though small, distance from the axis. For simplicity the electron is sometimes considered to be a small spherical ball, although for the purpose of this discussion the exact shape is not really critical.

If it is assumed that the electron's charge is distributed on the surface of a small spherical shell, as would be the case for a charged metallic sphere in a problem in electrostatics, the energy of such a system is distributed in an electrostatic field in accordance with the volume integral $\frac{1}{8}\pi \int \epsilon E^2 dv$. It will be seen in later chapters that an electron at rest possesses an energy $W = m_0 c^2$, where m_0 is the rest mass of the electron. If the observed rest energy of the electron is interpreted to be the energy associated with the electrostatic field of the electronic charge, the radius of the electron can be calculated, for both E and dv are functions of r, the radial distance from the center of the spherical shell repre-

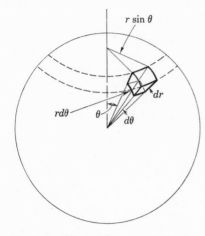

Fig. 2.6. Illustration to assist in the calculation of the energy in the electrostatic field of a charged spherical shell.

senting the electron. As seen in Fig. 2.6, the volume of an annular ring on the sphere surrounding the electron is

$$dv_r = 2\pi r \sin \theta r d\theta \, dr. \quad (2.19)$$

Hence the volume of an incremental spherical shell between r and $r + dr$ is

$$dv = 2\pi r^2 dr \int_0^\pi \sin \theta \, d\theta = 4\pi r^2 dr. \quad (2.20)$$

Since $E = e/\epsilon r^2$, the energy in the incremental volume dv is $dW = (\frac{1}{8}\pi)$ $(e^2/\epsilon r^4)(4\pi r^2 dr)$ and the energy in the electrostatic field produced by the electron (spherical shell of radius R) is

$$W = \frac{1}{8\pi} \int_R^\infty (e^2/\epsilon r^4)(4\pi r^2 dr) = (e^2/2\epsilon) \int_R^\infty dr/r^2 = e^2/2\epsilon R. \quad (2.21)$$

Since the energy of the electron is $m_0 c^2$, the electron radius by this calculation is

$$R = \frac{e^2}{2\epsilon m_0 c^2} = \frac{(4.80 \times 10^{-10} \text{ statcoulomb})^2}{2(9.11 \times 10^{-28}\text{gm})(3.00 \times 10^{10}\text{cm/sec})^2}$$

$$= 1.41 \times 10^{-13}\text{cm} \quad (2.22)$$

This is strictly a classical calculation based on a preconceived notion that the electron can be represented as a well-defined charged spherical shell. Other methods for calculating the classical radius of the electron give other multiples of $e^2/m_0 c^2$. It is customary to call the radius $R = e^2/m_0 c^2$ the classical radius of the electron. The size so calculated appears to be close to the right order of magnitude as seen from the size of the nucleus, based upon Rutherford scattering, and on the size of the atom, as will be seen in Chapter 4. With the introduction of quantum mechanics it will be seen that the electron possesses some properties which cannot possibly be explained by a particle having a finite, well-defined surface. In fact, certain observed phenomena require that the electron be spread over a volume exceedingly large compared to the volume calculated here, and indeed will lead to the question whether any definite size at all can be attributed to the electron.

References

H. H. Skilling, *Fundamentals of Electric Waves* (John Wiley and Sons, Inc., New York, 2nd Ed., 1948).

F. Bitter, *Currents, Fields, and Particles* (The Technology Press of MIT Cambridge, Mass., 1956).

E. R. Cohen, K. M. Crowe, and J. W. M. DuMond, *The Fundamental Constants of Physics* (Interscience Publishers, Inc., New York, 1957).

R. A. Millikan, *Electrons (+ and −), Protons, Photons, Neutrons, Mesotrons, and Cosmic Rays* (University of Chicago Press, Chicago, 1947).

R. G. J. Fraser, *Molecular Rays* (Cambridge University Press, London, 1931).

J. D. Stranthan, *The Particles of Modern Physics* (McGraw-Hill Book Co., Inc., New York, 1942).

Problems

1. To help in obtaining a feeling for the magnitude of the electronic charge, calculate the number of electrons required to produce a potential of 100 volts on a spherical shell 1.00 foot in diameter.

2. In a solution of silver nitrate the salt dissolves into positive ions (Ag^+) and negative ions (NO_3^-). Experiments show that, if two electrodes are placed into the solution and a potential applied between them, a current flows because of the motion of the positive ions to the negative electrode and the negative ions to the positive electrode. It is found that the passage of one coulomb of charge deposits 0.0011182 gram of silver on the negative electrode. Knowing the electronic charge and the atomic weight of silver in AMU (see Appendix 1.2), calculate Avogadro's number.

3. If a small amount of acid is added to distilled water and a potential applied between two electrodes placed in the water, an electric current is observed to flow across the solution between the electrodes. Oxygen gas is observed to be formed at the positive electrode and hydrogen gas at the negative. This process is known as the electrolysis of water. If 2.893×10^{14} statcoulombs of charge are passed through the solution, 8.000 grams of oxygen are formed at the positive electrode and 1.008 grams of hydrogen at the negative electrode. Calculate Avogadro's number from this information. What can be said about the charge carried on the oxygen ion? How is this related to the structure of the water molecule?

4. What is the temperature of a gas for which the most probable energy of the molecules is 1 ev?

5. If in the Millikan Oil Drop experiment the electric field between the plates M and N is 1000 volts/cm, what is the radius of the drop if a change of one electron charge on the drop produces a change in the rate of rise through air from 0.01535 cm/sec to 0.01000 cm/sec. Assume that the coefficient of viscosity of the air is 0.0001817 and that the density of the oil is 0.893 gm/cm³.

6. In Problem 5, what is the charge on the drop and the potential on the surface of the drop?

7. Rutherford and Geiger, and later Regener, measured the charge on the alpha particle by measuring the accumulation of charge on an electrometer connected to a screen which was being bombarded by alpha particles from a radioactive source emitting a known number of particles per unit time. In such an experiment it is found that a total charge of 3.77×10^{-4} esu is collected in 1 sec from a source of radium F which emits 393,500 particles per second. What is the charge on the alpha particle? What can be said about its charge relative to that on an electron?

8. Calculate how many electron volts of energy are required to lift a 200-pound man 3 feet from the surface of the earth against the force of gravity.

9. A method used by J. J. Thomson for determining the ratio e/m utilized crossed electric and magnetic fields in which the force of one field on a moving charged particle was in the opposite direction to the force of the other. Calculate the ratio of the electric field to the magnetic flux density necessary to maintain an electron moving in a straight line through these fields and perpendicular to both fields. If an electron moves with a kinetic energy of 500 ev in an evacuated chamber through these fields, what magnetic field must be maintained to balance the force exerted by an electric field of 2000 volts/cm?

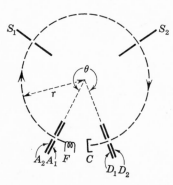

FIG. 2.7. Illustration of Dunnington's method for determining the ratio e/m. [*Phys. Rev.* **52**, 475 (1937)]

10. Dunnington determined the ratio e/m for the electron using the system illustrated in Fig. 2.7. A slowly alternating potential with a frequency f is applied between the electrodes A_1 and A_2 and between D_1 and D_2 such that the voltage on D_2 relative to D_1 is the same as the voltage on A_2 relative to A_1 at every instant. The electrodes A_1 and D_1 are at the same potential. Hence, an electron emitted by F is accelerated if it passes through the slits in the A electrodes when the potential on A_2 is positive with respect to that on A_1. If the time required for the electron to go from A to D is exactly one full cycle of the applied oscillatory frequency, the electrons lose all their kinetic energy at D and hence do not reach the collector C. In Dunnington's original experiments, $\theta = 5.9348$ radians, and the Helmholtz constant for the magnet field was $k = 17.3616$ gauss/ampere. For an applied frequency $f = 3.7920 \times 10^7$ cycles/sec, the minimum electron current at the collector C occurred at a magnet current $i = 0.71426$ ampere, and for $f = 2.9280 \times 10^7$ cycles/sec, at $i = 0.54498$ ampere. Calculate the ratio e/m.

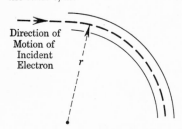

FIG. 2.8. Illustration for Problem 11.

Direction of Motion of Incident Electron

r

11. Another system for analyzing electrons into velocity groups utilizes electrodes that are bent into arcs having common centers of curvature, as indicated in Fig. 2.8. If an electron with a kinetic energy of 500 ev enters the plane midway between two electrodes 5 mm apart, for which the mean radius of curvature r is 20 cm, what voltage must be applied to the electrodes to maintain the electrons in the median plane?

12. Show that, if the coil of Fig. 2.3(c) had been rectangular, its magnetic moment would still be iA.

13. The magnetic moment produced by the spin of the electron is approximately 2×10^{-20} erg/gauss. If an atom having a single electron which interacts with the field passes through a magnetic field in which the inhomogeneity is $\Delta B/\Delta z = 10^4$ gauss/cm, what is the maximum displacement of an atom after it has passed through 10 cm of the inhomogeneous field? Assume that the electrons enter the field perpendicular to the z-direction with the most probable kinetic energy from an oven having a temperature of 1000° K.

Chapter III

RELATIVISTIC MECHANICS

3.1 Physical Laws for Atomic Dimensions. A physical theory is valid only if it is able to explain and predict the results of appropriate experiments. The study of atomic physics brings into being dimensional quantities several orders of magnitude smaller than those previously encountered by those theorists and experimentalists who derived the laws of Newtonian mechanics and Maxwellian electromagnetic wave theory. Much of the early experimentation showed that it was simply impossible to apply the existing physical laws to phenomena having atomic dimensions.

To overcome the dilemmas which ensued, relativistic mechanics and quantum mechanics were developed. Each is more general than the classical Newtonian mechanics. By extending each to conditions in which mass is large and velocity small, it can be found that either reduces to the same physical laws derived to explain the gross mechanical actions of nature. Because of this, Newtonian mechanics must be considered only a limited expression of more general mechanical laws and must be considered to apply only to objects having mass and other physical dimensions large compared to atomic dimensions and moving at speeds small compared to the speed of light. Relativistic mechanics has been developed to account for experimentally observed properties of matter moving at nearly the speed of light, properties which cannot be explained by Newtonian mechanics. Because it is relatively easy for particles as small as the electron or the atom to attain a speed approaching the speed of light, the laws of relativistic mechanics are important in the consideration of many atomic processes.

3.2 An Ether for Electromagnetic Radiation. The need for a theory of relativity initially arose from the success of Maxwell's theory of electromagnetic radiation. The ability of the Maxwell theory to explain the experimental observations of light and Hertzian wave phenomena left little doubt that both were waves of electric and magnetic fields propagated through space with a speed (experimentally measured) of

$c = 2.998 \times 10^{10}$ cm/sec. Based upon prior experiences, such as the propagation of sound through the air, or the motion of a ship on a moving current of water, it was natural for physicists to consider that electromagnetic radiation would be propagated relative to some stationary medium. The term *ether* arose to describe this medium. This ether would have to be some sort of frictionless fluid, uniformly distributed throughout space, which could not be affected by any mechanical interaction with matter.

To locate the ether, Michelson and Morley devised an experiment based upon the assumption that, because of the rotation of the earth on its axis and the revolution of the earth around the sun, the surface of the earth cannot *always* be at rest relative to the ether. If the sun is considered to be fixed relative to the ether, the earth is constantly moving through the ether with a speed of about 3×10^6 cm/sec, and the speed of light relative to the earth should change by about two parts in 10^4 during a six-month interval while the earth reverses its velocity relative to the ether. Even if the sun is not fixed in the ether, the same *change* in the speed of light should be observed. Such a small change could be detected only if extreme precision were obtained in determining the speed of light on the earth's surface.

The Michelson interferometer was the device used to give the required precision. The manner in which it is used when stationary relative to

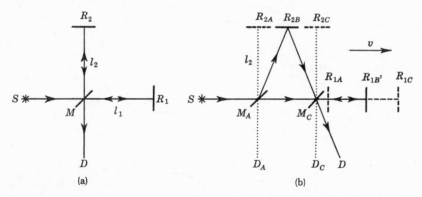

Fig. 3.1. Schematic illustration of light paths in a Michelson interferometer if (a) interferometer is stationary relative to the ether, and (b) if interferometer is moving in a direction parallel to the arm l_1 at a constant velocity, v, relative to the ether. In the illustration of the moving interferometer the subscript A shows the positions of mirrors M, R_1, and R_2, and detector D at the time an instantaneous beam of light from source S is initially reflected by half-silvered mirror, and the subscript C indicates the positions of these objects at the time the light from R_2 again reaches the half-silvered mirror. This beam is reflected from mirror R_2 at R_{2B} and from mirror R_1 at $R_{1B'}$. The reflection at $R_{1B'}$ occurs at a slightly later time than at R_{2B}.

the ether is shown in Fig. 3.1(a). Monochromatic light of wavelength λ is divided by the half-silvered mirror M such that part of the light passes to the mirror R_1 and part to the mirror R_2. The light is reflected back to the half-silvered mirror by the mirrors R_1 and R_2, and part of the light from each mirror is reflected or transmitted so as to reach the detector D. A series of interference fringes may be observed as either of the path lengths is extended or shortened. If the interferometer is moving with a velocity $\mathbf{v}$ relative to the ether, as indicated in Fig. 3.1(b), the time required for the monochromatic light to traverse each arm of the interferometer differs from the case illustrated in Fig. 3.1(a). For the path from M to R_1 and return, this time is now

$$t_1 = \frac{l_1}{c+v} + \frac{l_1}{c-v} = \frac{2l_1/c}{1 - v^2/c^2}. \tag{3.1}$$

The arm l_2 is perpendicular to the direction of motion of the ether. If the time required for the light to go from M to R_2 and return is t_2, $l_2 = (c^2 - v^2)^{1/2} t_2/2$, and

$$t_2 = \frac{2l_2/c}{(1 - v^2/c^2)^{1/2}}. \tag{3.2}$$

The difference in length of the two paths is $(t_1 - t_2)c$. This path length difference may also be expressed as $n_A \lambda$ in which n_A, the number of wavelengths difference in light path, is

$$n_A = (t_1 - t_2)c/\lambda = \frac{2/\lambda}{(1 - v^2/c^2)^{1/2}}\left[\frac{l_1}{(1 - v^2/c^2)^{1/2}} - l_2\right] \tag{3.3}$$

If, on the other hand, the apparatus is rotated 90° with respect to the direction of motion of the ether, the number of wavelengths difference in light path is

$$n_B = \frac{2/\lambda}{(1 - v^2/c^2)^{1/2}}\left[l_1 - \frac{l_2}{(1 - v^2/c^2)^{1/2}}\right]. \tag{3.4}$$

These two path length differences are not equal, and the inequality is

$$\Delta n = \frac{2}{\lambda}\frac{l_1 + l_2}{(1 - v^2/c^2)^{1/2}}\left[\frac{1}{(1 - v^2/c^2)^{1/2}} - 1\right]$$

$$\approx \frac{l_1 + l_2}{\lambda}\frac{v^2}{c^2} \quad \text{if} \quad v \ll c. \tag{3.5}$$

This expected shift in the number of fringes produced by the rotation of the interferometer through 90° is based upon the expectations from Newtonian mechanics, perhaps better called Newtonian relativity, that the transformation equations between systems of coordinates moving in the x-direction with a velocity $\mathbf{v}$ with respect to each other is

$$x' = x - vt, \quad y' = y, \quad z' = z, \quad t' = t. \tag{3.6}$$

If, under the experimental conditions actually used by Michelson and Morley, one arm of the interferometer were moving lengthwise relative to the ether, a shift Δn, of the order of magnitude of one-third of a fringe would have been expected. The apparatus was capable of detecting a fringe shift as small as 0.01 fringe. No fringe shift could be observed. Just in case the earth had been moving such that the frame of reference for the ether had been exactly the same as that for the interferometer, the experiment was repeated at different times of day and at different times of year in order to get the effects of the earth's motion on its axis and in different parts of its orbit. Completely negative results prevailed under all conditions.

3.3 Einstein's Theory of Relativity. If the results of the Michelson-Morley experiment are accepted (and, after many attempts at doing the experiment, there is no reason to doubt its validity), it is necessary to conclude that the laws of Newtonian mechanics are inadequate to explain experimental observations when the relative velocity of the observer to that of the phenomenon he is observing approaches the velocity of light. To explain the absence of interference fringes in the Michelson-Morley experiment it is necessary to assume that, if one frame of reference is moving with a uniform velocity relative to another frame of reference, a length l in the first frame appears in the second frame to be fore-shortened in the direction of motion. However, according to the Newtonian transformation, positions in the two frames that coincide at $t = 0$ will after a finite period of time be separated by a distance $x' = x - vt$, and

$$l' = \Delta x' = x'_2 - x'_1 = (x_2 - vt) - (x_1 - vt) = x_2 - x_1 = l$$

This equality does not agree with the results of the Michelson-Morley experiment. The transformation which must be used to give the experimentally observed results is $x' = \gamma (x - vt)$, where $\gamma = (1 - v^2/c^2)^{-1/2}$, from which it is found that

$$l' = l/(1 - v^2/c^2)^{1/2}. \tag{3.7}$$

This type of transformation was first proposed by Lorentz, and is hence known as the *Lorentz transformation*. For the other spatial coordinates $y' = y$ and $z' = z$, since there is no relative motion in these directions. However, if the x-coordinate is to transform in the way it does, the measure of time can no longer be the same in both frames of reference, for v is a function of t as well as x.

It was Einstein who introduced a theory which leads not only to a transformation for time consistent with experimental observations, but also presents a physical basis for the observed phenomena. Einstein's proposal to solve the dilemma in which the Michelson-Morley experiment left the scientific world was a fundamentally different type of assumption — there is no fixed ether in space through which electromagnetic radiation is propagated, and furthermore, the speed of light in a vacuum is a constant c, when measured in any frame of reference. More generally the relativity postulate states that all inertial systems are equivalent, meaning that the fundamental laws of physics are exactly the same in any frame of reference. Also, the velocity of light is independent of the motion of its source.

These statements may at first appear contradictory. How can a beam of light observed to be moving with a velocity c in one frame of reference also be observed in another frame of reference to be moving with the same velocity c? Further observation of atomic particles and their interactions reveals that new physical laws are required to explain many phenomena which cannot be explained by the classically established physical laws for the macroscopic world. The new laws, based upon Einstein's postulates, have for the most part been experimentally verified. Each law reduces under appropriate circumstances to those physical principles known as Newtonian mechanics.

Using Einstein's assumption of the constancy of the speed of light in vacuo in any frame of reference, it is possible to determine the relationship between time intervals in the primed and unprimed frames of reference for the Lorentz transformation. Since light moves with a velocity c in both frames of reference, the time t required to move a distance in the unprimed system is

$$x^2 + y^2 + z^2 = c^2 t^2,$$

and the time t' to move an equivalent distance in the primed system is determined from the equation

$$x'^2 + y'^2 + z'^2 = c^2 t'^2.$$

Transforming the space coordinates of the primed system in accordance with the known Lorentz transformations gives

$$\begin{aligned}
c^2 t'^2 &= \gamma^2(x^2 - 2xvt + v^2 t^2) + y^2 + z^2 \\
&= (\gamma^2 - 1)x^2 + x^2 + y^2 + z^2 + \gamma^2(-2xvt + v^2 t^2) \\
&= (\gamma^2 - 1)x^2 + c^2 t^2 + \gamma^2(-2xvt + v^2 t^2).
\end{aligned} \tag{3.8}$$

In terms of the variables x and ct, this equation is

$$c^2 t'^2 = [(c^2 + \gamma^2 v^2)/c^2]c^2 t^2 - (2\gamma^2 v/c)xct + (\gamma^2 - 1)x^2,$$

the solution of which must be of the form $ct' = Act + Bx$, with $A^2 = (c^2 + \gamma^2 v^2)/c^2$; $AB = \gamma^2 v/c$; and $B^2 = (\gamma^2 - 1)$. Thus

$$A = (\gamma^2 v/c)/(\gamma^2 - 1)^{1/2} = 1/(1 - v^2/c^2)^{1/2},$$

and

$$B = (\gamma^2 - 1)^{1/2} = (v/c)/(1 - v^2/c^2)^{1/2}. \tag{3.9}$$

The result is that $t' = \gamma\,(t - xv/c^2)$, and the complete set of Lorentz transformation equations is

$$x' = \gamma(x - vt), \quad y' = y, \quad z' = z, \quad t' = \gamma(t - vx/c^2). \quad (3.10)$$

From these transformation equations certain conclusions may be drawn with respect to the measurement of time in the two systems. If an event occurs in the unprimed system at a fixed position x_1, and is of duration $\Delta t = t_2 - t_1$, an observer in the primed system measures this time interval as

$$\Delta t' = t'_2 - t'_1 = \Delta t/(1 - v^2/c^2)^{1/2}, \quad (3.11)$$

since the second term of the time transformation is $vx_1/c^2 - vx_1/c^2 = 0$. This means that an observer standing in any frame of reference and observing an occurrence happening in another frame of reference, moving with respect to his, should observe that occurrence as happening at a slower rate than if he were in the frame of reference in which the event occurred.

3.4 Relativistic Effects of Mass and Energy. Even though the time dilation effect had not been verified as of this writing, several other predictions of the theory of relativity have been experimentally observed. From the point of view of atomic physics the most important of these are the observed effects relating to mass and energy.

From the Lorentz transformation equations it is seen that

$$dx' = \gamma(dx - vdt), \quad dy' = dy, \quad dz' = dz, \quad dt' = \gamma[dt - (v/c^2)dx]. \quad (3.12)$$

From the differential form of the velocity components, $v_x = dx/dt$, $v_x' = dx'/dt'$, etc., as obtained from Eq. 3.12, the relationship between velocity components in the primed and unprimed frames of references may be determined. These are

$$v'_x = \frac{v_x - v}{1 - vv_x/c^2}, \quad v'_y = \frac{v_y}{\gamma(1 - vv_x/c^2)}, \quad v'_z = \frac{v_z}{\gamma(1 - vv_x/c^2)} \quad (3.13)$$

Now suppose that a collision occurs between two spherical objects A and B, having masses m_A and m_B, respectively, such that the collision as observed in the unprimed frame of reference is shown in Fig. 3.2, and in the primed frame of reference in Fig. 3.3. The velocity of the point O relative to the point O' is $v = v'_x$; the x-component of velocity for the sphere B is v'_x relative to O'; the x-component of the sphere A is $-v'_x$ relative to O'; and the x-component of A relative to O is zero. According to both Newtonian and Einstein relativity, the magnitudes of the y-components of the spheres A and B are v'_y relative to O' after the collision. However the y-components relative to O are equal in magnitude only in Newtonian relativity. If the y-component of A relative

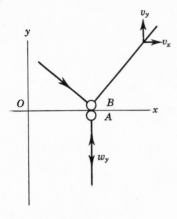

FIG. 3.2. The collision of two particles, A and B, in the unprimed frame of reference.

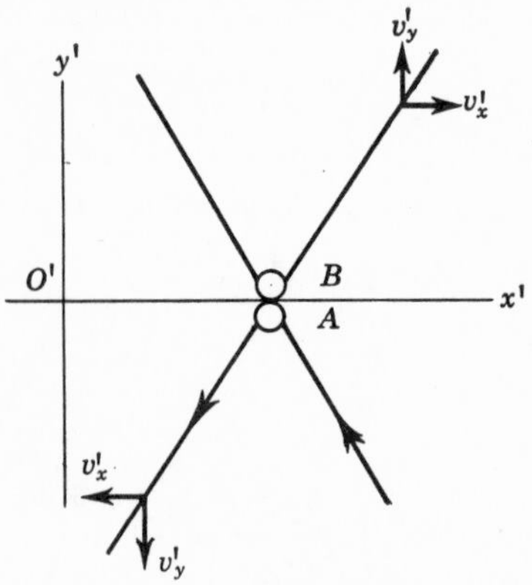

FIG. 3.3. The collision of the same two particles as in Fig. 3.2 in the primed frame of reference.

to O is w_y, its relation to v'_y according to Einstein relativity is $v'_y = w_y/\gamma$, since $w_x = 0$. But for the sphere B, $v'_y = v_y/\gamma(1 - vv_x/c^2)$.

Since the fundamental laws of physics must be valid in all frames of reference, momentum must be conserved in both the primed and unprimed frames of reference. Thus at the time of the collision there must be an equal change in the y-component of momentum for the two spheres, such that $2m_A w_y = 2m_B v_y$. From this

$$\frac{m_B}{m_A} = \frac{w_y}{v_y} = \frac{1}{1 - vv_x/c^2}. \tag{3.14}$$

The velocity of O relative to O', v, is v'_x which, according to the transformation of velocities, is

$$v = v'_x = \frac{v_x - v}{1 - vv_x/c^2} \rightarrow v(1 - vv_x/c^2) = v_x - v. \tag{3.15}$$

This reduces to the binomial expression $(v_x/c^2)v^2 - 2v + v_x = 0$, the solution of which is

$$v = [1 \pm (1 - v_x^2/c^2)^{1/2}]/(v_x/c^2). \tag{3.16}$$

Substituting this value for v into Eq. 3.14, we find

$$m_B/m_A = \pm(1 - v_x^2/c^2)^{-1/2}.$$

The negative sign preceding the right side of this equation has no physical significance, so it will be dropped.

If the y-component velocities are gradually reduced to zero, $w_y \rightarrow 0$ and $v_y \rightarrow 0$, and m_A is at rest, such that $m_A \rightarrow m_0$, the rest mass of the sphere. Under these conditions m_B moves with a velocity $v_x - v$, the mass of m_B relative to an equivalent mass at rest is

$$m_B = m = m_0/(1 - v^2/c^2)^{1/2} = m_0/(1 - \beta^2)^{1/2}, \quad \text{where } \beta = v/c. \quad (3.17)$$

The momentum of a particle having mass m and moving with a velocity v is thus

$$p = mv = m_0 v/(1 - v^2/c^2)^{1/2} = m_0 \beta c/(1 - \beta^2)^{1/2}. \quad (3.18)$$

By definition, force is time rate of change of momentum, $F = d(mv)/dt = m\, dv/dt + v\, dm/dt$. The first term is the customary $F = ma$ term, and the second term is of no consequence in Newtonian mechanics, since mass is assumed constant. This is no longer true in relativistic mechanics. The kinetic energy of an object of mass m moving with a velocity v is, where ds is an incremental length,

$$W_K = \int_0^v F ds = \int_0^v \frac{d}{dt}(mv) \frac{ds}{dt} dt = \int_0^v v\, d(mv)$$

$$= \int_0^v m_0 v\, d \left[\frac{v}{(1 - v^2/c^2)^{1/2}} \right]$$

$$= \int_0^v m_0 v \left[\frac{1}{(1 - v^2/c^2)^{1/2}} + \frac{v^2/c^2}{(1 - v^2/c^2)^{3/2}} \right] dv$$

$$= m_0 \int_0^v \frac{v\, dv}{(1 - v^2/c^2)^{3/2}} = m_0 c^2 \left[\frac{1}{(1 - v^2/c^2)^{1/2}} - 1 \right]$$

$$= mc^2 - m_0 c^2, \quad (3.19)$$

where m is the mass of the particle when moving with a velocity v, and m_0 is the rest mass.

Velocities, momenta, and kinetic energies of particles with atomic dimensions often are of the proper magnitude to require the use of relativistic equations. In fact, it was through the observation of atomic particles that many of the laws of special relativity initially were experimentally validated.

References

G. Joos and I. M. Freeman, *Theoretical Physics* (Blackie and Son, Glasgow, 1951).

F. K. Richtmyer, E. H. Kennard, and T. Lauritsen, *Introduction to Modern Physics* (McGraw-Hill Book Co., Inc., New York, 5th Ed., 1955).

W. H. McCrea, *Relativity Physics* (Methuen and Co., London, 3rd Ed., 1950).

D. C. Peaslee and H. Mueller, *Elements of Atomic Physics* (Prentice-Hall, Inc. Englewood Cliffs, N. J., 1955).

J. R. Pierce, "Relativity and Space Travel," *Proceedings of the IRE* **47**, 1053-1061 (1959).

W. Pauli, *Theory of Relativity* (Pergamon Press, New York, 1958).

H. Bondi, "Relativity," in *Reports on Progress in Physics* (The Physical Society, London, 1959), Vol. 22, pp. 97-120.

Problems

1. Assume that yellow light is used in the Michelson-Morley experiment and that the arms of the Michelson interferometer are of approximately equal length. It was stated that, had the ether existed, a fringe shift of approximately one-third of a fringe would have been expected when the interferometer was rotated through 90°. How long then were the arms of the interferometer?

2. Suppose a 24,000 megacycle/sec oscillator is placed in the nose cone of a rocket. If this nose cone is then put into orbit as a satellite 200 miles above the surface of the earth, what would be expected, according to the theory of relativity, to be the new frequency of the oscillator, as observed at the earth's surface?

3. One of the problems with an experiment of the type described in Problem 2 is that communication is difficult since the satellite is in direct line of sight for such a short time. At higher altitude, though, the satellite would move at a slower speed, so the observed change in frequency would be smaller. If an identical oscillator were operated on the surface of the earth, calculate the beat frequencies between this oscillator and oscillators in satellites in orbit at altitudes of 200 miles and 8000 miles. What would be the magnitude of the phase change between the earth and the satellite oscillators in each case during the period that the satellite is in line of sight? (It should be noted that another effect, part of the general theory of relativity, occurs because of the effects of the gravitational field in which the satellite moves. This effect, though, is not concerned with atomic theory, and is therefore beyond the scope of this book, so only the time dilation effect is to be calculated.)

4. Suppose there are two identical twins, one of whom remains on earth and the other of whom travels in a space ship to the star closest to our solar system (Alpha Centauri, which is four light years away), and returns. If the space ship makes the trip at a speed $\frac{1}{10}$th the speed of light, what will be the difference in age of the twins at the time the space ship returns to earth?

5. In Problem 4, because of the motion of the space ship, observers on the earth measure the passage of time on the ship as occurring at a slower rate than on the earth. People on the ship, though, note no change in the rate at which time passes in their frame of reference than it did when their frame of reference was the surface of the earth. What changes for them is an apparent shortening of the distance between the earth and Alpha Centauri, so they are apparently able to make the trip in a shorter period of time than expected prior to starting the trip. Suppose an observer on earth measures the distance between the earth and Alpha Centauri to be exactly four light years, what is the distance as measured by an observer on a space ship traveling between the two at a speed $\frac{1}{10}$th the speed of light? Compare the answers obtained in Problems 4 and 5.

6. As an electron approaches the speed of light, energy is added as an increase in mass rather than an increase in velocity. When an electron has a mass twice its rest mass, at what speed is it moving, what is its energy in electron volts, and what is its momentum?

7. Make the same calculations as in Problem 6 for the hydrogen atom and for the sodium atom.

8. Perry and Chaffee [*Phys. Rev.* **36**, 904 (1930)] found they had to use the relativistic formulation of kinetic energy in their determination of the ratio of the charge to mass of the electron. In their experiment, illustrated in Fig. 3.4, an oscillator applies a constant frequency to the plates P_1 and P_2. A group of electrons emitted by the cathode K are accelerated by a voltage V applied between the electrodes A and B. If the electrons pass through P_2 exactly one-

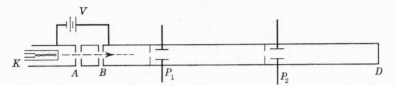

FIG. 3.4.   Schematic diagram of apparatus used to determine the ratio e/m_0 as described in Problem 8.

half cycle, or some multiple of one-half cycle, after they passed through P_1, they strike the detector D at its center. If the electrons arrive at P_2 either slightly earlier or slightly later than exactly one-half cycle they are deflected either up or down by the field between the plates of P_2, and strike the detector D either above or below its center. With an accelerating voltage $V = 10,766$ volts, Perry and Chaffee found that the time of passage for an electron between the two plates is exactly one cycle when there is an applied frequency of 80.683 megacycles/sec. The distance between P_1 and P_2 is 75.133 cm. Calculate e/m_0.

9. In Problem 10, Chapter 2, what is the percentage change in the value of e/m if the effects of the relativistic change in mass are considered?

10. Would there be any change because of relativistic effects in the answers to Problems 14 and 15, chapter 1?

11. Some high energy accelerators produce electrons with kinetic energies as high as 10^9 ev. At this energy what is the ratio of the mass of the electron to the electron rest mass? What is its mass in grams?

12. What is the velocity of a steel shot $\frac{1}{16}$th inch in diameter which has the same momentum as the electron of Problem 11? What would be the kinetic energy in electron volts of the steel shot if it were moving with a velocity equal to the velocity of the electron of Problem 11?

13. Convert the energies calculated for the electron in Problem 11 and for the steel shot of Problem 12 into watt-hours.

Chapter IV

THE WAVE PARTICLE DILEMMA

4.1 Particles or Waves? The preceding chapters assume that electrons, protons, and alpha particles are particles in the same sense as some small but visible object, such as a steel ball bearing, is a piece of matter. The assumption is also made that electromagnetic radiation is simply a continuing series of waves of electric and magnetic fields. However, much experimental evidence has been accumulated over the past several decades which indicates that such a clear distinction between waves and particles cannot be made when objects having atomic dimensions are observed. Electromagnetic radiation, for example, has been shown to possess certain characteristics distinctly applicable to particle mechanics. In addition, atomic size particles have been diffracted in much the same way as light is diffracted, and therefore must possess a characteristic wavelength. What, then, is there to distinguish a particle from a wave, or is there any real distinction? From this wave-particle dilemma have come the ideas fundamental to the development of quantum mechanics. The experimental evidence and the theoretical interpretations that led to the wave-particle dilemma, and ultimately to quantum mechanics, are discussed in this chapter.

4.2 Black-Body Radiation. The earliest evidence that casts doubt upon the simple assumption that particles and waves are distinctly different came from the study of the spectral characteristics of black-body radiation. A black body is simply an object that absorbs all the radiation incident upon it. A black body placed in an enclosure having uniform temperature comes to equilibrium with the temperature of the enclosure and emits as much radiation as it absorbs. In practice such conditions very nearly exist in the interior of a completely enclosed furnace in which a steady state has been established. If a small hole is opened in the side of the furnace, enough radiation can escape for experimental study of its spectral characteristics, without disturbing the equilibrium conditions of the interior. The emitted energy, which is directly proportional to the energy density within the furnace (see Problem 2), plotted as a function of wavelength, shows distributions of the type shown in Fig. 4.1. The exact form of this distribution of energy as a function of wavelength cannot be deduced from classical thermodymanics. Based on classical thermodynamics, though, Wien was able in 1893 to deduce that within the furnace the radiant energy density u_λ $(\lambda, T)d\lambda$ between the wavelengths λ and $\lambda + d\lambda$ is u_λ $(\lambda, T)d\lambda = (d\lambda/\lambda^5)f(\lambda T)$, in which the form of the function $f(\lambda T)$ is not determined, but is a function only of the wavelength λ of the radiation times the temperature T of the radiating body.

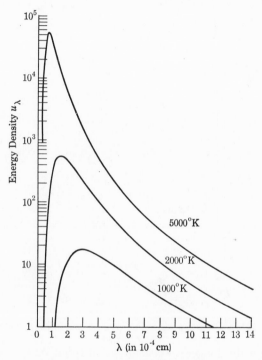

FIG. 4.1. Plots of the radiation energy density as a function of wavelength for the interior of enclosed furnaces at 1000°K, 2000°K, and 5000°K.

Subsequently, on the basis of classical theoretical considerations, Wien derived an energy distribution formula u_λ $(\lambda, T)d\lambda = C_1\lambda^{-5}$ exp $(-C_2/\lambda T)d\lambda$ and further showed that the energy maximum of the curve for any temperature T occurs at a wavelength λ_m, such that $\lambda_m T =$ a constant. A somewhat different approach was taken by Jeans who, basing his calculations upon earlier work by Rayleigh, showed (see Appendix 4.1), from considerations of statistical mechanics and electromagnetic theory, that the function f should be given by $f(\lambda T) = 8\pi\lambda kT$, where k is Boltzmann's constant.

Neither of these formulas agree with experimental observations. As seen in Fig. 4.2, the Wien distribution fits the experimental distribution at the shorter wavelengths and the Rayleigh-Jeans distribution ap-

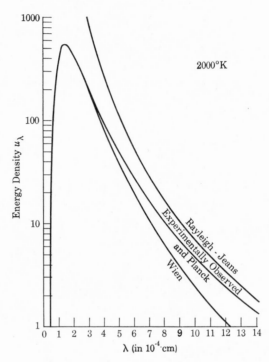

FIG. 4.2. Plots of experimentally observed (Planck) spectral distribution of radiation energy density for a furnace temperature of 2000°K, with comparative plots of the Wien distribution and the Rayleigh-Jeans distribution.

proaches it at the longer wavelengths. Although the Rayleigh-Jeans formulation seems farthest from the true distribution, it was the reasoning involved in the derivation of that law which led Planck to the correct formulation. By considering that radiation interacts with oscillators in the walls of the container, the Rayleigh-Jeans formula had been derived using the theory of the equipartition of energy. This derivation became entangled with the short wavelength dilemma, because the resulting Rayleigh-Jeans formula states that $u_\lambda \to \infty$ as $\lambda \to 0$, and the integral of u_λ over all λ, the total radiation density, does not converge. This lack of convergence means that there must be an infinite amount of energy in black-body radiation, a conclusion that clearly does not agree with experiment. Planck first decided that the key to the solution of the problem existed in a proper understanding of the emission and absorption of radiation by the oscillators in the walls. In due course, Planck came to the assumption, really radical for that time, that the radiation emitted by the oscillator is not emitted over a continuous energy range but in bundles or quanta, the energies of which are proportional to the frequency ν of the radiation. This conclusion is derived, as in Appendix 4.2, from the assumption that the oscillators can possess only selected energies, a conclusion that will later be derived from quantum mechanical considerations. The constant of proportionality is h, now known as *Planck's constant*. Through this line of reasoning he was able to derive a formula which did fit the distribution of black-body radiation energy density as a function of radiation wavelength:

$$u_\lambda(\lambda, T)d\lambda = \frac{d\lambda}{\lambda^5} \frac{8\pi ch}{\exp\left[\dfrac{ch}{k\lambda T}\right] - 1} = \frac{8\pi d\lambda}{\lambda^4} \frac{h\nu}{\exp\left[\dfrac{h\nu}{kT}\right] - 1}. \tag{4.1}$$

This was the beginning of the quantum theory of radiation, a really radical departure from the assumption that had existed prior to that time — that electromagnetic radiation is some sort of continuous wave phenomenon.

4.3 The Photoelectric Effect. The spectral distribution of radiant energy emitted by a black body as a function of wavelength led Planck to quantize the amount of energy emitted or absorbed at the walls of the radiator, but he made no assumption regarding the nature of light itself. However, concurrent experimentation on the photoelectric effect subsequently led Einstein to the conclusion that the radiation itself is also quantized.

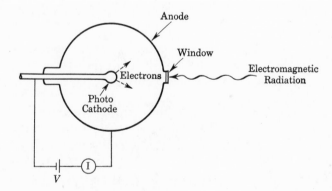

Fig. 4.3. Schematic diagram of the photoelectric effect experiment. [Based on experimental arrangement by L. Apker, E. Taft, and J. Dickey, *Phys. Rev.* **73**, 46 (1948)]

To illustrate the experimental observations that led Einstein to his conclusions, consider the photoelectric cell illustrated in Fig. 4.3. If a potential is applied between its electrodes, and a beam of light of sufficiently short wavelength is used to irradiate its cathode, an electric current is measured by the ammeter, I. Thus, under these conditions, a current must flow across the space between the electrodes of the photoelectric cell, electrons being emitted by the cathode and collected by the anode.

There is an upper wavelength limit for which the photoelectric process can occur. This wavelength limit (frequence threshold) at which the photoelectric process can be triggered has been found experimentally to depend on the type of material from which the cathode is made. For a cesium cathode the limit is about 6500 A in the visible region, but for tungsten (wolfram) the limit is at about 2800 A, in the ultraviolet. Thus, visible light can initiate the photoelectric effect from a cesium surface but not from a tungsten surface.

In the classical theory of electromagnetic radiation, energy is measured only in terms of intensity and is independent of wavelength. Experimentally, though, it is found that radiation having a wavelength greater than the wavelength limit for the photoelectric effect can produce no electrons regardless of its intensity. On the other hand, any radiation, even radiation of extremely low intensity, having a wavelength below the photoelectric limit causes photoelectrons to be ejected from the cathode.

If the wavelength of the incident radiation covers a limited spectral region, any change in wavelength produces changes in the distribution of photoelectron kinetic energies. On the other hand, if the radiation wavelength remains fixed, the distribution of electron energies also remains fixed, regardless of the radiation intensity, but the number of electrons increases by an amount directly proportional to the radiation intensity.

It was from this evidence that Einstein proposed that radiation itself is quantized, and that the energy of each quantum, or photon, as it is often called, is $W = h\nu$, the product of Planck's constant and the radiation frequency. The fact that a threshold energy $h\nu_0$ is required to eject an electron from a metal surface means that electrons are held in the metal with a binding energy, $h\nu_0$, sometimes called the *work function* of the metal. If an incident photon has an energy, $h\nu$, greater than the threshold energy, it can cause an electron to be released photoelectrically from a surface with a kinetic energy as high as

$$W_K = (m - m_0)c^2 = h\nu - h\nu_0 \qquad (4.2)$$

but no higher. The mechanism for the photoelectric emission of electrons from a surface is discussed in more detail in Chapter 10.

4.4 Relation of Electron Volts to Wavelength. The photon is one of the quantities for which the electron volt (see Section 2.5) is well suited as a measure of energy. Since the energy of a single photon is $h\nu$ and the relationship between frequency and wavelength is $\lambda = c/\nu$, the wavelength of a photon having an energy of 1 ev is

$$\lambda = hc/eV = \frac{(6.63 \times 10^{-27}\text{erg sec})(3.00 \times 10^{10}\text{cm/sec})}{(4.80 \times 10^{-10}\text{ statcoulomb})(1/300)(\text{statvolt})}$$

$$= 12.4 \times 10^{-5}\text{ cm} = 12400\text{ A}.$$

By a similar calculation, it can be seen that a photon in the visible region (say 5000 A) has energy

$$W = hc/\lambda = \frac{(6.63 \times 10^{-27}\text{ erg sec})(3.00 \times 10^{10}\text{ cm/sec})}{5.00 \times 10^{-5}\text{ cm}}$$

$$= 3.96 \times 10^{-12}\text{ erg} = 2.5\text{ ev}.$$

In the x-ray region a photon of 1 A wavelength has an energy

$$W = \frac{(6.63 \times 10^{-27}\text{ erg sec})(3.00 \times 10^{10}\text{ cm/sec})}{10^{-8}\text{ cm}}$$

$$= 1.98 \times 10^{-8}\text{ ergs} = 12400\text{ ev}.$$

Since energy is inversely proportional to wavelength, this equation is useful in relating electron volts to the most common unit of wavelength — angstroms. Note that the product of the wavelength of a photon in angstroms multiplied by the energy in electron volts is always numerically 12400.

It is customary to use the abbreviation kev for 1000 ev and the abbreviation Mev for a million electron volts energy.

4.5 The Compton Effect. Einstein's quantization of electromagnetic radiation led people to consider the photon as a type of particle. If this is true, the photon must demonstrate the same properties as other particles. Among these properties are conservation of energy and momentum in a collision with another particle, such as, for example, a free electron. If a photon having energy $h\nu$ and momentum $h\nu/c$ collides with a free electron at rest, as illustrated in Fig. 4.4, it should impart some of its energy and momentum to the electron in accordance with the customary laws of mechanics. This type of interaction is known as a Compton interaction, since it was A. H. Compton who first experimentally observed and explained this effect.

If, after the collision, the electron moves at an angle θ with respect to the direction of motion of the incident photon, and the photon is scattered at an angle ϕ with a scattered energy $h\nu'$, a series of three

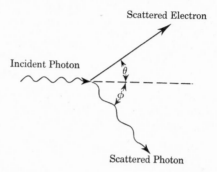

FIG. 4.4. The Compton type interaction.

equations expresses the conservation of energy and momentum of the interaction.

To conserve energy the sum of the electron kinetic energy and the energy of the scattered photon must be the same as the energy of the incident photon,

$$h\nu = h\nu' + m_0c^2[1/(1 - \beta^2)^{1/2} - 1]. \tag{4.3}$$

Since momentum is a vector quantity, two equations must be developed to express the conservation of momentum, one of which states that the x-component of momentum remains constant and the other that the y-component remains constant. These equations are:

$$h\nu/c = m_0\beta c \cos\theta/(1 - \beta^2)^{1/2} + h\nu' \cos\phi/c, \tag{4.4a}$$

$$0 = m_0\beta c \sin\theta/(1 - \beta^2)^{1/2} - h\nu' \sin\phi/c. \tag{4.4b}$$

In these three equations there are five variables, ν, ν', β, θ, and ϕ, all of which depend on the experimental conditions. If two of these quantities are experimentally known, the other three may then be calculated. Often, as in Compton's original experiment, it is the energy, $h\nu$, of the incident photon and the angle, ϕ, through which this photon is scattered that are experimentally known. If this is so, the problem becomes a matter of mathematically solving the three equations to determine the other three variables. One such method eliminates the variables β and θ to get an expression for the change in wavelength of the photon as a function of its angle of scattering. Such an algebraic solution of the three equations leads to the condition that

$$c/\nu' - c/\nu = \lambda' - \lambda = \Delta\lambda = (h/m_0c)(1 - \cos\phi). \tag{4.5}$$

This difference in wavelength of the incident and scattered photons is known as the *Compton shift*. The length $h/m_0c = 2.426 \times 10^{-10}$ cm is called the *Compton wavelength*. In magnitude it is the wavelength of a photon for which the energy is just equal to the rest energy, m_0c^2, of an electron.

It will appear again later when other wave properties involving the electron are discussed.

Other physical quantities may also be calculated, such as the energy of the scattered photon,

$$hv' = m_0c^2/[(m_0c^2/hv) + 1 - \cos \phi], \qquad (4.6)$$

or the kinetic energy of the scattered electron,

$$W_K = hv - hv'$$

$$= (hv)(hv/m_0c^2)(1 - \cos \phi)/[1 + (hv/m_0c^2)(1 - \cos \phi)]$$

$$= (hv)2(hv/m_0c^2) \cos^2 \theta/\{[1 + (hv/m_0c^2)]^2$$
$$- (hv/m_0c^2)^2 \cos^2 \theta\}. \quad (4.7)$$

That these processes do occur in the manner indicated, and that energy and momentum are conserved according to these equations has been shown in a number of experiments. In his original work Compton showed that the wavelength of the scattered photons differed from the wavelength of the incident photons in accordance with the equation for the Compton shift, depending on the angle of scattering but not upon the energy of the incident radiation nor upon the type of scattering material. The experimental arrangement is shown in Fig. 4.5. Characteris-

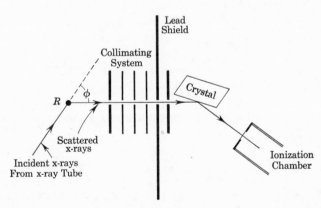

FIG. 4.5. Experimental arrangement used by Compton. [*Phys. Rev.* **22**, 409 (1923)]

tic molybdenum x-rays from an x-ray tube are scattered from a scattering block, R, through an angle ϕ. The radiations are analyzed by crystal diffraction (see next section). The results are shown in Fig. 4.6. In each case some radiation is scattered by another process with the original incident wavelength, but there is also radiation, the wavelength of which differs from the incident wavelength in accordance with the

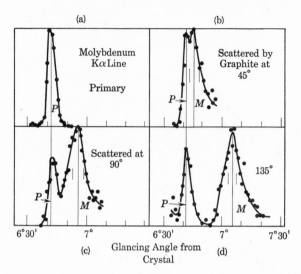

FIG. 4.6.   Results of Compton's original experiment. [*Phys. Rev.* **22**, 409 (1923)]

equation for the Compton shift, this being the radiation that is scattered from essentially free electrons in the scattering block.

4.6 X-Ray Diffraction.

From the results of the black-body radiation studies, the photoelectric effect and the Compton effect, it is relatively easy to begin to believe that electromagnetic radiation simply consists of beams of some sort of particle having zero rest mass. This experimental results certainly tend to lead toward this type of conclusion. In this radical departure from classical considerations, sight must not be lost of the fact that electromagnetic radiations of all wavelengths may still be shown to have the same wave properties that have characterized the longer wavelength electromagnetic radiations.

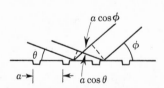

FIG. 4.7.   Cross sectional view of diffraction grating, illustrating schematically the principles of x-ray diffraction.

It is customary to use a diffraction grating for measuring the wavelength of electromagnetic radiation in the visible and near visible parts of the spectrum. A diffraction grating for the visible region is made by ruling a regular, repetitive pattern of scratches on a reflecting surface, as shown in Fig. 4.7, where adjacent scratches are separated by a distance a. If a wave front is incident upon this surface at a grazing angle θ, radiations reflected from various parts of the grating are out of phase at most angles of reflection. But those radiations which are reflected at a grazing angle ϕ such that $n\lambda = a(\cos \theta - \cos \phi)$, where n is an integer, are in phase from all the reflecting surfaces. The amplitudes of all the reflected beams of radiation interfere constructively at the angle of reflection ϕ, and the radiation intensity maximizes in that direction. There are certain limitations on the radiations which may be so diffracted. The maximum wavelength which may be diffracted in the first order $(n = 1)$ is $\lambda = 2a$. This occurs only if $\cos \theta = 1$ and $\cos \phi = -1$. On the other hand, if the wavelength of the incident radiation is much smaller than the grating spacing a, differences between the grazing angles of reflection, ϕ, for different orders (different values of n) are so small that diffraction is not easily observed. The best diffraction patterns are obtained when the grating spacing is just slightly larger than, but of the same order of magnitude as the wavelength of the incident radiation. Most ruled gratings are made with spacings appropriate to the study of radiations in the visible or near visible part of the spectrum. For x-rays scattered from such gratings the differences between the angles θ and ϕ are extremely small, and observation of diffraction patterns becomes very difficult, even though some of the longer wavelength x-rays have been successfully observed with a ruled diffraction grating.

Fortunately, nature provides a diffraction grating which has spacings of the correct dimensions for most x-ray wavelengths. These are crystalline substances, the atoms of which are regularly spaced in three-dimensional arrays with interatomic spacings d. The cross section for a cubic crystal, such as NaCl, is illustrated in Fig. 4.8. Since crystals are three-dimensional, additional conditions are imposed for successful diffraction of the radiation. Not only must waves diffracted by all atoms in a single plane be in phase, but waves diffracted from various planes within the crystal must also be in phase. The first condition may be met for all wavelengths by keeping $\phi = \theta$. By consulting Fig. 4.8 it can be seen that the second condition imposes the requirement that $n\lambda = 2d \sin \theta$. These two conditions are known as *Bragg's law* for x-ray reflection, and the angle θ is known as the Bragg angle. The atoms in many crystals are arranged in patterns other than cubic, so the distance d between the atomic planes may be a function of the direction of the planes within the crystal from which the x-rays are reflected. This is sometimes true even for cubic crystals, as x-rays may be reflected with constructive interference from planes formed by atoms other than those in

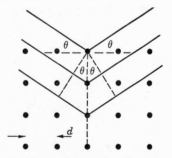

Fig. 4.8. Schematic illustration of principles of x-ray diffraction by a cubic crystal.

planes parallel to the sides of the cube. Such reflection is illustrated in Section 4.8 by means of Fig. 4.14.

A typical experimental arrangement for measuring x-ray wavelength is shown in Fig. 4.9. X-rays originating in the x-ray tube are analyzed by

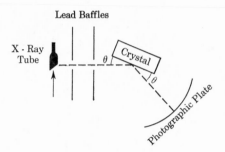

FIG. 4.9. Experimental arrangement for the diffraction of x-rays from a single crystal.

rotating the crystal on a platform. The relative intensity of the x-ray wavelength related to the corresponding Bragg angle is recorded at the appropriate place on the photographic film. Some sort of constant period of rotation of the crystal is required to maintain proper relative intensities on the film. This is the system of analysis used in Fig. 4.6 for the determination of the Compton scattered photon wavelength.

A method of x-ray diffraction not requiring mechanical motion of the apparatus is the powdered crystal method, illustrated in Fig. 4.10. The

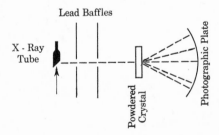

FIG. 4.10. Experimental arrangement for the diffraction of x-rays from a powdered crystal.

powdered sample used for diffraction is made up of an extremely large number of very small crystals which, when assembled as a powder, offer a complete assembly of random orientations, such that an appropriate Bragg angle can be found in some of the crystals for any x-ray wavelength. Uniform rotation of the diffracting crystal is no longer necessary. The diffracted radiations from a monochromatic incident x-ray beam appear as circles on the film, the center of each circle being at the point O at which the undeflected x-ray beam strikes the film.

Crystal diffraction experiments show the wave characteristics of x-rays. X-ray wavelengths as short as 0.00025 A have been measured by the crystal method. From such diffraction experiments it is seen that electromagnetic radiation retains its wave properties, even for photons, such as x-rays, that have quite predominant particle characteristics.

4.7 X-Ray Short Wavelength Limit. Additional experimental evidence which may be used to verify the quantum nature of electromagnetic radiation can be obtained through a study of the radiation produced when electrons are stopped by some target material. The spectrum of the radiation produced by such interactions consists of a continuous radiation that evolves as the electrons are stopped in the target material. Such spectra are shown in Fig. 4.11 for tungsten,

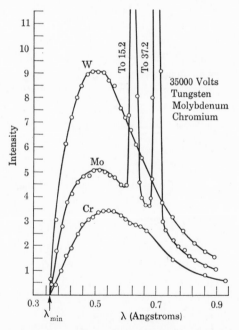

FIG. 4.11. Bremsstrahlung spectra, illustrating short wavelength limit λ_{min}. [C. T. Ulrey, *Phys. Rev.* **11**, 405 (1918)]

molybdenum, and chromium targets. Sometimes, as for molybdenum in Fig. 4.11, there are superposed on the continuous spectrum distinct peaks characteristic of the target material. The nature of these peaks will become evident in the later discussions of atomic structure. The continuous spectrum is known as *bremsstrahlung*.

According to classical theory, radiation should be produced by the very large accelerations or decelerations resulting from collisions between the incident electrons and the component parts of the atoms of the target material. This radiation is predicted to produce a continuous spectrum over all wavelengths. This is not quite what is actually seen, however, for there is a lower limit to the wavelength of the continuous spectrum. Below this lower limit the radiation intensity is zero.

Experimentally it is found that the energy of the incident electrons just equals the energy of a photon having a wavelength equal to the minimum observable wavelength of the bremsstrahlung spectrum. This further shows the quantum or particle nature of electromagnetic radiation because it indicates that a single photon cannot carry away more energy than the kinetic energy of the electron that initiated the interaction which produced it.

4.8 The Wave Properties of the Electron.

The past few sections have been devoted to the theories and experiments which establish a dual wave-particle nature for electromagnetic radiation. With this dual nature rather thoroughly proven, deBroglie proposed that the electron may have similar dual characteristics. If the momentum of the photon is h/λ, perhaps the same relationship holds for the electron as well. In this case the wavelength of the electron would be related to the momentum such that

$$\lambda = h/mv = (h/m_0c)(1 - \beta^2)^{1/2}/\beta. \tag{4.8}$$

Substitution of realistic magnitudes of electron momenta into this equation reveals that electron wavelengths should be about the same as those of x-rays. Thus experimental verification of the wave nature of an electron should be possible and would most probably use the same experimental techniques as were used for the study of the wave characteristics of x-rays. This type of experiment was performed by Davisson and Germer [*Phys. Rev.* **30**, 705 (1927)]. A schematic representation of the experimental arrangement is shown in Fig. 4.12. An electron beam was incident normally upon a nickel crystalline surface. It was found that electrons were reflected from this surface in all directions, but that the distribution as a function of scattering angle, ϕ, changed with energy of the incident beam. For incident electrons having 54 ev kinetic energy, a clear peak occurred at about 50° scattering angle, as illustrated in Fig. 4.13. This peak occurred at slightly different angles for other energies. The surface grating spacing, illustrated in Fig. 4.14, was 2.15 A for the crystal used in the experiment. For a scattering angle of 50° the grazing angles of incidence and reflection would be $\theta = 65°$ and diffraction would occur from a plane within the crystal in which the spacing $d = 0.91$ A.

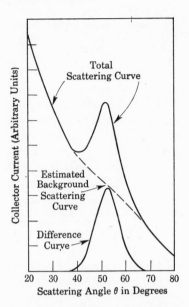

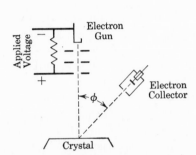

Fig. 4.12. Experimental arrangement used by Davisson and Germer for diffraction of electrons. [*Phys. Rev.* **30**, 705 (1927)]

Fig. 4.13. Results of Davisson and Germer experiment. [*Phys. Rev.* **30**, 705 (1927)]

Thus the experimentally measured wavelength of the electron is $\lambda = 2d \sin \theta = 2(0.91 \text{ A}) (\sin 65°) = 1.65 \text{ A}$. The wavelength for 54 ev electrons according to deBroglie's theory should be $\lambda = 1.67 \text{ A}$, in excellent agreement with experimentally observed results.

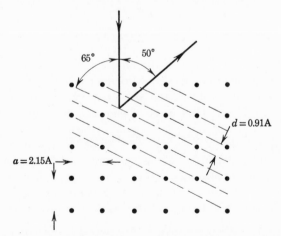

Fig. 4.14. Illustrating Bragg angle of electron diffraction in Davisson and Germer experiment.

These results entail an entirely new concept for the electron. No longer can it be considered just as a hard spherical particle resembling a miniaturized billiard ball. It possesses other properties for which there is no really good analogy in objects which can be seen visually. The electron, as well as the photon, is some sort of bundle of waves which are confined to a sufficiently small region in space so that this bundle can act as a whole in collisions with other particles. In such collisions both the electron and the photon conserve energy and momentum in accordance with the same laws of mechanics that were developed for Newtonian mechanical systems. Yet the wave properties of these physical entities, and hence the electrons or photons themselves, must be spread over a sufficiently large region that their wave fronts are presented to enough atoms in a crystal for them to be diffracted by that crystal in accordance with the laws developed for the diffraction of an incident plane wave by a diffraction grating.

G. P. Thomson experimentally observed the circular rings of powdered crystals when he sent beams of monoenergetic electrons through appropriate thin metallic foils. Had the electrons been strictly of a particulate nature, the angular distribution after penetration would have been a continuous function of angle. Diffraction rings, similar to the x-ray powdered crystal type of pattern were observed after electrons passed through a thin gold foil that had been rolled, a process which breaks the crystalline structure of the metal into innumerable small crystals.

Calculations of the grating spacing of crystals by the electron diffraction method yields results almost identical with those obtained by the x-ray diffraction method, indicating that the wave nature of electrons and photons must be quite similar.

4.9 The Heisenberg Uncertainty Principle. The dual wave-particle nature of photons and atomic particles leads to a problem in the exact determination of some of the physical characteristics of either of them. By using the principles of Newtonian mechanics, it is theoretically possible to observe an object and to determine exactly where it is and how fast it is moving. The degree of precision is determined simply by the ability of an experimenter to make measurements in the macroscopic world in which he lives. If the laws of Newtonian mechanics are strictly true, the problem of making more precise measurements is simply a matter of making more precise measuring instruments. This, though, is a fallacious assumption. In the world which can be seen in everyday living, all objects are so large and so massive that the wavelength of any object in motion is so tiny that it can be ignored in comparison with the dimensions of the object. Therefore only its particle characteristics are observed; measurements are made on only a part of it. When a very small particle, such as an electron for example, is observed, its wave characteristics cannot be ignored. Likewise in the interactions of electrons with electromagnetic radiation, the particle characteristics of the radiation must be considered. This dual wave-particle nature of matter leads to an indeterminacy in the ability to specify the exact nature of certain physical quantities, expressed by Heisenberg in his *uncertainty principle*.

The uncertainty principle states first of all that an experiment cannot be devised which simultaneously fixes the momentum and the location of a particle with unlimited precision, but only within a momentum-position range such that $\Delta p \Delta x \geq h$, where h is Planck's constant, Δp is the uncertainty in the momentum of the particle, and Δx is the uncertainty in the variable that fixes the position of the particle at the time of observation. It is possible to devise an experiment in which the determination of the momentum and position are much poorer than these requirements, but never better than $\Delta p \Delta x = h$. Based upon this uncertainty in the momentum and the location of a particle, a related equation can also be derived showing that the product of the uncertainty in the energy of a system and the duration of the time interval during which the system is at that energy is $\Delta W \Delta t \geq h$.

That this uncertainty exists can be shown by a hypothetical observation of the position and momentum of an electron, made by scattering a photon of light from the electron into a microscope, as illustrated in Fig. 4.15. If the photon is scattered from the electron below the objective lens of the microscope, it may scatter anywhere within the range of angles between $-\theta$ and $+\theta$ and still be focused by the microscope. If the

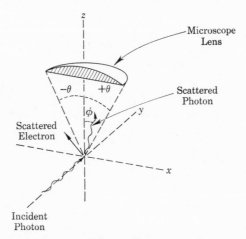

FIG. 4.15.   Illustrating the uncertainty principle by photon scattering from an electron.

J oe W orro

photon is incident from the y-direction, it initially has no x-component of momentum. If this photon is scattered by the electron into the xz-plane at an angle ϕ, the x-component of photon momentum is then $h \sin \phi /\lambda$. To conserve momentum an oppositely directed x-component of momentum must be imparted to the electron at the time of collision. Because the photon is observed through the microscope for all values of ϕ between $-\theta$ and $+\theta$, photons with all possible x-components of momentum between $-h \sin \theta /\lambda$ and $+h \sin \theta /\lambda$ will get into the microscope and be focused at the eyepiece. As a result the photon is observed throughout the range of momentum components p_x defined within the interval $\Delta p_x = 2h \sin \theta /\lambda$. There is no limit on the precision with which p_x may be determined, Δp_x may be made arbitrarily small, provided λ can be made very large or θ very small. This implies then that there is no limit on the precision with which the momentum of the electron can be determined.

It is known from physical optics that diffraction causes the image of a point source of light to appear broadened, the amount of broadening being dependent on the wavelength of the radiation used to observe the position of the particle. From the laws of physical optics the precision with which this broadening to the image can be located, the resolving power of the microscope,* is given by the equation $\Delta x = \lambda /2 \sin \theta$.

If λ can be made arbitrarily small there is no real limitation on the lower limit of Δx. This, though, is inconsistent with the fact that to define the x-component of the momentum of the electron within a small increment Δp_x requires a large λ. Furthermore a small θ, which can assist in defining the momentum, increases the magnitude of Δx. The conclusion that must be reached is that it is impossible to simultaneously make Δp_x and Δx arbitrarily small. The limiting accuracy for Δp_x and Δx is $\Delta p_x \Delta x = (2h \sin \theta /\lambda) (\lambda /2 \sin \theta) = h$.

Going now to the consideration of the energy of the system and the duration of the time interval in which the system is in that energy state, consider a particle moving with a momentum p. The kinetic energy of this particle is $W_K = p^2 /2m$. The rate at which the energy changes as a function of momentum is found by differentiation to be $dW_K /dp = p /m$ and, if the energy and momentum intervals are not infinitesimally small, $\Delta W_K /\Delta p = p /m$. For nonrelativistic speeds the quantity p /m is velocity, such that $p /m = \Delta x /\Delta t$, and $\Delta W_K = (\Delta x /\Delta t)\Delta p$. But it has already been shown that $\Delta p \Delta x \geq h$, such that $\Delta W_K \geq h /\Delta t$, from which it can be concluded that $\Delta W_K \Delta t \geq h$. The total energy W of a system is the sum of the rest energy and the kinetic energy. Because the rest energy is constant, $\Delta W = \Delta W_K$. Thus the product of the minimum uncer-

---

*See, for example, F. A. Jenkins and H. E. White, *Fundamentals of Optics* (McGraw-Hill Book Co., Inc., New York, 2nd Ed., 1950), pp. 297-299, or B. Rossi, *Optics* (Addison-Wesley Publishing Co., Inc., Reading, Mass.), pp 208-211.

tainty of the energy of the system and the duration of the time in which the system is at that energy is never less than h, Planck's constant.

This uncertainty in the ability of an experimenter to observe precisely certain quantities is an inherent part of the dual wave-particle nature of atomic entities. The laws of mechanics that are used for particles having atomic dimensions must take this into account. Therefore it is necessary to have mechanical laws that are different from those devised by Newton to explain the gross physical phenomena that can be observed visually. This new system of mechanics is found in quantum mechanics, which is introduced in Chapter 6.

References

R. A. Smith, F. E. Jones, and R. P. Chasmar, *The Detection and Measurement of Infra Red Radiation* (Oxford University Press, New York, 1957).

F. K. Richtmyer, E. H. Kennard, and T. Lauritsen, *Introduction to Modern Physics* (McGraw-Hill Book Co., Inc., New York, 5th Ed., 1955).

J. H. Jeans, *Philosophical Magazine* **10**, 91 (1905).

A. L. Hughes and L. A. DuBridge, *Photoelectric Phenomena* (McGraw-Hill Book Co., New York, 1932).

A. H. Compton and S. K. Allison, *X-Rays in Theory and Experiment* (D. Van Nostrand Company, Princeton, N. J., 2nd Ed., 1935).

C. F. Meyer, *The Diffraction of Light, X-rays and Material Particles* (J. W. Edwards, Publisher, Inc., Ann Arbor, Michigan, 2nd Ed., 1949).

J. D. Stranathan, *The Particles of Modern Physics* (McGraw-Hill Book Co., Inc., New York, 1942).

G. Gamow, "The Principle of Uncertainty," *Scientific American* **198**, No. 1, 51 (1958).

Problems

1. At what wavelength is the peak in the intensity of the radiation from a black body at 1000° K? At 5000° K? Which of these spectra would be best visible to the human eye? What is the ratio of the magnitudes of the peak in-intensities of these two spectra?

2. Equation 4.1 gives the energy density, u_λ, of the radiation within an enclosure that is in thermal equilibrium. Since this radiation is moving in all directions, its density is greater than the density of radiation from a single black surface. Furthermore, radiation intensity is usually measured by some sort of detector that collects the radiation over a period of time and does not measure the density of radiation in a unit volume at any instant in time. If a small surface of a black-body radiator, subtending a solid angle $\Delta\omega$, is observed at a detector show that the measured radiation intensity is $cu_\lambda\Delta\omega/4\pi$. If the radiation from an infinite plane surface emitting as a black body is observed, show that the radiation intensity is $cu_\lambda/4$. Note: In making the second calculation remember that a unit surface area appears smaller by a factor $\cos\theta$ when viewed from some angle θ with respect to a direction perpendicular to the surface.

3. The tungsten filament of a 100-watt light bulb operates at a temperature of about 2850° K. Assuming that it emits as a black body, what percentage of the radiation emitted is in the visible part of the spectrum?

4. Calculate the work function in electron volts of cesium and of tungsten from the wavelength limit for the photoelectric process, given in Section 4.3.

5. If monochromatic electromagnetic radiation of 4000 A wavelength is incident upon a cesium surface, what energy electrons are emitted? If these electrons are accelerated through a potential of 100 volts and then sent through an evacuated region into a magnetic flux density of 500 gauss, with what radius of curvature are the electrons bent?

6. Suppose a photon with an energy of 100 kev interacts by means of a Compton collision with a free electron at rest. What is the energy of the scattered electron if it moves in the same direction after the collision that the photon moved prior to the collision? At an angle of 30° with this direction? At an angle of 45° with this direction? At an angle of 85° with this direction?

7. In each of the cases of Problem 6, calculate the energy of the scattered photon, and the angle between its direction of motion and the direction of motion of the incident photon.

8. Suppose that, instead of being at rest, the electron had initially been moving with a kinetic energy of 9.7 kev toward the incident photon along line of approach of the latter. How would this change, in the laboratory system of coordinates, the equations for the energies of the scattered electron and for the scattered photon as a function of scattering angle?

9. Suppose the electron of Problem 8 had been initially moving at right angles to the direction of motion of the incident photon. What effect on the resulting equations for the scattered electron energy and the scattered photon energy would this have made?

10. Show that a photon cannot transfer all its energy and momentum to a single electron.

11. Sometimes an effective mass m is assigned to a photon in terms of the momentum relationship $h\nu/c = mc$. What is the effective mass of a 5000 A photon? Of a photon with an energy of 1 kev? Of a photon with an energy of 1 Mev?

12. A NaCl crystal is a simple cubic lattice with sodium and chlorine atoms in alternate positions in the lattice. The distance between any atom and its nearest neighbor is 2.820 A. With a monochromatic x-ray incident upon the surface of a NaCl crystal, the first Bragg angle is found to be at 10°. What is the wavelength of the incident x-radiation? At what angle would the second Bragg reflection occur?

13. At 18° C the density of KCl is 1.98930 gm/cm³. The crystalline structure of KCl is a simple cubic, as is NaCl (see Problem 12). Y. Tu [*Phys. Rev.* **40,** 662 (1932)] found that the Bragg angle for first order diffraction of molybdenum $K\alpha_1$ radiation (0.7093 A) is 6° 28′ 29.0″. Calculate Avogadro's number from this information.

14. If molybdenum $K\alpha_1$ x-rays are incident at a grazing angle of 10′ on a diffraction grating having 500 lines per cm, at what angle will the first order and second order diffraction maxima appear?

15. M. Siegbahn was able to rule gratings with 1800 lines to the millimeter. Under the same conditions as in Problem 14, at what angle would the first order diffraction maximum occur?

16. Compare the wavelength of an electron with a kinetic energy of 1 kev to the wavelength of a 1 kev x-ray. Make the same comparison for an electron kinetic energy and an x-ray energy of 100 kev.

17. Suppose electrons with a kinetic energy of 70 ev are incident at a grazing angle of 5′ on a diffraction grating with 1300 lines to the centimeter. At what angle are diffraction maxima expected?

18. Other atomic particles besides electrons also possess characteristic wavelengths. At room temperature (20° C) what is the wavelength of a helium atom moving with its most probable speed in a helium gas?

19. Compare the minimum uncertainty in locating a 1-gram mass moving with a velocity of 100 cm/sec with minimum uncertainty in locating an electron moving with a velocity of 10^8 cm/sec if the uncertainty in the momentum is $\Delta p = p/10^4$ in each case.

20. Calculate the Compton wavelength for a proton.

21. Show that the projections on the x-, y-, and z-axes of a unit vector having arbitrary direction are such that $\cos^2 A + \cos^2 B + \cos^2 \Gamma = 1$, where A, B and Γ are respectively the angles made by the unit vector with the directions of the x-, y-, and z-axes (see Appendix 4.1). Proof may be made by showing that $\cos^2 A + \cos^2 B = \sin^2 \Gamma$.

22. Calculate the energy of one photon of electromagnetic radiation having a frequency of 1 megacycle/sec. How many of these photons are required to produce 1 ev of energy? Why then are the quantum characteristics of radio waves not observed?

23. The wavelengths of objects in our everyday world of experience are negligibly small, so cannot be experienced. For example, calculate the wavelength of a baseball (mass of 145 grams) thrown by a pitcher at 100 ft/sec.

24. Even a very small macroscopic object moving with a slow speed still has a negligibly short wavelength. Suppose the 1-microgram object discussed in Section 2.5 were moving with a speed of 1 cm/min. What would be its wavelength?

Chapter V

THE BOHR MODEL OF THE HYDROGEN ATOM

5.1 The Hydrogen Atom. The simplest of all atoms is the hydrogen atom. Its nucleus consists of a single positively charged proton, which is electrically neutralized by a single electron. Mechanically it is a simple two-body system, held together by electrostatic attraction. It is this simplicity that makes the hydrogen atom a good starting point for the study of atomic structure, for many of the experimentally observed facts can be explained by quite simple assumptions. Even though some of these simple descriptions of atomic structure have now been superseded by more correct theories, many of them still provide considerable insight into the nature of the atom. Such a description was the Bohr model of the hydrogen atom.

5.2 Radiation from the Hydrogen Atom. The Rutherford scattering experiments have shown that an atom consists of a dense positively charged nucleus surrounded by much less massive electrons which occupy a space approximately 10^{12} times the volume of the nucleus. Normally there are just enough electrons to cancel the nuclear charge, to make the atom electrically neutral. This information led to a description of the atom as some sort of planetary system in which tiny electrons revolve about the nucleus in much the same manner as the earth revolves around the sun. The chief difference between the two systems is that in an atom electrons are bound to the nucleus by means of an electrostatic force, whereas the earth is held in its orbit by the gravitational force between it and the sun. There are gravitational forces between proton and electron but these are much smaller than the electrostatic forces.

Both theory and experiment show that an accelerated charge loses energy in the form of electromagnetic radiation. Thus, as the electron revolves about the proton, it should radiate because of the accelerating force of the proton. Classical theory thus predicts that, because of the gradual loss of kinetic energy by radiation, the electron should spiral in toward the nucleus and eventually coalesce with the nucleus.

This is not the case, though. The spectral characteristics of radiation from atoms is not continuous as would be expected if the electron were spiraling in toward the nucleus, but consists of radiations of discrete, specifically defined wavelengths. For a given type of atom these radiations always occur at the same wavelengths, as illustrated in Fig. 5.1.

FIG. 5.1.   The spectrum of the star Zeta Tauri, showing the Balmer series of the hydrogen spectrum from the Hγ line to the series limit. The Greek alphabet is used to indicate the order of the spectral lines in the series; hence Hγ is the third line of the Balmer series. Beyond the 24th and final letter of the Greek alphabet (ω), a numerical subscript is used, so H_{27} is the 27th line of the Balmer series. The line marked He is a line of helium at λ = 4026 A (see Section 7.16), and the lines marked H and K are the same as the H and K lines of the Frauenhofer spectrum of the sun. These are attributed to ionized calcium (CaII) (see Section 7.17). (*Photograph courtesy Dr. Dean B. McLaughlin, the Observatory, University of Michigan*)

In the visible spectrum from hydrogen there is always a radiation (normally called a line) at 6563.1 A (angstroms), there is also radiation in the blue at 4861.3 A and in the violet at 4340.5 A, but there is no other visible radiation. Other spectral lines of radiation appear at discrete energies in the ultraviolet. Experimental observations show that the spacing between two successive lines is smaller at the shorter wavelengths. Eventually a limiting wavelength is reached at which no two lines can be individually resolved. Empirically it has been determined that the *wave number* ($\bar{\nu} = 1/\lambda$) of any individual line in this series can be expressed by the equation:

$$\bar{\nu} = 1/\lambda = RZ^2(1/2^2 - 1/n^2), \qquad (5.1)$$

where n takes on all integral values above 2. The quantity R is a constant called the *Rydberg constant*, and Z is the nuclear charge, which for hydrogen is $Z = 1$. This series of spectral lines is known as the *Balmer series*, named for its discoverer.

Other series of spectral lines also have been found in the spectrum of hydrogen, one in the ultraviolet and the reminder in the infrared. An empirical equation expressing the wave number for each of these series has been found. Each of the equations is very similar to the one which describes the Balmer series. However, instead of the integer 2 in the denominator of the first fraction in the brackets, other integer values appear. In each equation the value of n is a series of integers beginning with the next higher integer than that which appears in the denominator of the first fraction. The wave numbers for each of the series of spectral lines in the ultraviolet are given by the equation:

$$\bar{\nu} = RZ^2(1/1^2 - 1/n^2). \qquad (5.1a)$$

This is known as the *Lyman series*. The series beginning in the infrared nearest the visible, known as the *Paschen series*, is composed of spectral lines whose wave number may be expressed by the equation:

$$\bar{\nu} = RZ^2(1/3^2 - 1/n^2). \qquad (5.1b)$$

Each succeeding series of lines may be expressed by an equation of a similar type, the number in the denominator of the first fraction being one integer higher for each succeeding series.

5.3 The Bohr Assumptions. Niels Bohr was able to explain these spectral series through a series of assumptions regarding the structure of the hydrogen atom. Based on the thinking of the times (1913), these were rather drastic assumptions, but no more so than the earlier theories proposed by Planck and Einstein, whose quantum theory of radiation was used by Bohr, along with the Rutherford model of the atom, as a basis for his proposed structure for the hydrogen atom. His assumptions were:

1. A static state for the hydrogen atom consists of an electron revolving about the nucleus in an orbit for which the angular momentum is

$$L = nh/2\pi, \qquad (5.2)$$

where n is an integer. The hydrogen atom can exist only in these particular states and in no others. There is no emission of radiation as long as an atom remains in one of these states.

2. Emission and absorption of radiation take place only in case of a transition from one of these static states to another. If there is a transition from a higher energy state to a lower one, radiation is emitted. On the other hand, radiation must be absorbed for an atom to be raised from a lower energy state to a higher one. If W_1 and W_2 are the energies of the atomic system in the two stationary states under consideration, the energy of the radiation, $h\nu$, emitted or absorbed at the time of the transition between these two states is

$$h\nu = W_1 - W_2. \qquad (5.3)$$

This is a rather distinct departure from the laws of classical mechanics and classical electromagnetic theory. It says that the electron revolves in well-defined orbits without gain or loss of energy except when it jumps to another one of these well-defined orbits. If there is a jump from one orbit to another, it is essentially instantaneous, and the energy gain or loss in the transition is absorbed from or given to a quantum of radiation. The electron cannot exist in any other orbit except the ones defined in the first Bohr assumption. Neither can it fall into the nucleus, for by Bohr's assumption it cannot get closer to the nucleus than the orbit for which the angular momentum is $h/2\pi$.

5.4 The Hydrogen Atom Radiations as Predicted by the Bohr Theory.

What radiant energies are predicted by the Bohr assumptions for the hydrogen atom? Bohr imposed the conditions of Eq. 5.2 for the angular momentum of the electron. Classical mechanics also states that $L = mvr$, in which m is the mass of the electron and v its speed in an orbit having radius r. If the hydrogen atom is to be pictured as a planetary system, classical mechanics then requires that the electron be held in its orbit by an electrostatic force between the nucleus and the electron in accordance with the force equation $mv^2/r = Ze^2/\epsilon r^2$, in which Ze is the charge on the nucleus. For the time being, the assumption is made that the nucleus is so massive that its motion may be neglected; hence no reduced mass effect need be considered. Utilization of the term Ze for the nuclear charge instead of simply e, as would be the case for hydrogen, allows for the more general consideration of all one electron hydrogen-like atoms such as once-ionized helium, twice-ionized lithium, etc. These atoms show similar spectral series as hydrogen but with each spectral series occurring at shorter wavelengths than the corresponding series in hydrogen (see Problems 2, 3, and 4 at end of this chapter).

Neither the radius of the electron orbit nor the speed of the electron can be experimentally determined. The mass of the electron is known, provided that the electron is moving with a speed which does not approach sufficiently close to the speed of light to impose relativistic effects. Solution of the momentum and force equations for r and v reveals that

$$r = \epsilon n^2 h^2/4\pi^2 me^2 Z \quad \text{and} \quad v = 2\pi Ze^2/\epsilon nh. \tag{5.4}$$

Numerical substitution of the appropriate values into the equations gives a value for hydrogen $(Z = 1)$ for the inner-most orbit $(n = 1)$ of $r = 5.234 \times 10^{-9}$ cm, and $v = 2.188 \times 10^8$ cm/sec. This velocity is sufficiently small that relativistic effects can be neglected. Thus the kinetic energy of the electron is simply $W_K = mv^2/2$.

The total energy of an electron in a Bohr orbit is the sum of its potential energy and its kinetic energy. The potential energy may be determined by calculating the energy lost when an electron falls from infinity into its orbit (negative of the energy required to remove it completely from the atom). This energy is given by the equation:

$$V = \int_{\infty}^{r} F\,dr = \int_{\infty}^{r} (Ze^2/\epsilon r^2)\,dr = \left[-Ze^2/\epsilon r \right]_{\infty}^{r} = -Ze^2/\epsilon r. \tag{5.5}$$

The potential energy is negative because it is produced by an attractive force. The kinetic energy is $W_K = mv^2/2$, which has already been shown by the force equation to be $W_K = Ze^2/2\epsilon r$. The total energy of the system, $W = W_K + V$, for an energy state defined by the quantum number n, the electron being in the nth orbit, is then

$$W_n = -Ze^2/2\epsilon r = -2\pi^2 me^4 Z^2/\epsilon^2 n^2 h^2. \tag{5.6}$$

Whenever the electron is bound to an atom, the system possesses negative energy according to the criteria used in the development of the atomic system. Zero energy is thus defined by the condition that the electron has just escaped from the electrostatic field of the atom, but has no kinetic energy. If the electron is free and possesses a finite amount of kinetic energy, the total energy of the system is positive. There may exist *any* positive energy state, but only those negative energy states defined by integral values of n in Eq. 5.6.

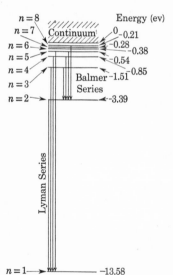

The possible energy states of an atomic system are often illustrated by an energy level diagram of the type shown in Fig. 5.2 for hydrogen. It will be seen later that similar energy level diagrams are also used to picture the energy states of a molecular or nuclear system, as well as those of an atomic system.

Under normal conditions all physical systems seek the lowest possible energy state. The lowest energy state of the hydrogen atom, also known as the *ground state*, is represented by the condition $n = 1$, which for $Z = 1$ (hydrogen) is at $W_1 = -13.58$ ev. The levels of several of the hydrogen atom energy states for which $n > 1$ are also indicated in Fig. 5.2. The energy of each of these states may be calculated from Eq. 5.6. It can be seen that the energy spacing between the higher energy levels is much less than between the lower levels. As the zero energy level (level at which the atom is ionized) is approached, the levels become

Fig. 5.2. Energy level diagram for hydrogen, showing the transitions that produce the first few spectral lines in the Lyman series and in the Balmer series.

so tightly packed that they cannot be individually detected.

If the hydrogen atom is in an energy state above the ground level, it will return to the ground state, according to Bohr's second assumption, by emitting electromagnetic radiation for which the energy is just equal to the energy difference, $W_n - W_1$, between the excited state under consideration and the ground state. The transition may occur directly from the excited state to the ground state with the energy difference being carried away by a single quantum of radiation, or, if energy states exist between the initial excited state and the final ground state, the atom may return to the ground state through these intermediate energy levels with the radiation of two or more quanta, the total energy of which is equal to the energy difference between the initial and final states.

The frequency of each quantum of radiation that is emitted by a transition from the nth level to the ground state level is $\nu = (W_n - W_1)/h$; the wave number is $\bar{\nu} = (W_n - W_1)/hc$. Using the values of W_n from Eq. 5.6 the wave number of the transition becomes

$$\bar{\nu} = (2\pi^2 me^4 Z^2/\epsilon^2 h^3 c)(1 - 1/n^2), \tag{5.7}$$

which corresponds to the empirically determined Eq. 5.1a for the Lyman series if $R = 2\pi^2 me^4/\epsilon^2 h^3 c$. The calculated value of R is 109737.309 cm^{-1}. For all other spectral series the calculated magnitude of R is the same.

5.5 The Rydberg Constant for Hydrogen. Using the calculated values of the Rydberg constant, the frequency of the radiation between the second and first energy levels in hydrogen should be

$$\nu = (2\pi^2 me^4 Z^2/\epsilon^2 h^3)(1 - \tfrac{1}{4}) = 2.46745 \times 10^{15} \text{ sec}^{-1}, \tag{5.8}$$

which corresponds to a wavelength of 1.21492×10^{-5} cm $= 1214.92$ A. But the experimentally observed wavelength for this transition is 1215.68 A. The difference between the calculated and experimentally observed values is not large, but it definitely exists.

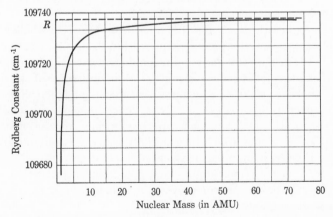

FIG. 5.3. Rydberg constant for hydrogen-like atoms as a function of nuclear mass.

The primary factor which contributes to the difference between the calculated and experimentally observed wavelengths is the finite mass of the nucleus around which the electron revolves. Even though the mass of the proton is approximately 1840 times the mass of the electron, the reduced mass of the electron is significantly different from the electron rest mass when results are measured to six significant figures. After replacing the electron mass m by the reduced mass $\mu = mM/(M + m)$, where M is the mass of the nucleus, the frequency of the radiation emitted during a transition from the first excited state to the ground state is calculated to be 2.46611×10^{15} sec $^{-1}$, corresponding to a wavelength of 1215.58 A, much closer to the experimentally observed value.

The effect of reduced mass results in a Rydberg constant for hydrogen, $R_H = 109677.576$ cm^{-1}, which is smaller than the constant R previously calculated. The Rydberg constants for hydrogen-like atoms, such as once-ionized helium, twice-ionized lithium, etc., are also smaller and are plotted as a function of nuclear mass in Fig. 5.3 to indicate how the constant approaches the value of R as the nuclear mass increases.

5.6 Introduction of the Electron Wavelength. The Bohr assumptions are quite arbitrary. The principal justification for such a set of assumptions appears to be that they can explain the experimentally observed radiation spectrum from the hydrogen atom and hydrogen-like atoms. The degree of arbitrariness can be greatly reduced if consideration is given to the fact that the electron possesses wave as well as particle characteristics. An electron in any orbit of the hydrogen atom is in motion and moving with speed v; hence, it has a characteristic deBroglie wavelength $\lambda = h/mv$. If it is assumed that the phase of the wave associated with an orbital electron must reenforce itself on each successive trip of the electron around its orbit, thereby producing constructive interference, then the distance around the orbit must be a whole number of wavelengths, such that, for a circular orbit, $2\pi r = n\lambda$, where r is the radius of the circular orbit and n is the number of wavelengths around the orbit. Using the deBroglie wavelength, the circumference of the circular orbit is $2\pi r = nh/mv$, from which it is seen that the angular momentum of the electron is $L = mvr = nh/2\pi$. Thus the assumption of wave properties for the electron leads quite naturally to the first Bohr assumption, an assumption which initially was made quite arbitrarily, primarily because it fit the experimental observations.

This sort of reasoning implies that something associated with the wave properties of the electron prevents it from getting any closer to the nucleus than the innermost Bohr orbit. To explain this situation the Heisenberg uncertainty principle is recalled. If the electron were able to fall into the nucleus, its position would have to be defined within a region as small as the nucleus, of the order of magnitude of 10^{-12}cm. But such definition can be shown by the uncertainty principle to be impossible. As the electron revolves about the nucleus in its orbit, its momentum cannot be defined closer than the limits $\Delta p = 2p$, for on opposite sides of the orbit it must be moving in opposite directions, in each case with a momentum having magnitude p. Also, because in the limit the electron may be on opposite sides of the orbit, its position cannot be defined closer than the interval $\Delta x = 2r$. Now, since the uncertainty principle states that $\Delta p \Delta x \geq h$, then $4pr \geq h$. Since $p = (2mW_K)^{1/2} = (me^2/\epsilon r)^{1/2}$, $4r(me^2/\epsilon r)^{1/2} \geq h$, and $r \geq \epsilon h^2/16me^2 = 1.31 \times 10^{-8}$cm, which is reasonably near the magnitude for the first Bohr radius, and is certainly much larger than the nuclear radius.

Because of this initial success using the wave properties of the electron, it is natural to ask what additional effects can be explained in atomic structure by the wave properties of atomic size particles. Is it necessary to consider the wave characteristics as well as the particle characteristics of all atomic systems? From this sort of questioning has grown the quantum mechanics, a much more general system of mechanics than Newtonian mechanics. Quantum mechanics considers both the wave and particle characteristics of matter, and results in a much more logical derivation of both atomic and macroscopic phenomena. The nature of quantum mechanics will be considered further in Chapter 6.

5.7 The Correspondence Principle. In his postulation of quantum theory Planck quantized the frequencies of the oscillators in the walls of a radiator, but he still assumed, as required by classical electromagnetic theory, that the frequency of the emitted radiation was simply the frequency of the oscillator. In Bohr's model of the hydrogen atom the oscillator is the electron orbiting around the hydrogen nucleus with an angular velocity $\omega = v/r$ and a frequency, based on Eq. 5.4, of

$$\nu_r = \frac{\omega}{2\pi} = \frac{v}{2\pi r} = \frac{4\pi^2 Z^2 m e^4}{\epsilon^2 n^3 h^3} = \frac{2RcZ^2}{n^3}. \qquad (5.9)$$

According to Eq. 5.7 and the accompanying discussion, though, the frequency of the radiation emitted from the hydrogen atom is given by the equation:

$$\nu = RcZ^2 \left(\frac{1}{n_1^2} - \frac{1}{n_2^2} \right) = RcZ^2 \left[\frac{(n_2 - n_1)(n_2 + n_1)}{n_1^2 n_2^2} \right]. \qquad (5.10)$$

Equations 5.9 and 5.10 are not equal for small values of n, but, if $n_2 \gg 1$ and $n_2 - n_1 = 1$,

$$\nu \approx \frac{2RcZ^2}{n_2^3} \approx \frac{2RcZ^2}{n_1^3}, \qquad (5.11)$$

exactly the frequency of the orbiting electron, which in this case is the oscillator of Planck's theory. For $n_2 - n_1 > 1$, the frequency of the hydrogen atom radiation, when $n_2 \gg 1$, is the product of an integer and the frequency of the orbiting electron.

Based upon these results it appears that, for large values of n, there is a correspondence between the Bohr quantum assumptions for radiation from the hydrogen atom and the classical theories of the emission of radiation. It also appears that classical theory favors a transition in the hydrogen atom for which $\Delta n = 1$. This statement of the correspondence between the classical ideas and the quantum ideas about the emission of radiation is known as *Bohr's correspondence principle*.

In the extension of the planetary model of the atom to other more complex atoms, it was found that Bohr's simple assumptions for hydrogen were inadequate and that it was necessary to make an arbitrary introduction of additional quantum numbers. From the spectra of the more complex atoms it was shown that one of these quantum numbers, dependent on n, did undergo unit changes for all allowed transitions. This appeared to present further confirmation of a correspondence between quantum and classical theories.

The sets of quantum numbers that were derived from the extension of the planetary model to more complex atoms will not be discussed in this book because the quantum mechanics based upon a solution of the wave equation for the electron, discussed in the following chapters, has replaced the older quantum mechanics of the planetary model. In the quantum mechanics discussed in succeeding chapters the complete set of quantum numbers appears in the solutions for all atoms, even hydrogen, and it is the orbital angular momentum quantum number, l, which undergoes only unit changes.

References

H. E. White, *Introduction to Atomic Spectra* (McGraw-Hill Book Co., Inc., New York, 1934).

G. Herzberg, *Atomic Spectra and Atomic Structure* (Dover Publications, Inc., New York, 1944).

A. Sommerfeld, *Atombau und Spectralinien* (F. Vieweg und Sohn, Braunschweig, 7th Ed., 1951).

Problems

1. Both the electron and the hydrogen atom nucleus (a proton) have finite mass. Therefore there must be a gravitational force between them. Calculate the magnitude of this force in the ground state of the hydrogen atom. Why is it not considered in the Bohr treatment of the hydrogen atom?

2. If one electron is removed from the helium atom, there remains a hydrogen-like atom. Calculate the binding energies of the remaining electron in the

energy levels for which $n = 1, 2, 3$ and 4. Compare these levels with those of hydrogen.

3. Make the same calculations for twice-ionized lithium.

4. What difference is expected in the magnitude of the wavelength of the longest wavelength lines of the Balmer series for ordinary hydrogen and for heavy hydrogen? (The nuclear mass of heavy hydrogen is twice that of ordinary hydrogen).

5. Calculate the kinetic energy (in ergs and in ev), and the speed (in cm/sec) of an electron in the most tightly bound orbit of once-ionized helium. Calculate the wavelength of this electron (in cm). Does this wavelength correspond to a standing wave on the first Bohr orbit for once-ionized helium?

6. Later in the text it will be found that there is a positively charged particle, the positron, with the same mass as the electron. The combination of a positron and an electron into a hydrogen like system is called *positronium*. Calculate the energy and radius of the first and second Bohr orbits of positronium. Note: Be sure to consider the effects of reduced mass.

7. Calculate the Rydberg constant for once-ionized helium and for oxygen ionized seven times.

8. Calculate the orbital frequency of electrons in the hydrogen Bohr orbits $n = 1, 2, 50, 51, 100$, and 101. Compare these frequencies with the frequencies of the radiations for the transitions from levels $n = 2$ to $n = 1$, $n = 51$ to $n = 50$ and $n = 101$ to $n = 100$.

9. Although the energy levels become tightly packed as n becomes large, the radii of the electron orbits become increasingly larger as n increases. Calculate for hydrogen the radius of the orbit for $n = 20$ and compare it to the radii at $n = 1$, $n = 5$, $n = 10$, and $n = 15$.

10. Make the same calculations as in Problem 9 for once-ionized helium.

Chapter VI

QUANTUM MECHANICS

6.1 The Wave Equation. Evidence has been introduced in Chapters 4 and 5 which questions the distinctive properties of particles and waves. Such questions do not arise in classical mechanics, since the characteristic wavelengths of moving particles of large mass are infinitesimally small compared to the dimensions of the particle. On the atomic scale, though, the electron, for example, cannot be considered simply as a particle — its characteristic wavelength is usually of the same order of magnitude as its physical size. In addition, electromagnetic radiation has been observed in many experiments to possess a particulate property. Surely there must then be some formulation of the laws of nature which takes into consideration all these facts. This formulation is provided by quantum mechanics, which applies to particles, such as electrons, and which develops a set of physical laws that make particle and wave aspects complimentary, not mutually exclusive.

The dual wave-particle nature of matter and of electromagnetic radiation can be summarized by stating that both matter and radiation display particle characteristics described by an energy W and a momentum p, and wave characteristics described by a frequency ν and a wavelength λ. Classically the energy density of a wave system is proportional to the sum of the squares of two functions from which the state of the wave is defined. In electromagnetic radiation these functions constitute the electric field E and the magnetic field H. In electromagnetic radiation E and H are in phase, so, if E and H are represented by a sinusoidally varying function such as $E = A \cos \beta(x - vt)$, where $\beta = 2\pi/\lambda$ (see Appendix 4.1), the function describing the energy density, $|f(x,t)|^2$ fluctuates in a manner proportional to $\cos^2 \beta(x - vt)$. From the quantum point of view, the function $|f(x,t)|^2$ can be described as a measure of the photon density such that, within an incremental volume of space $dx\ dy\ dz$, the number of photons, or the probability of finding a photon, is given by $|f(x,t)|^2\ dx\ dy\ dz$. By analogy, if the wave properties of those quantities, such as electrons, which have customarily been called particles, is represented by a function $\psi(x,t)$, the quantity $|\psi(x,t)|^2$ would be a measure of the electron density and $|\psi(x,t)|^2\, dx\, dy\, dz$ would be a measure of the probability of finding the electron in the incremental volume $dx\, dy\, dz$. No experimental evidence exists which clearly describes the nature of the two functions, comparable to E and H in electromagnetic radiation, from which the wave function $\psi(x,t)$ is defined. The function is therefore usually described rather generally either by the sum of a sine and cosine function:

$$\psi(x,t) = A \sin \beta(x - vt) + B \cos \beta(x - vt), \qquad (6.1)$$

or by an imaginary exponential (see Appendix 6.1):

$$\psi(x,t) = C \exp [i\beta(x - vt)]. \qquad (6.1a)$$

If the momentum and the energy of the electron wave are assumed to be related to wavelength and frequency in the same manner as for electromagnetic waves, $p = h/\lambda$ and $W_K = h\nu$, the wave function $\psi(x,t)$ may also be written in the form:

$$\psi(x,t) = C \exp [2\pi i(px - W_K t)/h]. \qquad (6.2)$$

Note that the energy is written as W_K since it is associated only with the motion of the particle, the kinetic energy. To express the wave function in terms of total energy W, equal to $W_K + V$, where V is the potential energy, Eq. 6.2 must be rewritten as:

$$\psi(x,t) = C \exp \{2\pi i[px - (W - V)t]/h\}. \qquad (6.2a)$$

Differentiation of Eq. 6.2 gives $\partial\psi/\partial t = (-2\pi i W_K/h)\psi$, and $\partial^2\psi/\partial x^2 = (-4\pi^2 p^2/h^2)\psi$. For nonrelativistic speeds $W_K = p^2/2m$ and

$$(ih/2\pi)(\partial\psi/\partial t) = -(h^2/8\pi^2 m)(\partial^2\psi/\partial x^2). \qquad (6.3)$$

This equation is the *one-dimensional, time-dependent Schroedinger equation*. For the more general case of a wave traveling in some arbitrary direction r, defined by $r = (x^2 + y^2 + z^2)^{1/2}$, Eq. 6.3 becomes:

$$\frac{ih}{2\pi} \frac{\partial\psi}{\partial t} = - \frac{h^2}{8\pi^2 m} \left(\frac{\partial^2\psi}{\partial x^2} + \frac{\partial^2\psi}{\partial y^2} + \frac{\partial^2\psi}{\partial z^2} \right). \qquad (6.4)$$

Because $\partial\psi/\partial t = (-2\pi i W_K/h)\psi$, Eq. 6.4 may also be written as:

$$\frac{\partial^2\psi}{\partial x^2} + \frac{\partial^2\psi}{\partial y^2} + \frac{\partial^2\psi}{\partial z^2} - \frac{8\pi^2 m}{h^2} (W - V)\psi = 0, \qquad (6.5)$$

this being the expression for the *Schroedinger equation* that will be used for solution of the problems described in this chapter.

6.2 Potential Well. The solution of the wave equation is critically dependent on the nature of the potential energy, V. The potential energy of immediate interest is that produced by the electrostatic field that holds the electron and the nucleus together in the hydrogen atom (see Section 5.4). It is a function only of the radial distance r since an electron approaching the nucleus along any radius follows the same function of potential energy. This function is then three-dimensional, and every part of any single spherical shell surrounding the nucleus at O in Fig. 6.1 has the same magnitude of potential energy. The closer the electron approaches the nucleus the stronger the force is that holds the two particles together, the larger the energy required to remove the electron from the influence of the positively charged nucleus, and the lower (more negative) the potential energy for the system.

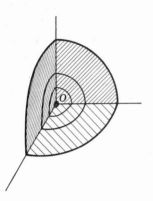

FIG. 6.1. Cutaway of one octant of space showing equipotential spheres around a charged nucleus.

In a diagram such as Fig. 6.1, the magnitude of the energy V cannot easily be shown. Since, however, V is the same function along any radius, a two-dimensional plot of V and r is identical along any line drawn through the center of the atomic nucleus. Such a plot of the potential energy of an atomic system as a function of radial separation of electron and nucleus is illustrated in Fig. 6.2. The resulting plot is called a *potential well*, a name which obviously arises from the shape of the

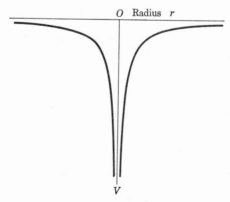

FIG. 6.2. The potential well of a hydrogen-like atom described by the equation
$$V = -Ze^2/\epsilon r.$$

curve. This method for diagramming the potential energy of an atomic system is quite standard and is used throughout this book.

As indicated in the discussion of the Bohr model of the hydrogen atom, an electron in a potential well can have kinetic as well as potential energy. Classically, then, the electron can have an energy-position relationship that lies anywhere above the line that describes the potential energy, V, of the system. In the system shown in Fig. 6.2, an electron at rest at very large distances from the nucleus, a free electron without kinetic energy, has an energy $W = 0$. When free, an electron with kinetic energy has an energy $W > 0$. If an electron has an energy $W < 0$ its kinetic energy is determined by its distance above the potential energy curve V. Thus it has no kinetic energy when on the potential energy curve; and, since a particle, according to classical mechanics, cannot possess negative kinetic energy, an electron with energy $W < 0$ apparently can occupy only a limited region of space, being confined to the interior of the potential well. According to the laws of quantum mechanics, though, this requirement is no longer strictly necessary, as will be seen in the following discussion.

When considering a graphical representation of energy as a function of position, such as Fig. 6.2, an electron in a position $x = 0$ is always at the center of the nucleus, for, even though it may have an energy $W \geq 0$, the position $x = 0$ is the center of the nucleus everywhere along the energy (W) axis.

6.3 Quantum Mechanical Solution for Rectangular Potential Well. It has already been seen in Section 5.6 that discrete energy levels in the hydrogen atom apparently result from the deBroglie wave properties of the electron. If this is true, then the solution of the Schroedinger wave equation using the potential energy function, $V = -e^2/\epsilon r$, of the hydrogen atom should give the same set of energy levels. This is a three-dimensional problem, though, and becomes relatively complex from a mathematical point of view. The solution of the wave equation for the allowed energy levels in the hydrogen atom is therefore deferred to

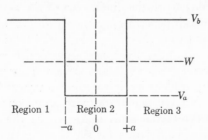

FIG. 6.3.   A rectangular potential well.

Chapter 7, for the basic principles upon which quantum mechanics is founded can be shown with much simpler mathematical manipulations, such as those required for the solution of the wave equation for the one-dimensional rectangular potential well shown in Fig. 6.3. A rectangular potential well of this type can be used to show the principles of quantum mechanics even though the exact numerical solutions are quite different from those obtained from a real physical situation because, from a qualitative point of view, the principles involved in arriving at a solution are similar.

The wave equation of a particle in a one-dimensional potential well is:

$$\frac{d^2\psi}{dx^2} + \frac{8\pi^2 m}{h^2}(W - V)\psi = 0. \tag{6.5a}$$

If the total energy of the system is greater than the potential energy, the second term of the equation is positive and the solution of the equation is:

$$\psi = A \sin \alpha x + B \cos \alpha x, \tag{6.6}$$

where $\alpha = (2\pi/h)[2m(W - V_a)]^{1/2}$. On the other hand, if the energy of the system is less than the potential energy the solution of the equation is:

$$\psi = C \exp(-\beta x) + D \exp(\beta x), \tag{6.7}$$

where $\beta = (2\pi/h)[2m(V_b - W)]^{1/2}$. The solution of the former is an oscillatory function which may pass through zero any number of times, whereas the solution of the second is an exponential function.

For these solutions of the wave function ψ to be valid, a number of interpretations of their physical significance must be made. The first interpretation involves the solution given by Eq. 6.7. This solution says that the function ψ may have a finite magnitude even though $W < V$. There is no way, though, for the function ψ to have infinite magnitude, for under these conditions there must be an infinite energy density at some point in space. Therefore, beyond the edges of the well the solution of the function ψ is limited to that part of Eq. 6.7 for which there is a zero magnitude at an infinite distance from the edge. This may be looked upon as being analogous to the diminution of the amplitude of electromagnetic radiation as it penetrates an energy absorbing medium, such as an electrically conducting material. A potential barrier for the electron may then, by analogy, be compared to a physical barrier of conducting material for electromagnetic radiation. When an electromagnetic wave comes to such a physical barrier, it is not instantaneously and completely stopped at the surface but penetrates with an exponentially decreasing amplitude into the material (this is known as the skin effect). By analogy, then, the wave function for the electron has an exponentially decreasing, but finite value inside the potential barrier. From this it may be concluded that, in the one-dimensional potential well of Fig. 6.3, the only significant part of the wave function that may be used in the region of positive x in which the potential energy is greater than the energy of the system is $\psi = C \exp(-\beta x)$. In the equivalent region of negative x that part of the wave function which has significance is $\psi = D \exp(\beta x)$.

For the rectangular potential well shown in Fig. 6.3 all changes in the potential energy are finite for every region in space. This situation establishes the requirement that any change in $d^2\psi/dx^2$ be finite, and, under these conditions, both the first derivative of the wave function, $d\psi/dx$, and the wave function, ψ, itself, must be continuous at every point in space. This requirement means that there cannot exist anywhere an arbitrarily abrupt change in the probability for finding an electron, a consideration which is especially important in the region near the edge of the potential barrier.

For essentially every real physical situation all changes in potential energy within a small region of space are finite in magnitude. Therefore the requirement that ψ and $d\psi/dx$ be everywhere continuous and finite, under which conditions ψ is said to be *well-behaved*, is a very realistic requirement.

Based upon the above considerations, the mathematical equations describing the wave function in the three areas of Fig. 6.3 are thus: $\psi_1 = D \exp(\beta x)$, $\psi_2 = A \sin \alpha x + B \cos \alpha x$, and $\psi_3 = C \exp(-\beta x)$. If these are to satisfy the three conditions specified above then the equations for regions 1 and 2, and their first derivatives, must be equal at $-a$, and the equations for regions 2 and 3, and their first derivatives, must be equal at $+a$. Thus:

$$\text{at} - a \begin{cases} D \exp(\beta x) = A \sin \alpha x + B \cos \alpha x, \\ \beta D \exp(\beta x) = \alpha A \cos \alpha x - \alpha B \sin \alpha x; \end{cases} \quad (6.8a)$$

$$\text{at} + a \begin{cases} C \exp(-\beta x) = A \sin \alpha x + B \cos \alpha x, \\ -\beta C \exp(-\beta x) = \alpha A \cos \alpha x - \alpha B \sin \alpha x. \end{cases} \quad (6.8b)$$

Elimination of D from the first two of these equations shows that, at $x = -a$,

$$A = B(\beta \cos \alpha a - \alpha \sin \alpha a)/(\alpha \cos \alpha a + \beta \sin \alpha a),$$

and, similarly, elimination of C from the second two of these equations shows that, at $x = +a$,

$$A = B(\alpha \sin \alpha a - \beta \cos \alpha a)/(\beta \sin \alpha a + \alpha \cos \alpha a).$$

For any individual energy level, both solutions must simultaneously exist if a wave function is to exist at that level. The condition for such simultaneous existence of both solutions is:

$$\frac{\beta \cos \alpha a - \alpha \sin \alpha a}{\alpha \cos \alpha a + \beta \sin \alpha a} = \frac{\alpha \sin \alpha a - \beta \cos \alpha a}{\beta \sin \alpha a + \alpha \cos \alpha a}, \quad (6.9)$$

the solution of which is $2(\beta^2 - \alpha^2) \sin \alpha a \cos \alpha a = 2\alpha\beta (\sin^2 \alpha a - \cos^2 \alpha a)$ or $(\beta^2 - \alpha^2) \sin 2\alpha a = -2\alpha\beta \cos 2\alpha a$, which, upon substitution of the original values for α and β, shows that

$$\tan \{(4a\pi/h)[2m(W - V_a)]^{1/2}\}$$
$$= 2[(W - V_a)(V_b - W)]^{1/2}/(2W - V_a - V_b). \quad (6.10)$$

This equation has a solution for the energy W only for certain discrete values of W, as seen from a plot of the two sides of the equation in Fig. 6.4. Before an actual solution can be made, the depth of the potential well must be determined. For the current explanatory purposes the

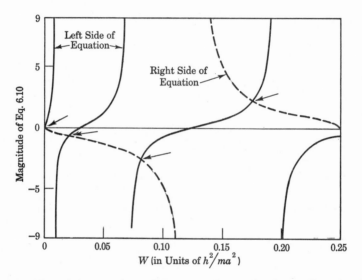

Fig. 6.4. Plot of the two sides of Eq. 6.10. Energy levels are allowed only at the points of intersection, those energies for which the two sides of Eq. 6.10 are equal.

choice of well depth is rather arbitrary, so for simplicity the origin for the energy axis is set at the bottom of the well, such that $V_a = 0$. Suppose, too, $V_b = h^2/4ma^2$. The choice of the type of units is determined by the nature of the trigonometric function on the left side of the equation. Using these arbitrarily chosen values for V_a and V_b, $\tan \{(4a\pi/h)[2m(W - V_a)]^{1/2}\}$ is plotted as a solid line in Fig. 6.4 and $2[(W - V_a)(V_b - W)]^{1/2}/(2W - V_a - V_b)$ as a dashed line. It can be seen that the two curves have only four common values. Thus the equation has a solution at only four values of W for the chosen conditions. If the height of the walls of the potential well is raised, the number of levels at which solutions can exist is increased, but, for a potential well of finite magnitude, the number of levels is always finite. Increasing the width of the potential well, that is, increasing the magnitude of a for a constant V_b, also increases the number of energy levels within the potential well.

6.4 The Hydrogen Atom.

It is now possible to explain qualitatively some of the features of the hydrogen atom by means of quantum mechanics. The potential well of a hydrogen-like atom, $V = -Ze^2/\epsilon r$, illustrated in Fig. 6.2, has an infinite depth, but approaches a zero width at large depths. At the top of the potential well there is no abrupt change from finite to infinite width, as was the case for the rectangular well, but the widening is continuous.

Because of the extreme widening at the top of the hydrogen potential well, the density of possible wave functions ψ, hence the density of possible energy levels, increases very rapidly as a function of energy. At lower levels, because of the ever-narrowing of the width of the well, the spacing of levels continually increases. There is a minimum width of the well for which the function ψ can produce a wave which satisfies the three requirements specified in Section 6.3. Thus there must be a lowest energy level in the well. These qualitative features, based upon the observations of a square well potential, are just those that are observed experimentally for hydrogen and hydrogen-like atoms.

6.5 The Potential Barrier.

Although there are, in addition to the potential well, many rectangularly shaped distributions of potential energy which may be treated in accordance with the laws of quantum mechanics, the only additional one to be considered in detail in this chapter is the potential barrier. The well and the barrier are relatively fundamental since most physical phenomena in which quantum mechanical principles play a part in atomic and nuclear structure involve either the potential well or the potential barrier, or some combination of the two. For example, the potential well and the potential barrier play significant roles in later discussions of the energy levels in a crystal and of alpha-particle decay of the atomic nucleus. The potential barrier to be treated here is illustrated in Fig. 6.5.

Even an intuitive approach based upon the results from the potential well provides some idea as to what should be expected. Since the wave function, ψ, must have finite values all the way through the barrier, the wave function for a particle that is on one side of a potential barrier must still have a finite magnitude on the other side. This says that there is a finite probability that the particle can penetrate the barrier. The magnitude of the probability depends on the height and width of the barrier, as well as the energy level of the particle.

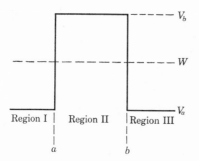

Region I | Region II | Region III

a b

FIG. 6.5. A rectangular potential barrier.

Assume that an atomic particle exists in region I of Fig. 6.5. Then the equation which describes its wave function in that region is:

$$\psi_I = A \exp (i\alpha x) + B \exp (-i\alpha x), \quad (6.11)$$

where α is the same as for the potential well. For simplicity in the mathematical manipulations, the exponential form of the sinusoidal wave is used in these equations (see Appendix 6.1). In region II the equation for the wave function is:

$$\psi_{II} = C \exp (\beta x) + D \exp (-\beta x), \quad (6.12)$$

with β again having the same meaning as for the potential well, and in region III the wave equation is

$$\psi_{III} = F \exp (i\alpha x) + G \exp (-i\alpha x). \quad (6.13)$$

As in the case of a plane wave of electromagnetic radiation, a wave function originating from a particle in region I is reflected from either of the walls of the potential barrier. Thus the resulting wave has components moving in either direction in regions I and II, but only in the one direction of positive x in region III, so $G = 0$ (see Appendix 6.1).

Applying the quantum mechanical rules already discussed for the potential well, the equations on both sides of the barrier for the wave functions and for their first derivatives are set equal at the barrier. Thus, at $x = a$,
for the equation:

$$A \exp (i\alpha a) + B \exp (-i\alpha a) = C \exp (\beta a) + D \exp (-\beta a), \quad (6.14a)$$

and for the derivative:

$$i\alpha A \exp (i\alpha a) - i\alpha B \exp (-i\alpha a)$$
$$= \beta C \exp (\beta a) - \beta D \exp (-\beta a). \quad (6.14b)$$

and at $x = b$,
for the equation:

$$C \exp (\beta b) + D \exp (-\beta b) = F \exp (i\alpha b), \quad (6.14c)$$

and for the derivative:

$$\beta C \exp (\beta b) - \beta D \exp (\beta b) = i\alpha F \exp (i\alpha b). \quad (6.14d)$$

Thus there are four equations but five unknown coefficients: A, B, C, D, and F. But this is all that is really needed to get the ratio, F/A, of the magnitudes of the wave function on the two sides of the barrier, from which can be found the ratio of the probabilities, $|F|^2/|A|^2$, for the existence of an atomic particle on the right side of the barrier as compared to its existence on the left side.

The solution of these four simultaneous equations is obtained by the relatively straightforward mathematical manipulations presented in Appendix 6.2. The result is

$$\frac{|F|^2}{|A|^2} = \frac{1}{1 + \dfrac{(V_b - V_a)^2 \sinh^2\left\{\dfrac{2\pi}{h}(b - a)[2m(V_b - W)]^{1/2}\right\}}{4(V_b - W)(W - V_a)}} \cdot \quad (6.15)$$

That this ratio is different from zero for finite values of V_b means that, according to the quantum mechanical picture, an atomic particle possesses a finite probability for penetrating a potential barrier of finite height. Its wave properties permit this penetration of a barrier and produce other effects not in keeping with the properties generally attributable to a classical particle. Many properties usually associated with a particle are still present, but these properties give only part of the description and are still found in the quantum mechanical treatment. It is therefore necessary to consider the quantum mechanical treatment of any atomic phenomenon to arrive at a true representation of its characteristics.

6.6 The Linear Harmonic Oscillator. Before proceeding to the quantum mechanical solution for the energy levels in the hydrogen atom it is perhaps best that a somewhat simpler, but still real, physical problem be investigated. The problem selected is that of the one-dimensional harmonic oscillator that was assumed by Planck to be quantized (see Appendix 4.2) in his solution for the energy spectral distribution of black body radiation. The solution of the Schroedinger equation for the energy states of the linear harmonic oscillator follows the same general pattern as the solution of the Schroedinger equation for many other physical processes, such as for the energy states of the hydrogen atom. Hence it can serve as a guide for other similar problems.

For any harmonic oscillator, such as an oscillating spring, there is a restoring force which tries to return the system to its equilibrium condition. The magnitude of this force is taken as being directly proportional to the magnitude of the displacement of the oscillator from its equilibrium condition, which for a system oscillating in the x-direction is $F = -kx$, where k is a constant. This constant can be shown from classical mechanics (see Problem 1) to be $k = 4\pi^2 m\nu^2$, where m is the mass of the object performing the oscillations and ν its frequency. At any displacement x, the potential energy of a system describing simple harmonic motion is the energy that would be transformed into kinetic energy in going from a displacement x to its equilibrium position,

$$V(x) = \int_x^0 F\,dx = \int_x^0 (-kx)\,dx = \tfrac{1}{2}kx^2. \qquad (6.16)$$

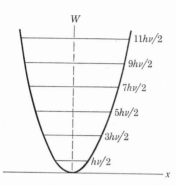

FIG. 6.6. The harmonic oscillator potential well and energy levels according to quantum mechanics.

The potential well described for the harmonic oscillator by this equation is shown in Fig. 6.6.

The Schroedinger equation for the one-dimensional harmonic oscillator is then

$$\frac{d^2\psi}{dx^2} + \frac{8\pi^2 m}{h^2}(W - \tfrac{1}{2}kx^2)\psi =$$
$$\frac{d^2\psi}{dx^2} + \left(\frac{8\pi^2 mW}{h^2} - \alpha^2 x^2\right)\psi = 0, \qquad (6.17)$$

in which $\alpha = 4\pi^2 m\nu/h$. The solution of an equation of this type is of the form $\psi = Au \exp(\pm\alpha x^2/2)$, where u is some function of x and A is a constant. The plus sign must be eliminated from the exponential since, as $x \to \pm\infty$ in the positive exponential, the potential energy $V \to \infty$ and $\psi \to \infty$. However this violates the principles enumerated in Section 6.3 for, to be physically interpretable, as $V \to \infty$ the wave function ψ must become zero. The solution then must be $\psi = Au \exp(-\alpha x^2/2)$, from which

$$d\psi/dx = -A\alpha xu \exp(-\alpha x^2/2) + Au' \exp(-\alpha x^2/2)$$
$$= A[u' - \alpha xu] \exp(-\alpha x^2/2), \qquad (6.18)$$

in which $u' = du/dx$. The second derivative, in which $u'' = d^2u/dx^2$, is

$$d^2\psi/dx^2 = A[(u' - \alpha xu)(-\alpha x) + (u'' - \alpha u - \alpha xu')] \exp(-\alpha x^2/2)$$
$$= A[u'' - 2\alpha xu' + (\alpha^2 x^2 - \alpha)u] \exp(-\alpha x^2/2), \qquad (6.19)$$

and Eq. 6.17 becomes:

$$u'' - 2\alpha xu' + (8\pi^2 mW/h^2 - \alpha)u = 0. \qquad (6.20)$$

The simplest solution for this equation is $u = a_0 x^0$, for which $u'' = u' = 0$, and, since $\alpha = 4\pi^2 m\nu/h$, the equation becomes $(2W/h - \nu)a_0 = 0$, from which it is seen that $W = h\nu/2$. Terms containing higher powers of x may also appear in a solution for Eq. 6.20. For example, if $u = a_0 + a_1 x + a_2 x^2$, the equation becomes:

$$2a_2 - 4\alpha a_2 x^2 + (8\pi^2 mW/h^2 - \alpha)a_2 x^2$$
$$- 2\alpha a_1 x + (8\pi^2 mW/h^2 - \alpha)a_1 x + (8\pi^2 mW/h^2 - \alpha)a_0$$
$$= (8\pi^2 mW/h^2 - 20\pi^2 mv/h)a_2 x^2 + (8\pi^2 mW/h^2 - 12\pi^2 mv/h)a_1 x$$
$$+ [2a_2 + (8\pi^2 mW/h^2 - 4\pi^2 mv/h)a_0] = 0.$$

A power series of this type can equal zero only if each term of the series is individually zero. This equation therefore determines a relationship between the coefficients a_2 and a_0, and that the possible magnitudes of the energy W are $W = hv/2$, $3hv/2$ and $5hv/2$.

The most general solution of Eq. 6.20 is the infinite series:

$$u = \sum_{n=0}^{\infty} a_n x^n = a_0 + a_1 x^1 + a_2 x^2 + a_3 x^3 + \dots, \qquad (6.21)$$

where a_0, a_1, a_2, a_3, etc., are constants and the n's are integers. Also any polynomial formed by a finite number of terms of this series is a solution to Eq. 6.20. The first and second derivatives of the infinite series are:

$$u' = \sum_{n=0}^{\infty} n a_n x^{n-1} = a_1 + 2a_2 x + 3a_3 x^2 + 4a_4 x^3 + \dots \qquad (6.22)$$

and

$$u'' = \sum_{n=0}^{\infty} n(n-1) a_n x^{n-2} = 2a_2 + 6a_3 x + 12a_4 x^2 + \dots . \qquad (6.23)$$

Equation 6.20 becomes, upon substitution of these values for u, u', and u'':

$$\sum_{n=0}^{\infty} x^n \{a_{n+2}(n+2)(n+1) + a_n[-2\alpha n + (8\pi^2 mW/h^2) - \alpha]\} = 0. \quad (6.24)$$

The requirement that each term of the power series be zero leads to the recursion formula relating the coefficients of the power series:

$$a_{n+2}/a_n = (2\alpha n + \alpha - 8\pi^2 mW/h^2)/(n+2)(n+1).$$

If the value determined by this recursion formula is placed into Eq. 6.24, it is seen that each power of x has a coefficient $[(2n+1)4\pi^2 mv/h - 8\pi^2 mW/h^2]$. Thus the general requirement for the power series (6.21) to be a solution to Eq. 6.20 is that $W = (n + \frac{1}{2})hv$, in which n has all integer values between 0 and the maximum magnitude of n in the polynomial that is used for the solution. From this solution for W it can be said then that the simple harmonic oscillator is quantized almost, but not quite, as Planck had assumed. The lowest energy level, instead of occurring at $W = 0$, occurs at $W = \frac{1}{2}hv$, as indicated in Fig. 6.6.

It appears from quantum mechanics therefore that Planck's quantizing of the harmonic oscillator was completely valid, although his assumptions were quite arbitrary at the time. Perhaps it should also be indicated at this point that such a quantum mechanical solution for the harmonic oscillator is not inconsistent with observations in classical mechanics, for the ratio of the magnitude of the quantum jumps of a spring, for example, are so small compared to the total energy in the spring that they cannot be individually observed (see Problem 2).

References

V. Rojansky *Introductory Quantum Mechanics* (Prentice-Hall, Inc., Englewood Cliffs, N. J., 1938).

L. Pauling and E. B. Wilson, *Introduction to Quantum Mechanics* (McGraw-Hill Book Co., Inc., New York, 1935).

D. Bohm, *Quantum Theory* (Prentice-Hall, Inc., Englewood Cliffs, N. J. 1951).

L. I. Schiff, *Quantum Mechanics* (McGraw-Hill Book Co., Inc., New York, 1949).

L. D. Landau and E. M. Lifshitz, *Quantum Mechanics — Non Relativistic Theory* (Addison-Wesley Publishing Co., Inc., Reading, Mass., 1958).

N. F. Mott and I. N. Sneddon, *Wave Mechanics and Its Application* (Oxford University Press, Inc., New York, 1948).

F. Mandl, *Quantum Mechanics* (Academic Press, Inc., New York, 1957).

Problems

1. Simple harmonic motion is performed by an object moving along the diameter of a circle in such a way that it is the projection on that diameter of a point describing uniform circular motion with an angular velocity $d\theta/dt = \omega = 2\pi\nu$. Using the equation of force for a classical simple harmonic oscillator, show that $k = 4\pi^2 m\nu^2$. If needed, Fig. A.4 (Appendix 6.1) can be used for assistance in comparing uniform circular motion with simple harmonic motion.

2. To show that quantum mechanics gives the same results as Newtonian mechanics for macroscopic objects, assume that a pendulum when swung through small arcs undergoes simple harmonic motion. If a 1-kg mass swings at the end of a 6-foot long string through an arc 4° on either side of equilibrium, calculate the magnitude of the integer n for this condition. Why then does the change in energy of a pendulum as it loses energy appear to be a continuous function?

3. If the potential well of Fig. 6.3 is 1 ev in depth and 1 A wide, at what energies are there allowed energy states for an electron?

4. Suppose the depth of the potential well of Problem 3 is increased to 100 ev, but the width remains the same; at what energies are there allowed energy states for the electron?

5. Suppose the depth of the potential well of Problem 3 remains the same but the width is increased to 100 A, at what energies are there allowed energy states for an electron?

6. Calculate the allowed energy states for a proton in the potential wells of Problems 3, 4, and 5. How then does mass affect the position of energy levels in potential wells?

7. Suppose an electron with an energy of 1 ev encounters a potential barrier 2 ev high and 1 A thick; what is the probability that the electron will penetrate this barrier?

8. Make the same calculation as in Problem 7 for a barrier of 100 times the height but the same thickness, and another calculation for a barrier of the same height as in Problem 7 but 100 times the thickness.

9. Suppose an alpha particle exists between two potential barriers each of which is 25 Mev high and 5×10^{-12} cm thick. If the alpha particle is at an energy of 5 Mev above the bottom of the barrier, what is the probability that it will penetrate the barrier in any single encounter?

10. Suppose the alpha particle of Problem 9 oscillates at the 5 Mev level in a region between the two barriers that is 2×10^{-12} cm wide. Upon each encounter with a barrier its probability of escape is the same as calculated in Problem 9. How long must it oscillate in this region before the probability of escape is $\frac{1}{2}$? This is the time required for half the alpha particles to escape from a large number of such systems and is known as the *half-life* of the system. Assume that within the well all the energy of the alpha particle is kinetic energy, that is, $mv^2/2 = W$.

11. The potential energy diagram for electrons near the edge of a metal generally rises quite sharply as one goes from the interior to the exterior of the metal. This potential energy can be approximated by the square barrier of Fig. 6.7. According to classical mechanics, an electron inside the metal, having an energy W in excess of the depth, V_0, of the potential barrier, would always be able to escape, since it is above the barrier. However, in the quantum mechanical picture the barrier

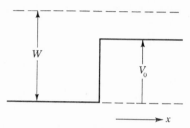

Fig. 6.7. The potential step function of Problem 11.

can be effective, even for an electron with an energy $W > V_0$, for some of these electrons are reflected by the barrier at these energies. Calculate the ratio of electrons reflected at the barrier to those transmitted through the barrier for electron energies $W > V_0$.

12. Suppose $W = V_0$. What is the probablity of reflection in Problem 11?

13. Suppose the electron approaches the potential step from the right side of Fig. 6.7. Calculate the probability of reflection at the step for $W > V_0$ and for $W = V_0$.

14. In going from the somewhat idealized one-dimensional examples of quantum mechanical potential wells in Chapter 6 to the potential well of a hydrogen-like atom, it is necessary to transform the Schroedinger equation into spherical coordinates. This is a two-step process in which the first partial derivative must be determined before the second partial derivative can be determined. Based upon the knowledge (see Sections 1.4, 2.6, and 2.7) that

$$\frac{\partial u}{\partial z} = \frac{\partial r}{\partial z}\frac{\partial u}{\partial r} + \frac{\partial \theta}{\partial z}\frac{\partial u}{\partial \theta} + \frac{\partial \phi}{\partial z}\frac{\partial u}{\partial \phi},$$

$x = r \cos \phi \sin \theta$, $y = r \sin \phi \sin \theta$, $z = r \cos \theta$, and $r = (x^2 + y^2 + z^2)^{1/2}$, show that:

$$\partial r/\partial x = \cos \phi \sin \theta, \quad \partial \theta/\partial x = \cos \theta \, \cos \phi/r,$$

$$\partial \phi/\partial x = -\sin \phi/r \sin \theta, \quad \partial r/\partial y = \sin \phi \sin \theta, \quad \partial \theta/\partial y = \cos \theta \sin \phi/r,$$

$$\partial \phi/\partial y = \cos \phi/r \sin \theta, \quad \partial r/\partial z = \cos \theta, \partial \theta/\partial z = -\sin \theta/r, \text{ and } \partial \phi/\partial z = 0,$$

and hence that:

$$\frac{\partial u}{\partial x} = \sin\theta\cos\phi\,\frac{\partial u}{\partial r} + \frac{1}{r}\cos\theta\cos\phi\,\frac{\partial u}{\partial\theta} - \frac{1}{r}\frac{\sin\phi}{\sin\theta}\frac{\partial u}{\partial\phi},$$

$$\frac{\partial u}{\partial y} = \sin\theta\sin\phi\,\frac{\partial u}{\partial r} + \frac{1}{r}\cos\theta\sin\phi\,\frac{\partial u}{\partial\theta} + \frac{1}{r}\frac{\cos\phi}{\sin\theta}\frac{\partial u}{\partial\phi},$$

$$\frac{\partial u}{\partial z} = \cos\theta\,\frac{\partial u}{\partial r} - \frac{1}{r}\sin\theta\,\frac{\partial u}{\partial\theta}.$$

Note: To get $\partial\phi/\partial x$, $\partial\phi/\partial y$, $\partial\theta/\partial x$, and $\partial\theta/\partial y$, eliminate the unwanted angle from the above expressions for x and y as functions of r, θ, or ϕ.

15. If the function u is dropped from the results of Problem 14, the quantities $\partial/\partial x$, $\partial/\partial y$ and $\partial/\partial z$ that remain are called *differential operators*. They indicate that any function that immediately follows them must undergo partial differentiation. Show then that:

$$\left(\frac{\partial}{\partial x}\right)^2 + \left(\frac{\partial}{\partial y}\right)^2 + \left(\frac{\partial}{\partial z}\right)^2 = \frac{1}{r^2}\frac{\partial}{\partial r}\left(r^2\frac{\partial}{\partial r}\right)$$
$$+ \frac{1}{r^2\sin\theta}\frac{\partial}{\partial\theta}\left(\sin\theta\,\frac{\partial}{\partial\theta}\right) + \frac{1}{r^2\sin^2\theta}\frac{\partial^2}{\partial\phi^2}.$$

This is the spherical coordinate form that must be used for the solution of the Schroedinger equation for a hydrogen-like atom.

16. If the walls of the potential well of Fig. 6.3 approach infinite height, $V_b \to \infty$ and the wave function ψ is everywhere zero outside the potential well. Calculate the allowed energy levels for a rectangular one-dimensional well of this description.

Chapter VII

ATOMIC STRUCTURE AND ATOMIC SPECTRA

7.1 The Franck and Hertz Experiment. In addition to the rather clear evidence that the monochromatic atomic spectra give for discrete atomic energy states, another, even more direct, experimental verification of discrete energy states in atoms was found by Franck and Hertz in the study of collisions of electrons with atoms of mercury vapor. Similar experiments were performed later by several experimenters using other elements, always with similar results.

The basic arrangement for the experiment by Franck and Hertz is shown in Fig. 7.1. In an electron tube filled with mercury vapor, a positive potential with respect to the cathode K is applied to the grid G. The plate P of the tube is kept at about 0.5 volt negative with respect to

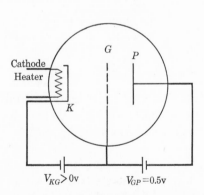

FIG. 7.1. Experimental arrangement for the Franck and Hertz experiment.

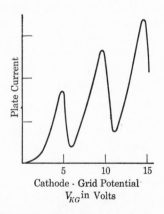

FIG. 7.2. Experimental results for mercury vapor for the Franck and Hertz experiment.

the grid. The positive potential on G accelerates the electrons emitted at K, and, if the electrons pass through G with a kinetic energy greater than 0.5 ev, they generally reach the plate, P. For electron kinetic energies below 4.9 ev, collisions between electrons and mercury vapor atoms are elastic and, since the mercury atoms are so much more massive than the electrons, there is no measurable loss of kinetic energy by the electrons at each collision, only a change in direction. Thus the higher the voltage between K and G the greater the chance that the electron has a component kinetic energy toward P of $W_K > 0.5$ ev at the time of its passage through G, and hence reaches P.

When the voltage difference between K and G passes 4.9 volts, though, there is a sudden drop in the number of electrons reaching the plate of the tube, as illustrated in Fig. 7.2 in a plot of the plate current as a function of cathode-grid potential difference. This relatively abrupt drop occurs again at 9.8 ev, twice 4.9 ev, and again at three times 4.9 ev. The interpretation of this phenomenon is that electrons with kinetic energies $W_K > 4.9$ ev can undergo inelastic collisions with the mercury atoms, in which case the kinetic energy lost by the electron goes into raising the mercury atom from its ground state energy level to a first excited state 4.9 ev above the ground state. The effect at 9.8 ev occurs because the electron undergoes two such collisions in the space between K and G. If the collision occurs close to the grid, which it does if the electron finally acquires 4.9 ev of kinetic energy just prior to passing the grid, the electron does not retain sufficient kinetic energy to overcome the retarding potential of 0.5 ev between G and P and hence is forced to return to G if it passes into the intermediate region.

If a mercury atom is raised to an excited energy level by an inelastic collision, it returns to the ground state by emission of a quantum of electromagnetic radiation having an energy characteristic of the energy difference between the two levels. Such characteristic radiation has been observed in the spectrum of mercury vapor.

By correlating the inelastic collision observations in the Franck and Hertz type of experiment with an observation of the appropriate characteristic spectral line of mercury it can be seen that the discrete spectral line is controlled by the excitation of the mercury atom. Thus the spectral lines that are observed are valid indications of the decay of excited atomic states.

7.2 Schroedinger's Wave Equation for the Hydrogen Atom.

Calculation of the energy levels in the atoms other than hydrogen is possible but difficult, primarily because of the effect of the forces between individual electrons as well as the forces between electrons and the atomic nucleus. However, all the basic principles of the Schroedinger description of atomic structure can be seen by solving the Schroedinger equation for hydrogen. Extension to other atoms can then be made by a qualitative explanation of the physical processes that produce the variations in the observed spectra, and in other experimental observations that can be made on the more complex atoms. The structure of all atoms is sufficiently similar that such treatment gives results that are reasonably accurate.

As seen in Chapter 5, the electron is held in the hydrogen atom, or in a hydrogen-like atom, by an electrostatic force for which the potential energy of the system is $V = -Ze^2/\epsilon r$. Since this potential energy is spherically symmetric about the nucleus, the solution of the Schroedinger equation is most easily determined if it is solved in terms of the spherical coordinates r, θ, and ϕ. The development of the Schroedinger equation in the spherical coordinate system has been made in Problems 14 and 15 of Chapter 6. For hydrogen-like atoms it is:

$$\frac{1}{r^2}\frac{\partial}{\partial r}\left(r^2\frac{\partial\psi}{\partial r}\right) + \frac{1}{r^2\sin^2\theta}\frac{\partial^2\psi}{\partial\phi^2} + \frac{1}{r^2\sin\theta}\frac{\partial}{\partial\theta}\left(\sin\theta\frac{\partial\psi}{\partial\theta}\right)$$
$$+ \frac{8\pi^2 m}{h^2}\left(W + \frac{Ze^2}{\epsilon r}\right)\psi = 0, \quad (7.1)$$

where m is the mass of the electron in an electron-nucleus system in which the nucleus is infinitely massive. For finite nuclear masses the reduced mass μ must be used. This equation can be solved by the separation of variables (see Appendix 7.1 for an outline of the solution). The result is that

$$\psi = KR_{nl}(r)P_l{}^{m_l}(\cos\theta)\exp{(im_l\phi)}. \quad (7.1a)$$

Here K is a constant, n, l, and m_l represent sets of integers which appear as a part of the solution of the Schroedinger equation for the central force problem, $R_{nl}(r)$ is a function of r that is dependent on the values of the integers n and l, and $P_l{}^{m_l}(\cos\theta)$ is what is known as an *associated Legendre polynominal*, a function of $\cos\theta$ that is dependent on the values of the integers l and m_l. The integers n, l, and m_l are *quantum numbers* which describe the energy state of the atom. The quantum number, n, is the same as introduced by Bohr in his development of a model for the hydrogen atom. However, the solution of the Schroedinger equation introduces two additional quantum numbers, each of which must be interpreted in terms of its appropriate physical significance. These quantum numbers (see Appendix 7.1) may have only certain well-defined values. The quantity n may be any integer value, but not zero. The quantities l and m_l may have only those integer values such that $n > l \geq |m_l|$. It should be noted that n and l have only positive values, but m_l may have both positive and negative values. These same quantum numbers appear in the solution of the wave equation for any atom and have the same limitations on allowed numerical magnitudes.

7.3 Physical Interpretation of the Quantum Numbers. Using only the hydrogen atom as a model, the significance of the three quantum

numbers n, l, and m_l, which arise as a result of the wave mechanical solution, is not at once apparent. The existence of standing waves for electrons in hydrogen atom orbits, the orbital angular momentum of which is $L = nh/2\pi$, appears to be sufficient reason for the splitting of the hydrogen atom into discrete energy levels. This is a good logical explanation for the energy states of the hydrogen atom, and is adequate as long as the situation is confined to a two-body problem, an electron plus a nucleus, in which force is always in the radial direction, r.

When one or more additional electrons are introduced into the system, not only are there forces between each electron and the nucleus, but there are also forces between individual electrons taken in pairs. The forces are no longer entirely radial, and three quantum numbers are necessary to provide a complete description of the electron in the three spatial dimensions.

The quantum number n is called the *principal quantum number*. Even as it did in the hydrogen atom, in any other individual atom it also describes rather generally the distance between the nucleus and the electron and, because of this feature, is sometimes called the *radial quantum number*. Since the quantum number n does describe in a rather general way the distance of the electron from the nucleus, all electrons having the same principal quantum number are confined to a relatively limited range of energies. They are said to be in an *atomic shell* which is defined by the principal quantum number.

Introduction of the second quantum number l permits the electron a second degree of freedom. In the solution of the Schroedinger equation the quantum number l is a function both of the radial variable r and of the angular variable θ. Hence it must describe some characteristic that is applicable to a plane, such as the orbital motion of the electron in a planetary model for the atom. The electron orbital angular momentum is the physical characteristic that is now ascribed to the quantum number l, rather than to the quantum number n.

In a planetary model of the atom, an electron with small orbital angular momentum is pictured as having an elliptical orbit with high eccentricity, and hence is capable of penetrating other electron shells closer to the nucleus. Because of this penetration, electrons with small orbital angular momentum quantum numbers are expected at some point in their orbit to get closer to the nucleus, and to experience larger electro-static attractive forces than other electrons in the same shell. Hence in any single shell (n = constant), electrons with smaller orbital angular momentum (l small) are more tightly bound in the atom, and are at lower energy levels than those with larger orbital angular momentum. Because of the nonexistence of inner shells of atoms, this effect is not present in the hydrogen atom; there is no separation of energy levels in accordance with the magnitude of the quantum number l, and description of the orbital angular momentum of an electron by the quantum number n is valid.

In the quantum mechanical solution it is found (see Appendix 7.1) that the magnitude of the orbital angular momentum of an electron in an atom is not simply $lh/2\pi$, but is $l^*(h/2\pi) = [l(l+1)]^{1/2}h/2\pi$. Thus, for an $l = 0$ state the orbital angular momentum is zero; for an $l = 1$ state the orbital angular momentum is $\sqrt{2}\ h/2\pi$. Higher quantum number states have appropriately greater orbital angular momenta, but as l becomes very large l^* approaches l in magnitude. In the quantum mechanical solution the energies of the low orbital angular momentum states are lower than those of the high orbital angular momentum states, just as in the planetary model.

The magnetic quantum number m_l appears in the solution to the Schroedinger equation as a function of the angular variables θ and ϕ. In the planetary model, it is used to describe the possible spatial orientations in the $r\theta$-plane, relative to an external magnetic field, which can be taken by each of the orbits that have been described by the quantum numbers n and l. Since there is a limited number of available quantum numbers, the number of such orientations is therefore limited. In the quantum mechanical solution the quantum number m_l similarly defines the orientation in the $r\theta$-plane relative to a magnetic field of the orbital angular momentum of the electron within the atom, but there is no basis for drawing a well-defined orbit in which the electron moves. Since there is usually no applied magnetic field to provide a reference direction within the atom, orientation at some angle θ is usually not possible. Hence, under most circumstances, there is no difference in the energy levels of electrons in the same shell having the same orbital angular momentum but with different magnetic quantum numbers.

The angle ϕ appears only as a part of the imaginary exponential term of the wave function ψ. The significance of this fact will be deferred until after discussion of probability density distributions in the following section.

7.4 Wave Functions and Probability Density Distributions.
The Heisenberg uncertainty principle states that an electron cannot be located exactly in terms of both its space and momentum coordinates, or in terms of both its time and energy coordinates. If the energy of a particular atomic state is precisely defined, the time at which an electron is found in that energy state cannot be so defined. Likewise, if the momentum of an electron within an atomic state is precisely defined, its position in space cannot be so defined. It is possible, though, to determine the probability that an electron can be found at a particular spot

relative to its probability for being found somewhere else. These probability density distributions are given by the solutions to the Schroedinger wave equation.

To plot a clearly understandable probability density distribution for finding the electron at some point around the nucleus is made difficult by the limitation of dimensions available on the surface of a page — the probability density distribution $|\psi|^2$ is a function of all three spatial variables r, θ, and ϕ. When using only the two variables available on the plane of a page, it is sometimes necessary to picture the results as a series of graphs, which then must be assembled in the imagination of the reader to picture the complete three-dimensional distribution.

That part of the probability density distribution given by $|R(r)|^2$ is a function only of r, not of θ and ϕ. Along any radial direction the relative

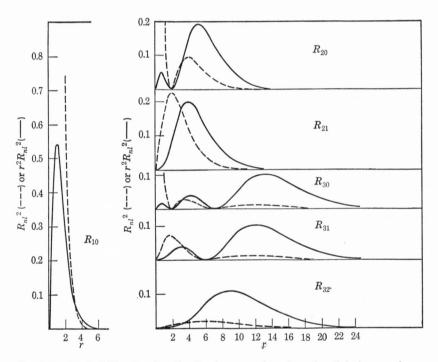

FIG. 7.3. Probability density distributions as a function of radial distance from the nucleus for several energy states of the hydrogen atom. The dashed lines are proportional to the probability for finding the electron in an incremental volume dv at the indicated radial distance. The solid lines are proportional to the probability for finding the electron in an incremental ring of volume $4\pi r^2 dr$ at the indicated radius. Radial distances are given in units of Bohr radii, the distance from the nucleus of the $n = 1$ orbit in the Bohr planetary model of the hydrogen atom. The subscripts on R indicate the appropriate values of the quantum numbers n and l as R_{nl}.

probability of finding an electron in a small volume element dv which can be moved anywhere in space is given by the function $|R(r)|^2 dv$. This distribution is plotted as dashed lines in Fig. 7.3 for three values of the quantum number n. The more customary plot, though, is one which gives the probability density distribution for finding the electron in the spherical shell bounded by spheres with radii r and $r + dr$. The volume of this shell is very nearly $4\pi r^2 dr$; hence the probability density distribution in any spherical shell between r and $r + dr$ is $4\pi r^2 |R(r)|^2$. These distributions are plotted as the solid lines in Fig. 7.3.

The equations describing the probability density distribution for an electron with zero orbital angular momentum ($l = 0$) do not contain either the variable θ or the variable ϕ (see Appendix 7.1). The probability of finding an $l = 0$ electron is therefore uniformly distributed in each spherical shell surrounding the nucleus. Depending on the value of n, the probability density distribution shows some sort of maximum density in one or more of these shells. It should also be noted that there is a finite probability that an $l = 0$ electron can occupy the same small region of space dv in which the nucleus is found, a fact that becomes much more important in the discussion of some of the principles of nuclear physics.

For electron energy states having measurable orbital angular momentum ($l > 0$), the equations describing the probability density distribution are functions of both θ and ϕ as well as r, the type of function depending on the magnitude of the quantum numbers l and m_l. To have an observable angle θ or ϕ, though, some force or torque external to the electron under consideration must define a direction from which either angle may be measured. This externally determined direction is generally that of a magnetic field which interacts with the magnetic moment of the electron, thereby providing an axis for orienting in the $r\theta$-plane the various energy states of an atomic electron. Since for $l = 1$, m_l may have any of the three values $1, 0,$ or -1, there are three possible distributions for the electrons with quantum number $l = 1$. For the case $m_l = 0$, the probability density distribution in the $r\theta$-plane for the hydrogen atom is given in Fig. 7.4. For either $m_l = +1$, or $m_l = -1$, the distributions are identical and are given in Fig. 7.5. Because the angle ϕ appears only in the imaginary exponential term (see Appendix 6.1), there is no definition of a $\phi = 0$ direction. The angle ϕ must therefore be averaged over all times, with the result that all distributions are symmetrical about ϕ. The $m_l = 0$ distribution in three-dimensional space is then a modified dumbbell shape and the $m_l = \pm 1$ distributions are ring-shaped. That part of the probability density distribution factor, $|\Theta_{m_l l}|^2$, which is a function of the coordinate θ, has twice the magnitude for the $m_l = 0$ condition that it has for either of the $m_l = 1$ conditions. For $m_l = 0$, $|\Theta_{m_l l}|^2 = \frac{3}{2} \cos^2 \theta$, and for $m_l = 1$, $|\Theta_{m_l l}|^2 = \frac{3}{4} \sin^2 \theta$. A

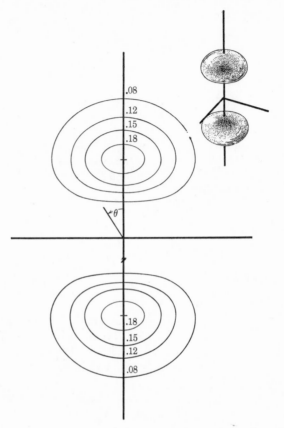

Fig. 7.4.   Contours of constant probability density in the $r\theta$ plane for an $n = 2$, $l = 1$, $m = 0$ hydrogen atom electron. The magnitude of each contour is in arbitrary units. Along the directions defined by $\theta = 0°$ and $\theta = 180°$ the magnitude of the probability density distribution as a function of r is the same as in Fig. 7.3. Along other radial directions the magnitude of this distribution is reduced by a factor $\cos^2 \theta$. In the upper right corner is a schematic, three-dimensional representation of this probability density distribution.

summation over all m_l then gives a probability density distribution for $l = 1$ that is independent of the angle θ. This means that, when all possible states in a subshell of an atom defined by a given value of the quantum number l are occupied by electrons, the orbital angular momenta of the various electrons are oriented in such a way that no residual angular momentum can be observed external to the system. This condition forms what is known as a *closed*, or *filled*, *shell*, and the summed probability density distribution for all electrons in such a filled shell has no means for providing a reference direction, just as was the case for the individual $l = 0$ electron. Thus, even with an externally applied

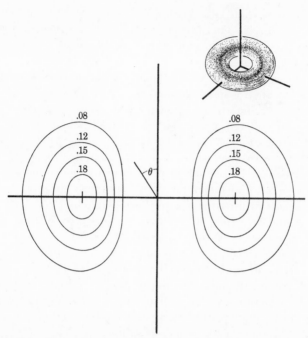

FIG. 7.5. Same as Fig. 7.4 but for the $n = 2$, $l = 1$, $m = \pm 1$ electron energy states of the hydrogen atom. In this case the maximum of the probability density distribution given in Fig. 7.3 exists along the radial directions $\theta = 90°$ and $\theta = 270°$.

magnetic field the probability of finding an electron in a closed shell is symmetric around the nucleus.

Similar probability density distributions can be constructed for larger values of l.

7.5 Pauli Exclusion Principle.

Atomic nuclei having $Z > 1$ attract a single electron with an electrostatic force greater than the attractive force of the hydrogen nucleus. In Section 5.4 it was seen that, if the atom is hydrogen-like (has only one orbital electron), the energy levels may be calculated in the same manner as the hydrogen atom energy levels. The ground state energy level of such an atom is lower than the ground state energy level of hydrogen since the electron is more tightly bound to the nucleus by the larger nuclear charge.

Normal atoms with nuclear charge $Z > 1$ are not hydrogen like, but are electrically neutral, hence have more than a single orbital electron. With more than one electron in the atom, it is necessary to determine the relationship of one electron to its neighbors. Does each electron fall into the lowest possible energy state and remain there until excited to a higher energy level? The answer is no, for in any neutral atom it is experimentally observed that the energy required to remove some atomic electrons is much greater than the energy required to remove other atomic electrons. In other words, the potential energy which holds some electrons in an atom is much greater than the energy which holds other electrons in the same atom. From the results of the detailed observations, Pauli formulated a principle which stated that no two electrons within the same atom may have exactly the same wave function. In atomic structure two electrons possess the same wave function if their momenta and positions are identical. Within a single atom two electrons with the same set of quantum numbers would have the same wave function. To avoid this situation, the rule formulated by Pauli, known as the *Pauli exclusion principle*, states that no two electrons within a single atom may possess exactly the same set of quantum numbers. Thus, if any energy level in an atom is occupied by an electron, that level is forbidden to all other electrons. If each electron falls to its lowest possible energy state, the next electron to enter the atom must remain in some higher energy level. In quantum mechanics this principle is equivalent to the statement in Newtonian mechanics that no two objects can occupy the same space at the same time.

7.6 The Spin Quantum Number. In addition to the conditions imposed by the principal, orbital, and magnetic quantum numbers, the electron has also been observed to have an intrinsic magnetic moment of its own. Thus, the electron can perhaps be pictured as a tiny, spinning, electrically charged top which sets up its own magnetic field. All electrons possess the same intrinsic spin, and this spin may be characterized by a spin quantum number s, the magnitude of which is always $\frac{1}{2}$. Since this is the same for all electrons, it need not be considered in the set of quantum numbers which describe an atomic state. However, its associated magnetic quantum number $m_s = \pm\frac{1}{2}$ must be considered, since this now gives two possible orientations for the electron.

That such a magnetic moment exists, and that the magnetic quantum number m_s has only two values, can be shown experimentally by passing a beam of neutral atoms, the valence electron for which is a single $l = 0$ electron, through an inhomogeneous magnetic field. This type of experiment was described in detail in Section 2.6. Since the orbital angular momentum is zero, any observed effect must be that of the magnetic moment of the spinning electron. The only other magnetic moment which could effect the results would be that of a spinning nucleus, which, if the observations are made on hydrogen, would be a single proton. As discussed in Chapter 2, though, the magnetic moment of the proton is of the order of magnitude 10^{-3} times smaller because of the large mass of the proton relative to the electron. Other nuclei are even more massive and hence have even smaller moments.

This type of experiment was first performed by Gerlach and Stern using silver atoms. Later experiments using hydrogen and other atoms were also performed. The experiment showed that in an inhomogeneous magnetic field, a beam of hydrogen or other atoms with intrinsic orbital angular momenta of zero splits into two components, deflected equally on either side of an undeflected beam. Classically it would have been expected that a magnetic dipole such as the spinning electron could have been oriented in any arbitrary direction relative to the applied magnetic field and hence deflections of all magnitudes between the two extremes should have taken place. But the fact that only two deflections exist, corresponding to the maximum amount of deflection expected in either direction, shows the quantized nature of the orientation of spin.

7.7 Energy Levels and Optical Spectra. To determine the structure of the many electron atoms, quantum mechanical calculations become relatively complex, and well beyond the scope of this book. But many of the gross features of the hydrogen atom remain the same in the more complex atoms, and thus are usable for a qualitative description of the physical characteristics of these atoms. It must be remembered that the wave functions and the probability density distributions discussed in Section 7.4 were calculated only for the hydrogen atom. However, in other atoms the distributions are similar.

In the more complex atoms the same physical interpretations as were developed in the discussion in Section 7.3 may be given to the quantum numbers. The quantum number n still defines a shell of electron energy levels that fall within a specified upper and lower bound, but in the many electron atoms the upper energy limit for one shell may overlap the lower energy limit of the next higher shell. Within a given shell the quantum number l always separates electrons in accordance with the magnitude of their orbital angular momentum (and ability to penetrate inner shells of electrons), and the quantum number m_l defines the magnitude of the component of the orbital angular momentum that orients itself parallel to an external magnetic field.

To illustrate the separation of energy levels, the sodium atom has been chosen. The energy level scheme of sodium, along with that of hydrogen, is shown in Fig. 7.6. In this diagram the spectroscopic notation is used to designate the magnitude of the orbital angular momentum quantum number for each state. Optical spectroscopists customarily call an $l = 0$ state an s state, an $l = 1$ state a p state, an $l = 2$ state a d state, an $l = 3$ state an f state, with consecutively higher letters above f in the

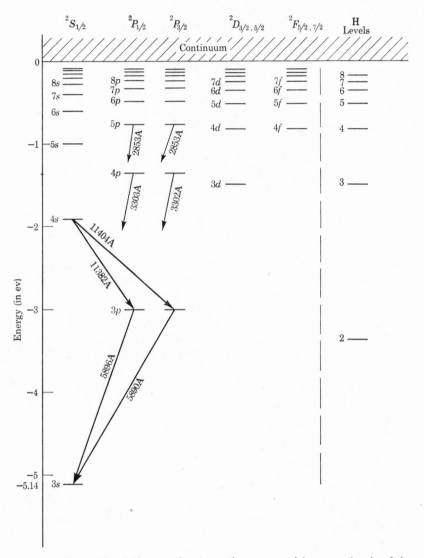

FIG. 7.6. Energy level diagram for the sodium atom with energy levels of the hydrogen atom shown at the right for comparison. The notation at the top of the figure, such as $^2S_{1/2}$, is the spectroscopist's notation (see Section 7.10) for the type of atomic energy state in the column below it. Based on information from C. E. Moore, *Atomic Energy Levels*, Vol. I, *NBS Circular* 467 (U.S. Government Printing Office, 1949).

alphabet designating each succeeding value of l.† The number that accompanies the state designation for each level is the value of n associated with that level. For example the $3p$ level is an $n = 3$, $l = 1$ state. In sodium all the $n = 2$ and $n = 1$ states are filled and there is but a single electron remaining to go into an $n = 3$ state. This electron must therefore be the least tightly bound electron. Unlike those in the hydrogen atom, all $n = 3$ states are no longer at the same energy in sodium. As discussed in Section 7.3, for any single shell — for example, the $n = 3$ shell — the lower energy levels are those in which the electron has the smaller orbital angular momentum. For example, the $3s$ level is lower than the $3p$ level which in turn is lower than the $3d$ level.

If a small amount of energy is given to the atom, as for instance by an incident photon, it is generally the least tightly bound electron that absorbs that energy and is raised to an excited energy level. The excited electron then returns to its ground state through a series of transitions from higher to lower energy states of the atom. Some such transitions are indicated in Fig. 7.6. The energy released by any single transition usually appears in the form of a photon of radiation. If there are a sufficient number of excited atoms of the same type, a line spectrum characteristic of the atom can be observed, in this case a spectrum characteristic of sodium.

Only certain transitions are allowed within an atom. These rules governing these transitions state that: n may change by any value, l must change by a single integer ($\Delta l = \pm 1$), and m_l may change by a single integer or not change at all ($\Delta m_l = 0, \pm 1$).

The spinning electron also has its effect on an atomic energy level scheme. An electron having measurable orbital angular momentum ($l > 0$) sets up an inhomogeneous magnetic field in which the spin may be oriented. There are then two possible orientations of the spin relative to the orbital angular momentum. Thus the total angular momentum of the system is slightly increased or decreased with the result that there is either a slight increase or decrease in the total energy of the system. As a result, some levels appear as closely spaced *doublets*. Such is the case for all levels in sodium except the s states, as illustrated in Fig. 7.6 by the existence of two levels for each p state. The energy differences between the d and f state doublets are too small to show in Fig. 7.6. In the case of the s states the magnitude of the orbital angular momentum is zero, so

†The sequence s, p, d, f, g, h, . . . was determined historically by considerations that are no longer important, and so is easier tolerated than understood.

there is no reference frame from which the spin direction of the electron may be determined.

7.8 The Periodic Table of Elements. With the basic knowledge that has been generated in this chapter regarding quantum numbers and their effect on atomic shells, it is possible to relate these quantum numbers to certain of the chemical and physical properties of atoms.

The first item of importance is to note that in any orderly arrangement of the atoms the primary influence is exerted by the nuclear charge. Normally an atom is electrically neutral. Therefore, the greater the nuclear charge, the larger the number of electrons in the atom. Also, the larger the nuclear charge the greater the force on the most tightly bound electrons. In atoms having high atomic number (large nuclear charge Z), the more tightly bound electrons are spatially closer to the nucleus and are held in lower energy levels than in atoms of lower atomic number. The least tightly bound electron is always bound by the same order of magnitude of energy in all atoms since it is held by an effective charge not much different from $Z = 1$. This is illustrated in Fig. 7.6; the least tightly bound electron (the valence electron) in sodium is bound to the atom in energy states comparable to the energy with which the single electron is bound to the hydrogen atom (-5.14 ev as compared to -13.58 ev).

For the innermost shell, $n = 1$, there can be only a single value, $l = 0$, for the orbital angular momentum quantum number. However, there are two possible states in this shell since the spin magnetic quantum number may be either $m_s = +\frac{1}{2}$ or $m_s = -\frac{1}{2}$. In the case of hydrogen ($Z = 1$) only one of these states is occupied, but it may be either state. In the case of neutral helium ($Z = 2$) both the states are occupied, and the $n = 1$ shell is closed, for there are no more states in it which can be filled.

If the nuclear charge is larger than 2, such as for lithium ($Z = 3$), beryllium ($Z = 4$), boron ($Z = 5$), carbon ($Z = 6$), etc., further electrons must be added to keep the atom electrically neutral. To do so though requires that the $n = 2$ shell be occupied. Two values of the orbital angular momentum quantum number may exist in the $n = 2$ shell, either $l = 0$ or $l = 1$. For $l = 1$ there are three possible values of the orbital magnetic quantum number $m_l = 0, +1,$ or -1. For each of these states there are two possible spin states, $m_s = +\frac{1}{2}$ or $-\frac{1}{2}$. Thus there are a total of eight possible nonrepetitive states in the $n = 2$ shell. In their lowest energy states lithium has a single $l = 0$ electron and beryllium fills the $l = 0$ states in the $n = 2$ shell. The next six elements of the periodic table (boron, carbon, nitrogen, oxygen, fluorine, and neon) complete the $n = 2$ shell by filling the $l = 1$ states.

With the completion of the $n = 2$ shell, the $n = 3$ shell is the next to be

TABLE 7.1. FILLING ORDER FOR ELECTRON SHELLS IN ATOMS

Element	Atomic Number (Z)	n=1 l=s	2 s	2 p	3 s	3 p	3 d	4 s	4 p	4 d	4 f	5 s	5 p	5 d	5 f	6 s	6 p	6 d	7 s
H	1	1																	
He	2	2																	
Li	3	2	1																
Be	4	2	2																
B	5	2	2	1															
C	6	2	2	2															
Ne	10	2	2	6															
Na	11	2	2	6	1														
Mg	12	2	2	6	2														
Al	13	2	2	6	2	1													
Si	14	2	2	6	2	2													
A	18	2	2	6	2	6													
K	19	2	2	6	2	6		1											
Ca	20	2	2	6	2	6		2											
Sc	21	2	2	6	2	6	1	2											
Ti	22	2	2	6	2	6	2	2											
Zn	30	2	2	6	2	6	10	2											
Ga	31	2	2	6	2	6	10	2	1										
Kr	36	2	2	6	2	6	10	2	6										
Rb	37	2	2	6	2	6	10	2	6			1							
Sr	38	2	2	6	2	6	10	2	6			2							
Y	39	2	2	6	2	6	10	2	6	1		2							
Zr	40	2	2	6	2	6	10	2	6	2		2							
Cd	48	2	2	6	2	6	10	2	6	10		2							
In	49	2	2	6	2	6	10	2	6	10		2	1						
Xe	54	2	2	6	2	6	10	2	6	10		2	6						
Cs	55	2	2	6	2	6	10	2	6	10		2	6			1			
Ba	56	2	2	6	2	6	10	2	6	10		2	6			2			
La	57	2	2	6	2	6	10	2	6	10		2	6	1		2			
Ce	58	2	2	6	2	6	10	2	6	10	1	2	6	1		2			
Yb	70	2	2	6	2	6	10	2	6	10	14	2	6			2			
Lu	71	2	2	6	2	6	10	2	6	10	14	2	6	1		2			
Hg	80	2	2	6	2	6	10	2	6	10	14	2	6	10		2			
Tl	81	2	2	6	2	6	10	2	6	10	14	2	6	10		2	1		
Rn	86	2	2	6	2	6	10	2	6	10	14	2	6	10		2	6		
Fr	87	2	2	6	2	6	10	2	6	10	14	2	6	10		2	6		1
Ra	88	2	2	6	2	6	10	2	6	10	14	2	6	10		2	6		2
Ac	89	2	2	6	2	6	10	2	6	10	14	2	6	10	?	2	6	?	?
Th	90	2	2	6	2	6	10	2	6	10	14	2	6	10	?	2	6	2	2
Pa	91	2	2	6	2	6	10	2	6	10	14	2	6	10	?	2	6	?	?
U	92	2	2	6	2	6	10	2	6	10	14	2	6	10	3	2	6	1	2
No	102	2	2	6	2	6	10	2	6	10	14	2	6	10	13	2	6	1	2

filled. The next element in the periodic table after neon is sodium, which has complete $n = 1$ and $n = 2$ shells and a single electron in the $n = 3$ shell. In its lowest energy level this electron is in an $l = 0$ state (an s state electron). The levels which this $n = 3$ electron may occupy if it is given additional energy have been illustrated by Fig. 7.6.

The completion of the various shells occurs in regular order through the $n = 3$, $l = 1$ states. However the $n = 4$, $l = 0$ states have a lower energy than the $n = 3$, $l = 2$ states and are filled first. This also occurs for the $n = 5$ and $n = 6$ shells. The $n = 5$, $l = 0$ states are filled prior to the $n = 4$, $l = 2$ states and the $n = 6$, $l = 0$ states are filled prior to the $n = 5$, $l = 2$ states. This sequence for the filling of specific energy states can be understood at least qualitatively by considering the degree of penetrability of the electrons through the inner electron cores, which influences the effective charge acting upon the individual electron. Basically, the $n = 4$, $l = 0$ electron penetrates farther through the inner cores of electrons than the $n = 3$, $l = 2$ electron, with the result that it is influenced by a larger effective charge, and is held in a lower energy state. The filling of the $l = 3$ states, which are even less penetrating than the $l = 2$ states, occurs much farther along in the periodic table. For example, the $n = 4$, $l = 3$ states are not filled until after the $n = 6$, $l = 0$ states are filled. The filling of the $n = 4$, $l = 3$ states produces the rare earths in the periodic table. Because of the similar nature of the outer shells of all the rare earth elements, all show remarkably similar chemical characteristics.

The manner in which the filling of shells occur can be seen in Table 7.1. A simple rule for the order of filling of the atomic shells is that shells with the smallest values of the sum $n + l$ are always filled first. For example, the $n = 4$, $l = 0$ shell for which $n + l = 4$ is filled before the $n = 3$, $l = 2$ shell for which $n + l = 5$. In case two sets of n, l quantum numbers give the same value of the sum $n + l$, the shell with the lowest n is filled first. For example, the $n = 4$, $l = 2$ shell is filled before the $n = 5$, $l = 1$ shell which in turn is filled before the $n = 6$, $l = 0$ shell.

Elements may also be arranged in what is known as the periodic table of elements, such as is shown in Table 7.2. Elements in the same column of a tabular periodic table of elements possess similar chemical properties, because each column represents atoms having similar electronic structure in their outer shells.

7.9 The Vector Model of the Atom. Sometimes the easiest way to get a good physical picture of what is happening in an atom is to revert to a modified form of the planetary representation of the atom with what is known as the *vector model* of the atom. According to the planetary interpretation of the atom, each electron moves in an orbit around the nucleus

Table 7.2. Periodic Table of Elements*
(With Energy State Notation for Ground State†)

Period		Group I	II	III	IV	V	VI	VII	VIII	0
1		1 H $^2S_{1/2}$								2 He $^1S_0$
2		3 Li $^2S_{1/2}$	4 Be $^1S_0$	5 B $^2P_{1/2}$	6 C $^3P_0$	7 N $^4S_{3/2}$	8 O $^3P_2$	9 F $^2P_{3/2}$		10 Ne $^1S_0$
3		11 Na $^2S_{1/2}$	12 Mg $^1S_0$	13 Al $^2P_{1/2}$	14 Si $^3P_0$	15 P $^4S_{3/2}$	16 S $^3P_2$	17 Cl $^2P_{3/2}$		18 A $^1S_0$
4		19 K $^2S_{1/2}$	20 Ca $^1S_0$	21 Sc $^2D_{3/2}$	22 Ti $^3F_2$	23 V $^4F_{3/2}$	24 Cr $^7S_3$	25 Mn $^6S_{5/2}$	26 Fe $^5D_4$ 27 Co $^4F_{9/2}$ 28 Ni $^3F_4$	
		29 Cu $^2S_{1/2}$	30 Zn $^1S_0$	31 Ga $^2P_{1/2}$	32 Ge $^3P_0$	33 As $^4S_{3/2}$	34 Se $^3P_2$	35 Br $^2P_{3/2}$		36 Kr $^1S_0$
5		37 Rb $^2S_{1/2}$	38 Sr $^1S_0$	39 Y $^2D_{3/2}$	40 Zr $^3F_2$	41 Nb $^6D_{1/2}$	42 Mo $^7S_3$	43 Tc $^6S_{5/2}$	44 Ru $^5F_5$ 45 Rh $^4F_{9/2}$ 46 Pd $^1S_0$	
		47 Ag $^2S_{1/2}$	48 Cd $^1S_0$	49 In $^2P_{1/2}$	50 Sn $^3P_0$	51 Sb $^4S_{3/2}$	52 Te $^3P_2$	53 I $^2P_{3/2}$		54 Xe $^1S_0$
6		55 Cs $^2S_{1/2}$	56 Ba $^1S_0$	57-71 *	72 Hf $^3F_2$	73 Ta $^4F_{3/2}$	74 W $^5D_0$	75 Re $^6S_{5/2}$	76 Os $^5D_4$ 77 Ir $^4F_{9/2}$ 78 Pt $^3D_3$	
		79 Au $^2S_{1/2}$	80 Hg $^1S_0$	81 Tl $^2P_{1/2}$	82 Pb $^3P_0$	83 Bi $^4S_{3/2}$	84 Po $^3P_2$	85 At		86 Rn $^1S_0$
7		87 Fr $^2S_{1/2}$	88 Ra $^1S_0$	89- **						

*Lanthanide Series Rare Earths	57 La $^2D_{3/2}$	58 Ce	59 Pr $^4I_{9/2}$	60 Nd $^5I_4$	61 Pm	62 Sm $^7F_0$	63 Eu $^8S_{7/2}$	64 Gd $^9D_2$
	65 Tb	66 Dy	67 Ho	68 Er	69 Tm $^2F_{7/2}$	70 Yb $^1S_0$	71 Lu $^2D_{5/2}$	
**Actinide Series	89 Ac $^2D_{3/2}$	90 Th $^3F_2$	91 Pa	92 U $^5L_6$	93 Np	94 Pu	95 Am $^8S_{7/2}$	96 Cm
	97 Bk	98 Cf	99 E	100 Fm	101 Mv	102 No		

*Names of each of the elements and their chemical atomic weights are given in Appendix 1.2.

†Based on C. E. Moore, *Atomic Energy Levels, NBS Circular 467* (U. S. Government Printing Office), Vol. I, 1949; Vol. II, 1952; Vol. III, 1958. For discussion of energy state notation, see Section 7.10.

with an angular velocity ω. The associated angular momentum is $lh/2\pi$, where l is an integer. However, according to the quantum mechanical results of Appendix 7.1 and Sections 7.2 and 7.3, the magnitude of the orbital angular momentum of an orbital electron is $h/2\pi[l(l+1)]^{1/2}$ not $lh/2\pi$. For large l, though, the two terms are approximately the same. The simple formulation $lh/2\pi$ for the angular momentum, even for small values of l, sometimes presents an adequate picture of the physical situation in an atom. In the vector model it is therefore often found convenient to assume that the orbital angular momentum is $lh/2\pi$. Diagrammatically it is customary to show angular momentum as a vector along the axis of rotation, perpendicular to the plane of the orbit. The magnitude of the vector then is set equal to the angular momentum quantum number, l, or to $l^* = [l(l + 1)]^{1/2}$, depending on the assumptions that are made regarding the magnitude of the orbital angular momentum. Similarly a vector representing the spin angular momentum, equal to s or $s^* = [s(s + 1)]^{1/2}$, is used in the vector model.

Because a magnetic field is established when a charged particle moves or spins in such a manner as to have angular momentum of finite magnitude, it is anticipated that one electron in an atom should interact with other electrons in the same atom through the fields established by their respective motions. The vector model has been developed to describe in relatively simple terms the nature of these interactions. It must be remembered that the vector model is only a means for easily picturing some characteristics of the atom, and can be considered only as an aid that assists in the understanding of the workings of the atom. If a picture of the atom is to be used, though, the vector diagram is probably as good a picture as can be drawn that still retains a reasonable representation of the quantum mechanical aspects of atomic structure.

To obtain an initial understanding of the workings of the vector model, consider as an example the interaction of the orbital angular momenta of two p electrons. These orbital angular momenta combine to give a resultant orbital angular momentum for which the quantum number is L.† Since each p electron has an orbital angular momentum quantum number $l = 1$, the maximum possible resultant orbital angular momentum quantum number for two p electrons is $L = 2$. This results from simple addition of the two parallel vectors each of which has a magnitude l, proportional to the angular momentum, $lh/2\pi$, of each of the two electrons. Vector addition of the quantum numbers for the two p electrons may also be such that one orbital electron vector is directed oppositely to the first, with the result that $L = 0$. Both of these types of vector additions are illustrated in Fig. 7.7(a). The resultant orbital angular momentum quantum number not only is limited to integer values, but must be able to assume all integer values between the maximum and minimum values. Therefore, besides $L = 2$, and $L = 0$, two p electrons must also combine to give an orbital angular momentum $L = 1$, also shown in Fig. 7.7(a).

Assuming that the magnitude of the orbital angular momentum vector is proportional to l has the advantage that all possible magnitudes of the resultant quantum numbers can be determined easily and quickly. How-

†It is standard practice to use a capital letter, such as L or S, to represent quantum numbers resulting from the combined effects of two or more electrons.

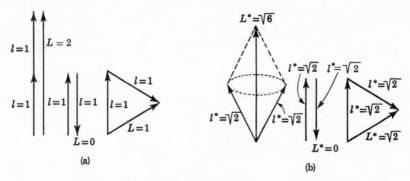

FIG. 7.7. Vector model addition of the angular momentum vectors of two $l = 1$ electrons to produce resultant angular momentum states of $L = 0, 1$, and 2. Part (a) shows the vector addition based on the simple planetary model of the atom, and part (b) the vector addition based on the quantum mechanical model.

ever, this method gives inadequate information regarding the relative directional characteristics of the angular momentum vectors. If directional properties of the vectors are also desired, correct quantum mechanical values of the orbital angular momentum, $l^*h/2\pi = [l(l + 1)]^{1/2}h/2\pi$ and $L^*h/2\pi = [L(L + 1)]^{1/2}h/2\pi$, must be used. Now, though, the vectors for two $2p$ electrons must be aligned as indicated in Fig. 7.7(b). Alignment of the angular momentum vectors in this manner further induces a precession of these vectors around the resultant vector direction. Such precession may be at least qualitatively understood by reference to Fig. 2.3(b). The most stable orientation in a magnetic field for a charged particle orbit is a plane perpendicular to the direction of the magnetic flux, for then the angle ϕ of Fig. 2.3(b) is zero, and $B_z \sin \phi = 0$. However, if $B_z \sin \phi \neq 0$, a net torque is exerted upon the orbit. This torque tries to move the plane of the orbit into a plane perpendicular to the direction of B_z, but is restrained by the interaction between the individual electron angular momenta. Under such circumstances, though, a time averaged equilibrium condition can be attained because of a precession of the plane of the orbit around the direction of the applied magnetic flux, provided that the period of the precession is slow compared to the orbital period of the electron. With such precession the net force on the orbital electron averages to zero. In the specific case under consideration the orbital precession (precession of the individual vectors) is around the direction of the resultant orbital angular momentum vector in the manner indicated by the dotted path at the top of the appropriate vectors in Fig. 7.7(b).

According to the vector model, the individual spin angular momenta of two electrons interact in exactly the same manner as the orbital angular

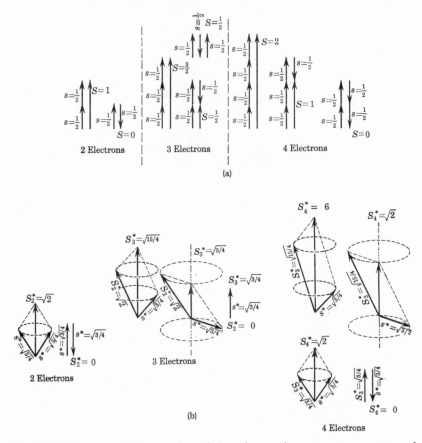

Fig. 7.8. Vector model summation of the spin angular momentum vectors of two, three, and four electrons. Again part (a) is based on the planetary model and part (b) on the quantum mechanical model. The subscript on the capital S (as S_3^*) denotes the number of electrons contributing to this vector. Note that there is more than one way to arrive at all resultant vectors S for which the magnitude is less than the maximum (examples are given for $S_3^* = \sqrt{3/4}$ and $S_4^* = \sqrt{2}$). This means that these states are degenerate.

momentum vectors. But the spin quantum number s is always $\frac{1}{2}$, so if the spin angular momentum is assumed to be $sh/2\pi$, the resultant spin quantum number of two electrons can have only two values, $S = 0$ or $S = 1$, as illustrated in Fig. 7.8(a). Also in Fig. 7.8(a) are shown the possible resultant spin quantum numbers for the combination of three electrons ($S = \frac{1}{2}$ and $\frac{3}{2}$) and for four electrons ($S = 0, 1$ and 2). When the quantum mechanical magnitudes $s^*h/2\pi$ are used for the spin angular momentum vector, the resultant spin angular momentum vectors for two electrons are determined in an analogous manner to that used for the

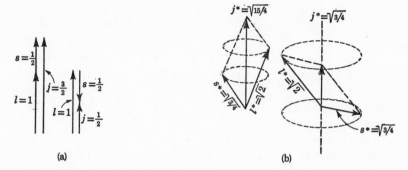

FIG. 7.9.   Vector model addition of spin and orbital angular momentum vectors to produce the total angular momentum vectors belonging to the energy states of a single atomic electron.   In this case the specific electron chosen for illustration is an $l = 1$, $s = \frac{1}{2}$ electron.

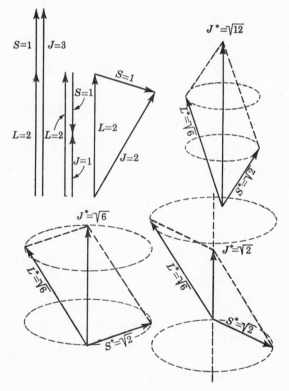

FIG. 7.10.   Vector model addition of spin and orbital angular momentum vectors for atomic energy states produced by the interactions of more than a single electron.

addition of two orbital angular momentum vectors, and are appropriately shown in Fig. 7.8(b). In this system the resultant spin vectors for three electrons are obtained by addition of the angular momentum vector for the third electron with the vectors resulting from the combination of two electrons. This results in the same spin quantum numbers, $S = \frac{1}{2}$ and $\frac{3}{2}$, also illustrated in Fig. 7.8(b), as determined in the simpler analysis discussed above. Similarly the addition of the spin angular momentum vector for a fourth electron to the resultant vectors for three electrons gives precisely the same results, $S = 0, 1$, and 2, as previously determined. The spin vectors also precess about the resultant vector in the same manner as has been discussed for the case of the orbital angular momentum vectors.

Spin and orbital angular momenta interact with each other to give a total angular momentum for each atomic state, the quantum number for which is designated by j or by J, depending on the number of electrons contributing to the energy state. The magnitude of this quantum number is found by a vector type of addition of the spin and orbital quantum number vectors. As an example, the total angular momentum vector for an $l = 1$, $s = \frac{1}{2}$ electron is $j = \frac{1}{2}$ or $\frac{3}{2}$, as illustrated in Fig. 7.9. If more than a single electron contributes to the total angular momentum vector J, the magnitude of this vector usually is found by vector addition of the resultant L and resultant S vectors, as illustrated in Fig. 7.10 for the condition that $L = 2$ and $S = 1$, in which case the total angular momentum vectors are $J = 1, 2$, or 3. This type of spin-orbit coupling is known as *Russell-Saunders* or *L–S* coupling, and is the type of coupling prevalent in most atoms. Under certain circumstances, though, especially at the high atomic number end of the periodic table of elements, *j–j coupling* is prevalent. In *j–j* coupling, vector addition of the *l* and *s* angular momentum vectors must be made for the individual electrons prior to a final vector addition of the individual *j* vectors to determine the resultant total quantum numbers, J.

In addition to the s, S, l, L, j, and J quantum numbers, there have already been introduced earlier in this chapter the magnetic quantum numbers which, with the introduction of the total quantum numbers, j and J, now have grown to six in number, m_s, M_S, m_l, M_L, m_j, and M_J. This group of six is more than enough to describe fully the energy state configuration of any single set of electrons. Depending on the physical situation only the m_j's (M_J's) or a combination of m_l's (M_L's) and m_s's (M_S's) need be used in any single situation, since the magnitude of m_j depends on the magnitude of m_l and m_s. In Section 7.3 it was stated that the quantum number m_l describes the orientation in the $r\theta$-plane of the orbital angular momentum vector relative to an external magnetic field. Coupling of the orbital (or spin) angular momentum vectors of two or more electrons or coupling of the spin and orbital angular momentum vectors of a single electron fixes the orientation of the momentum vectors relative to each other. The relative directions of the coupled vectors cannot be changed by an external magnetic field unless the external field is strong enough to overcome the interactions between the magnetic moments that produce the coupling. The introduction of an external magnetic field does, though, bring about an orientation of the system as a whole. The physical characteristics of the resulting phenomena are explained in more detail in Section 7.12, but for the present a discussion of the effect of an external magnetic field on the total angular momentum vector, J, will suffice.

Suppose a group of coupled electrons has a total angular momentum quantum number $J = 3$. The possible magnetic quantum numbers M_J for this group include all integers between $+3$ and -3. According to the vector model each of these magnetic quantum numbers results from an electron for which the vector J is oriented in a distinct direction, as in Fig. 7.11, defined so that the projection of J on the direction of an applied magnetic field gives the value of M_J. When there is no applied

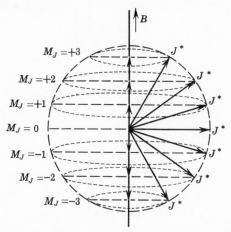

F IG. 7.11. Diagram showing possible orientations of the total angular momentum vector J relative to the direction of an externally applied magnetic field and the magnitudes of the associated magnetic quantum state vectors M_J.

magnetic field it is impossible to distinguish between different magnetic states, and all energy states of this group having the same total quantum number are at the same energy level. If an external magnetic field is applied the levels split and an additional number of monoenergetic radiations resulting from transitions between individual atomic levels are observed. The additional spectral lines resulting from this type of splitting of atomic energy levels produce what is known as the *Zeeman effect* (see

Section 7.12). A new reference direction is now introduced by the externally applied magnetic field and the total angular momentum vectors precess around this magnetic field. Under these conditions the component of each vector perpendicular to the magnetic field direction averages to zero, and the only angular momentum that can be experimentally observed is $M_J h/2\pi$. The energy level, characteristic of a particular value of J, that existed prior to the introduction of the external magnetic field now splits into $2J + 1$ levels.

7.10 Energy State Notation. Before proceeding further it is perhaps best to introduce the notation used by spectroscopists to describe an atomic energy state. This notation must describe the magnitude of L, S, and J for the state. Since the inner shells of the atom are generally filled and hence do not contribute to the magnitude of the resulting orbital, spin, and total quantum numbers, only the outer shell, or valence, electrons must be considered. These valence electrons either may all be in their respective ground states, or one or more may be in an excited state.

In the spectroscopist's energy state notation a central capital letter is used to describe the orbital angular momentum of the atomic system. These capital letters are the same set used in lower case to describe the orbital angular momentum quantum state of a single electron. For instance, if the orbital angular momentum of the atom is $L = 0$, the atomic state of the atom is an S state. If the orbital angular momentum quantum number is $L = 1$, the atom is in a P state. Sodium (Fig. 7.6) is a simple example with which to begin, since all its electrons except one are in closed shells and only the one valence electron is responsible for the atomic state. In its ground state the atom is in an S state. By appropriate addition of energy to the system it may be raised either to other S states, or to P, D, F, G, and other states.

To describe completely the state, though, not only the orbital angular momentum quantum number must be known, but also the spin angular momentum quantum number s, or S (this capital S must not be confused with the S which describes the $L = 0$ state, and will not when the complete atomic state description is completed, since the S which describes the atomic state is always accompanied by appropriate superscripts and subscripts). The spin angular momentum quantum state is described by a number superscript to the left of the capital letter describing the orbital angular momentum quantum state. The magnitude of this number is $2s + 1$, or $2S + 1$. Thus the ground state of the sodium atom, for which the spin angular momentum quantum number is $s = \frac{1}{2}$, is described by a superscript 2. Since there is only one electron producing all of the sodium states, this superscript is 2 for all states.

To describe completely an atomic state, the magnitude of the quantum number j, or J, must also be known. This magnitude is given as a numerical subscript to the right of the capital letter. Thus the ground state of sodium is completely described as a $^2S_{1/2}$ state, since there is only a single value of j possible for the quantum numbers $s = \frac{1}{2}$ and $l = 0$. If the atom is raised to a P state (an $l = 1$ state), the vector model shows that for sodium there are two possible values for J, $\frac{1}{2}$ and $\frac{3}{2}$. Thus there are two possible $l = 1$ atomic states, a $^2P_{1/2}$ and a $^2P_{3/2}$ state. The energy levels of these two states are very nearly, but not quite, the same. They are therefore described as *doublet* states.

With the exception of the $l = 0$ and $L = 0$ states, the superscript to the left gives the number of energy states for any single set of values of the n, l, or L, and s, or S, quantum numbers. It is called the *multiplicity* of the state. This type of descriptive notation for each state is shown in Fig. 7.6 for sodium. All levels in each vertical column are the same type of state, each being in a different shell (different n quantum number).

The rules for allowed transitions between multi-electron atomic states are $\Delta L = \pm 1$, $\Delta S = 0$, and $\Delta J = 0$ or ± 1. To distinguish between levels described by the same state configuration but in different shells of the same atom, the magnitude of the quantum number n is sometimes added as a prefix to the state description; thus the ground state of sodium is a $3^2S_{1/2}$ state. The next higher levels are the $3^2P_{1/2}$ and $3^2P_{3/2}$ states. Transitions from these two states to the ground state produce two characteristic yellow spectral lines which are separated by only about six angstroms. It is this radiation which gives a sodium flame or sodium arc its distinctive yellow color.

If there are two or more valence electrons, it is possible to have something other than doublet states. For example, consider the magnesium atom, which has one more electron than sodium. Outside the closed $2p$ shell magnesium has two electrons, each of which are $l = 0$ electrons. The atomic state is described by the configuration produced by the interaction between these two electrons. Since each of these electrons has a spin quantum number $s = \frac{1}{2}$, the spin of the system, as determined from the vector model, must be $S = 0$ or 1. If $S = 0$ there is only a single value of J regardless of the magnitude of the quantum number L, but, if $S = 1$, use of the vector model shows that there are three possible values of J for every L, with the one exception $L = 0$. Thus the superscript in the description of the atomic state once again describes the number of levels in the configuration since the numerical magnitude of $2S + 1$ indicates that magnesium has both singlet and triplet states. The ground state, when both electrons are in the $n = 3$ shell, is a $^1S_0$ state. No $^3S_1$ state may exist in this shell since the existence of a spin $S = 1$ implies, both according to the planetary atom version of the vector model, and according to the quantum mechanical version of the vector model, provided the spin vector direction is averaged over a sufficiently long period of time, that the spins of the two individual electrons are parallel. To have parallel spins requires that either $m_s = +\frac{1}{2}$ for both electrons or $m_s = -\frac{1}{2}$ for both electrons. On the other hand, a vector addition of the two electron spins to give a resultant spin $S = 0$ implies that the spins of

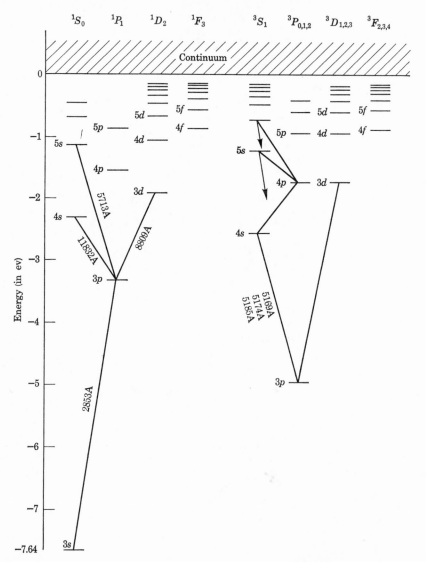

Fig. 7.12.   Energy level diagram for magnesium.

the two individual electrons are antiparallel. Now the Pauli exclusion principle states that no two electrons in the same atom may have the same set of quantum numbers. Both electrons in the ground state, $n = 3$ shell of the magnesium atom have an orbital quantum number $l = 0$. Hence, $m_l = 0$ for both electrons. The spin quantum number for both electrons is $s = \frac{1}{2}$, so the only quantum number that can assume different values for these two electrons is the spin magnetic quantum number, m_s. The two electrons cannot then line up with parallel spins, with a resultant spin $S = 1$, for this would be a violation of the Pauli exclusion principle. But if one of the electrons is raised to the $n = 4$ or a higher shell, a $^3S_1$ state is possible. The energy level diagram for the magnesium atom is shown in Fig. 7.12. All the excited energy levels of this diagram are generated when one electron is in the ground state and the other is raised to the indicated excited state. The energy state notation is that which results from the L–S coupling of the two electrons.

For elements having more than two valence electrons, systems of higher multiplicity exist. Quartets and quintets are relatively common, and in some elements ground state multiplicities as high as eight (octets) have been observed.

7.11 Equivalent Electrons. There are a number of cases when two or more electrons in an atom have the same set of n, l, and s quantum numbers. To determine what atomic states can exist in this situation, it is necessary to determine the magnetic quantum numbers. This has been done in Section 7.10 in considering the rather special case of two s electrons in the same shell. To give a more general treatment to the subject, two equivalent p electrons are considered in this section. Generally it is not necessary to make use of these magnetic quantum numbers to determine all possible atomic states. But for the situation that exists when two electrons in an atom have the same n, l, and s quantum numbers, it is necessary to bring into consideration the magnetic quantum numbers M_L and M_S that result from the effects of combining the magnetic quantum numbers of the individual electrons, as well as those multi-electron quantum numbers that have already been described.

To describe this situation consider for example the possible atomic energy states that can exist for carbon, which has two 2s electrons and two 2p electrons beyond the closed $n = 1$ shell. In this particular case the two 2s electrons can be ignored since they represent a closed subshell for which $L = 0$ and $S = 0$. It is only the two 2p electrons which produce the observed atomic energy states. If the two 2p electrons were completely independent, the vector model indicates that states should be expected for which $L = 0$, 1, or 2 and $S = 0$ or 1. There would then be six states in all, the $^1S_0$, $^1P_1$, $^1D_2$, $^3S_1$, $^3P_{0,1,2}$, and $^3D_{1,2,3}$ states. But for two $2p$ electrons not all of these states can exist.

In Table 7.3 the six possible combinations of magnetic quantum numbers that can be formed by two $2p$ electrons are tabulated. Since the Pauli exclusion principle states that duplicate sets of quantum numbers

TABLE 7.3. COMPUTATION OF POSSIBLE GROUND STATES OF CARBON

$m_s = +\frac{1}{2}$ $m_l = +1$ (a) $m_s = -\frac{1}{2}$ $m_l = +1$ (d)

$m_l = 0$ (b) $m_l = 0$ (e)

$m_l = -1$ (c) $m_l = -1$ (f)

	ab	ac	ad	ae	af	bc	bd	be	bf	cd	ce	cf	de	df	ef
M_S	1	1	0	0	0	1	0	0	0	0	0	0	-1	-1	-1
M_L	1	0	2	1	0	-1	1	0	-1	0	-1	-2	1	0	-1

cannot exist in a single atom, the combinations aa, bb, cc, dd, ee, and ff are forbidden for carbon, but all other combinations of quantum numbers must be used to determine possible energy states. These allowed combinations and the resulting magnetic quantum numbers M_L and M_S are also listed in Table 7.3.

To determine the values of L and S, note the largest value of M_L. In the carbon example it is 2. Associated with $M_L = 2$, the largest value of M_S is 0. This means that an $L = 2$, $S = 0$ state is allowed under the conditions that have been imposed. This state requires five values of M_L ranging from $+2$ to -2, consuming the combinations ad, ae, af, ce, and cf. It is necessary then to conclude that a $^1D_2$ state is allowed. After removal of the combinations of M_S and M_L required for a $^1D_2$ state, the maximum value of M_L that now remains is 1, and associated with this is a maximum M_S of 1. To satisfy this state requires that each quantum number $M_L = +1$, 0, and -1 combine with each quantum number $M_S = +1$, 0, and -1, a total of nine possible combinations. These combinations consume all the remaining possible sets of magnetic quantum numbers with the exception of a single $M_L = 0$, $M_S = 0$ combination. Thus the two remaining possible states are a $^3P_{0,1,2}$ state and a $^1S_0$ state. The other three which would have been obtained by the originally described vector model analysis are therefore forbidden. Remember, though, that, if one of the two $2p$ electrons is raised to a higher energy shell, say for example the $n = 3$ shell, all six possible states are allowed. In this case one electron is a $2p$ electron and the other a $3p$ electron. The quantum number n is then different for the two electrons, so both electrons can have simultaneously the same set of magnetic quantum numbers.

Analyses for other equivalent electrons follow the same general pattern, but, of course, the analysis becomes more difficult for the higher orbital angular momentum states and for larger numbers of electrons. As previously indicated, two s electrons in the same shell can have only the $^1S_0$ state. Two d electrons in the same shell can have only five states, the $^1S_0$, $^1D_2$, $^1G_4$, $^3P_{0,1,2}$, and $^3F_{2,3,4}$ states, rather than the ten that would have been predicted by the general treatment of the vector model.

7.12 The Zeeman Effect. An external magnetic field provides an axis upon which the electron distributions in the various atomic energy states can be oriented. According to the vector model, an atom in an external magnetic field is quantized with J oriented such that the vector associated with its magnetic quantum number, M_J, is aligned at some angle to the direction of the magnetic field. The introduction of a magnetic field then splits each atomic state into $2J + 1$ energy levels.

It is the magnetic moment of any dipole, such as an orbiting electron or a spinning electron, that interacts with a magnetic field to produce a change in the energy of the system. For an electron current flowing in a loop, it was seen in Eq. 2.16 that the magnetic moment produced by and the angular momentum of the electron moving in the loop are related by the gyromagnetic ratio, such that $\mu = Le/2mc$ where L is the angular momentum. If the value $l^*h/2\pi$, now known to be the angular momentum of the orbiting electron, is substituted into this equation, the magnetic moment of the electron is found to be

$$\mu_l = l^*(h/2\pi)(e/2mc), \tag{7.2}$$

where, to give correct numerical values, $l^* = [l(l+1)]^{1/2}$. Just as experimental evidence shows that the angular momentum of the spinning electron is $s^*h/2\pi$, where $s^* = [s(s+1)]^{1/2}$, and $s = \frac{1}{2}$, experimental evidence also shows that, for the spinning electron μ_s is twice the expected gyromagnetic ratio, such that

$$\mu_s = 2s^*(h/2\pi)(e/2mc). \tag{7.3}$$

Because of the effect of this value for the magnetic moment of the spinning electron, the resultant magnetic moment vector $\mu_{l,s}$ is not parallel to the resultant angular momentum vector j. This is indicated in Fig. 7.13. The magnetic moment parallel to the j angular momentum vector must be formed by the projections of the l and s magnetic moments upon the j direction, such that

$$\mu_j = [l^* \cos (lj) + 2s^* \cos (sj)](h/2\pi)(e/2mc), \tag{7.4}$$

where $\cos (lj)$ means the cosine of the angle formed by the direction of l and the direction of j.

The magnitude j^* must be multiplied by some factor g to be equal to the bracketed quantity of Eq. 7.4; thus

$$j^*g = l^* \cos (lj) + 2s^* \cos (sj). \qquad (7.5)$$

By the laws of plane trigonometry,

$$s^{*2} = l^{*2} + j^{*2} - 2l^*j^* \cos (lj) \quad \text{and} \quad l^{*2}$$
$$= s^{*2} + j^{*2} - 2s^*j^* \cos (sj), \qquad (7.6)$$

so that

$$l^* \cos (lj) = (j^{*2} + l^{*2} - s^{*2})/2j^* \quad \text{and} \quad s^* \cos (sj)$$
$$= (j^{*2} + s^{*2} - l^{*2})/2j^*. \qquad (7.7)$$

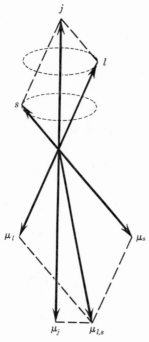

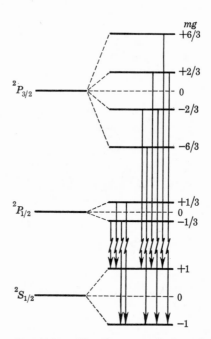

FIG. 7.13. Diagram illustrating the magnitudes and directions of the angular momentum vectors and magnetic moment vectors for an atomic energy state. The specific case shown is that of an $l = 1$, $s = \frac{1}{2}$ electron.

FIG. 7.14. The Zeeman splitting of the ground state energy level and first excited state of the neutral sodium atom, and the allowed transitions between the various Zeeman levels. The break in each transition is made to indicate the large energy interval between the ^2P and the ^2S energy states in the $n = 3$ shell of sodium.

Substitution of these two values into Eq. 7.5 gives

$$g = 1 + (j^{*2} + s^{*2} - l^{*2})/2j^{*2} = 1$$
$$+ [j(j+1) + s(s+1) - l(l+1)]/2j(j+1). \quad (7.8)$$

It is this factor g by which $e/2mc$ must be multiplied to determine the ratio of the total magnetic moment to the total angular momentum, with the result that

$$\mu_j = j^*g(h/2\pi)(e/2mc) = j^*g(eh/4\pi mc). \quad (7.9)$$

The quantity g is known as the *Landé g factor*, and the unit of magnetic moment $eh/4\pi mc$ is called the *Bohr magneton*, equal in magnitude to 0.918×10^{-20} ergs/gauss.

In a magnetic flux density B the energy of precession is $\mu_j B \cos (jB)$, this being the energy that must be added to the already existing energy level because of the effects of precession. This increment of energy is then

$$\Delta W = Bgj^*(eh/4\pi mc) \cos (jB) = Bm_j g(eh/4\pi mc). \quad (7.10)$$

The effects of a magnetic field in splitting the $3^2P_{1/2}$, $3^2P_{3/2}$ and $3^2S_{1/2}$ energy levels of sodium are illustrated in Fig. 7.14. Also shown in Fig. 7.14 are the allowed transitions between the sodium atom energy levels when the radiating atom is situated in a magnetic field. It is this splitting of atomic spectral lines into a number of component parts by a magnetic field that is known as the *Zeeman effect*. The magnitude of g from which the amount of splitting in each of the levels is determined is $g = 2$ for the $^2S_{1/2}$ state, $g = \frac{2}{3}$ for the $^2P_{1/2}$ state, and $g = \frac{4}{3}$ for the $^2P_{3/2}$ state. It is this difference in splitting in the different atomic energy states that produces the rather large numbers of lines in the spectra for the two different types of transitions. Had g been the same for all states, the splitting of the levels would have been equal in each state and each of the yellow spectral lines of sodium would have split into three lines as a result of the effects of the magnetic field. Splitting of the energy levels because of the effects of a magnetic field occurs in all types of atomic state configurations, the number of spectral lines depending on the type of energy state in which the splitting occurs.

As the magnitude of the magnetic field is increased, the coupling between the magnetic moments of the orbital and spin angular momenta becomes less significant than the interaction between the individual magnetic moments and the magnetic flux density. As a result, the coupling between spin and orbit magnetic moments is broken and the spin and orbital vectors precess individually around the direction of the magnetic flux density vector. This produces a further change in the splitting of the energy levels for any atomic energy state beyond that observed in the Zeeman effect. The resulting effect is known as the *Paschen-Back effect*, detailed information about which can be found, if desired, in the more advanced texts on atomic structure given in the references at the end of the chapter.

7.13 The Photoelectric Effect and Characteristic X-Rays.

If radiation of very high energy, such as x-rays from an x-ray tube, is incident upon an atom, a photon from this radiation may interact with an electron which is in one of the inner shells, an electron which is much more tightly bound than the valence electron. For example, an incident photon having an energy greater than the binding energy of an electron in the $n = 1$ shell may eject from the atom by a photoelectric process one of these most tightly bound electrons. The electron is released with a kinetic energy $W_K = h\nu -$ B.E., where $h\nu$ is the energy of the incident photon and B.E. is the binding energy of the electron. This is simply a form of the photoelectric effect discussed earlier.

After the ejection of an electron from the innermost shell of an atom, a vacancy exists in that shell. Since electrons in the outer shells are less tightly bound than the electron that was ejected, a transition by one of these electrons into the $n = 1$ shell is possible with a loss of energy that is radiated as electromagnetic radiation. These less tightly bound electrons are in well-defined energy levels and a transition by one of them to the $n = 1$ shell releases a discrete amount of energy. The resulting electromagnetic radiations appear as monochromatic lines in an x-ray spectrum, each line characteristic of a specific transition between two energy levels of the atom. This is the explanation for the characteristic x-rays observed above the continuous spectrum of Fig. 4.11.

The characteristic x-rays arise from transitions within the atomic structure already discussed, and hence can be described in terms of the already familiar quantum numbers. However, x-ray spectroscopists introduced their own distinctive notation for the spectral lines that they found. This notation became so entrenched that it remains in the literature and is still used in much of the discussion of characteristic spectra in the x-ray region. A British physicist, Moseley, was able to systemize (in 1913–1914) the frequencies of the characteristic x-rays as a function of the atomic number, Z, of the element from which the x-rays were emitted. Two series of lines were observed by Moseley, one of which was associated with fluorescent x-ray radiation which Barkla, a Swedish physicist, had earlier (1908) called *K*-radiation, and another of which was associated with the fluorescent x-ray radiation Barkla had called *L*-radiation. It so happens that the *K*-radiation is produced when an electron falls from a less tightly bound shell into the $n = 1$ shell, and the *L*-radiation is produced when an electron falls into the $n = 2$ shell.

From the use of this notation the $n = 1$ shell was known to the x-ray spectroscopists as the K-shell and the $n = 2$ shell as the L-shell. Successive shells are called the M $(n = 3)$, N $(n = 4)$, O $(n = 5)$, etc., shells, following through the alphabet for the shells which optical spectroscopists have denoted by successively higher principal quantum numbers n. Further subdivision of the x-ray shell notation, indicated in Table 7.4, relates it to the quantum number notation for individual electron states in the atom. Thus any atomic transition can be designated either in terms of the x-ray notation or in terms of the quantum number.

TABLE 7.4. IDENTIFICATION OF ATOMIC SHELLS

X-Ray Notation	Corresponding Quantum Numbers			X-Ray Notation	Corresponding Quantum Numbers		
	n	l	j		n	l	j
K	1	0	$\frac{1}{2}$	N_I	4	0	$\frac{1}{2}$
L_I	2	0	$\frac{1}{2}$	N_{II}	4	1	$\frac{1}{2}$
L_{II}	2	1	$\frac{1}{2}$	N_{III}	4	1	$\frac{3}{2}$
L_{III}	2	1	$\frac{3}{2}$	N_{IV}	4	2	$\frac{3}{2}$
M_I	3	0	$\frac{1}{2}$	N_V	4	2	$\frac{5}{2}$
M_{II}	3	1	$\frac{1}{2}$	N_{VI}	4	3	$\frac{5}{2}$
M_{III}	3	1	$\frac{3}{2}$	N_{VII}	4	3	$\frac{7}{2}$
M_{IV}	3	2	$\frac{3}{2}$				
M_V	3	2	$\frac{5}{2}$				

7.14 The Auger Effect. An electron sometimes falls into a more tightly bound vacant shell without the emission of a characteristic x-ray. Instead the transition energy is transferred to one of the other bound electrons in the atom and that electron is ejected from the atom with sufficient kinetic energy to carry away the transition energy. Such a transition is then a *radiationless transition*. The process is also known as the *Auger effect*, after Pierre Auger, the discoverer of such radiationless transitions.

To demonstrate the Auger effect suppose, for example, that one of the K-shell electrons is missing from an atom of silver, having been ejected by some means, perhaps by a high energy incident photon which has photoelectrically ejected a K-shell electron. Suppose an N_{II} electron falls into the vacant spot in the K-shell. The N_{II}–K energy difference for silver is 25.46 kev. If an x-ray photon is emitted, its energy is $h\nu = 25.46$ kev. But, if instead of photon emission, an L_I-shell electron is ejected as an Auger electron, the total energy given to this electron would be 25.46 kev. The binding energy of an L_I electron is 3.83 kev, and since this energy must be consumed in getting the L_I electron out of the atom, the kinetic energy of the electron after escape is only 21.63 kev.

7.15 X-Ray Absorption Edges. If a beam of x-rays from an x-ray tube passes through a piece of material, some of the photons are photo-electrically absorbed, as described in the previous section. To be so absorbed the photon must have sufficient energy to eject a bound elec-tron from the target atom. If the incident radiation has a wavelength slightly too long (the energy is not quite sufficient) to eject an electron, no photoelectric absorption can take place. But for any wavelength shorter than the critical wavelength (energy greater than electron binding energy) there is a finite probability that the photon can interact with the bound electron and cause its removal from the atom. As a result there are a series of discrete breaks in the continuity of the attenua-tion coefficient of the material. The *attenuation coefficient* describes the rate of removal of photons from a beam of radiation by some material that is placed in the beam to act as a shield, and is expressed mathe-matically by the formula $dI/dx = -\mu x$, where I is the intensity of the radiation at any point x and μ is the attenuation coefficient.

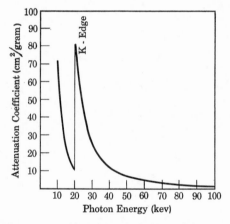

Fig. 7.15.   Plot of the attenuation coefficient for molybdenum as a function of photon energy, showing the absorption edge for the K-shell. (Based on informa-tion from G. W. Grodstein, *X-ray Attenuation Coefficients from 10 kev to 100 Mev, NBS Circular 583*)

Generally the attenuation coefficient decreases for any given material with increasing photon energy. This is shown in Fig. 7.15. But there are sudden breaks in this curve at photon energies equal to the binding energy of the various shells of the atom. These are known as the *absorption edges*.

7.16 Absorption Spectra. The characteristic line spectra arising from transitions between atomic energy levels usually are seen in observations of terrestrial sources as bright line spectra on a dark background. This kind of spectrum appears when an atom falls from a higher energy state into a lower energy state, releasing in the process a photon of radiation. It is possible, though, to have dark line, or absorption, spectra, such as the spectrum of the Balmer series of hydrogen shown in Fig. 5.1. Such spectra can be observed terrestrially if a source of radiation (such as a carbon arc) that is emitting a continuous spectrum is observed by a spectrometer through an intermediate layer of gas, shown schematically in Fig. 7.16. In the case of Fig. 5.1 the radiation from the opaque body of Zeta Tauri is observed through a gaseous atmosphere. If

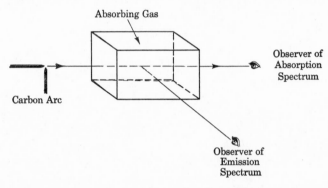

FIG. 7.16.   Experimental arrangement for observing absorption spectra.

a photon with exactly the right energy to raise one of the atoms of the gas from a lower energy state to a higher energy state interacts with that atom, there is a finite probability that the transition will occur. If the transition does occur, the photon which initiates the interaction is removed from the radiation beam. After many such interactions the radiation passing through the gaseous atmosphere from the surface of the star underneath will have been sufficiently depleted of photons of this characteristic frequency to produce a reduction in the intensity of the radiation passing through the gas. Hence the resulting dark lines in the spectrum.

Typical of such dark line spectra is the spectrum of the sun. The radiation which is emitted by the surface of the sun is observed in the visible region to be approximately that of a black body at slightly less than 6000° K. As the radiation passes through the gaseous envelope surrounding the sun, radiation is absorbed by the atoms in the gas, with a resultant dark line spectrum appearing superposed on the continuous spectrum. These dark absorption lines are known as the *Frauenhofer lines*, and two of them also appear in the spectrum of Zeta Tauri of Fig. 5.1, the H and K lines of ionized calcium (see Section 7.17).

When the atoms in the gas are raised to excited states they must, of course, return to the lower energy states by reradiation of photons of the same or lower frequencies than were absorbed. However, the photons that are reradiated are emitted isotropically, whereas the incident absorbed radiation all came from one direction, so, even though all the energy is released after absorption, the energy is released in all directions, and the dark lines appear as prominent features in spectra observed in the manner indicated in Fig. 7.16. The emitted characteristic radiation can be seen by observing the radiations from the gas at right angles to the direction of the incident beam. The most prominent characteristic lines of the Frauenhofer spectrum are similarly seen as bright line spectra in the gaseous shell surrounding the sun at the time of a total eclipse of the sun.

The relative intensities of the characteristic lines appearing in an absorption spectrum always are quite different from the relative intensities of the lines in the emission spectrum of the same element. For a gas at low temperature the only absorption lines that can be observed are those arising from an allowed transition between the ground state energy level and some level above the ground state. Only if the absorbing gas is at such high temperature that an appreciable fraction of the gaseous atoms are continually in excited states will other absorption lines appear (see Problems 15, 16, and 17). For example, the only lines observed in an absorption spectrum in hydrogen at room temperatures are the Lyman series, in the ultraviolet, which arise from transitions from the ground level to higher energy states. That the Balmer series shows up so prominently in the spectrum of Fig. 5.1 is evidence that the gaseous shell surrounding Zeta Tauri is at relatively high temperature, such that an appreciable number of hydrogen atoms are in the $n = 2$ shell at all times.

7.17 Spectra of Ionized Atoms. If a valence electron is given sufficient energy that it escapes from the atom, it leaves the atom with a net positive charge, a positive ion. Unlike the situation discussed in Section 7.13 in which x-rays photoelectrically eject electrons from inner shells of the atom, the removal of a valence electron does not disturb the arrangement of electrons throughout the rest of the atom. However, electrons in the ionized atom can also be raised to excited energy levels and there is a characteristic discrete energy spectrum associated with each ionized element. With the removal of one electron the spectrum of the ion assumes characteristics similar to the spectrum of the atom next lower in the periodic table. For example, ionized magnesium has only one valence electron, hence its energy levels are somewhat similar to those of neutral sodium, and the spectra are also similar, except that the lines are shifted to different wavelengths because of the different energy levels of the corresponding energy states in the two cases.

Among spectroscopists it is customary to use a roman numeral to designate the degree of ionization of an atom in referring either to its energy states or its spectral lines. The numeral I is used to designate the neutral atom, II the once ionized atom, III the twice ionized atom, etc. For example, MgI refers to neutral magnesium and MgII to once ionized magnesium. It is difficult to get very highly ionized atoms in terrestrial sources but from sources in interplanetary and interstellar space radiations characteristic of very highly ionized atoms have been observed. For instance, in the corona of the sun, lines characteristic of FeXIV, FeXV, CaXIII, and other highly ionized atoms have been observed.

The lines marked H and K in Fig. 5.1, the H and K lines of the Frauenhofer spectrum, are absorption lines from transitions in CaII, transitions from the $^2S_{1/2}$ ground state of CaII to the first excited levels, the $^2P_{1/2}$ and the $^2P_{3/2}$ states. Note that calcium, after removal of one of its two valence electrons, which leaves only a single valence electron, has the same ground state and first excited states as neutral sodium, as in Fig. 7.6.

References

H. E. White, *Introduction to Atomic Spectra* (McGraw-Hill Book Co., Inc. New York, 1934).

G. Herzberg, *Atomic Spectra and Atomic Structure* (Dover Publications, Inc., New York, 1944).

A. C. Candler, *Atomic Spectra and the Vector Model* (Cambridge University Press, New York, 1937).

G. P. Harnwell and W. E. Stephens, *Atomic Physics* (McGraw-Hill Book Co., Inc. New York, 1955).

J. C. Slater, *Quantum Theory of Matter* (McGraw-Hill Book Co., Inc., New York, 1951).

G. Gamow, "The Exclusion Principle," *Scientific American* **201**, No. 1, 74, (July 1959).

W. Finkelnburg, *Atomic Physics* (McGraw-Hill Book Co., Inc., New York, 1950).

D. C. Peaslee and H. Mueller, *Elements of Atomic Physics* (Prentice-Hall, Inc., Englewood Cliffs, N. J., 1955).

A. H. Compton and S. K. Allison, *X-Rays in Theory and Experiment* (D. Van Nostrand Co., Inc., Princeton, N. J., 2nd Ed., 1935).

R. B. Leighton, *Principles of Modern Physics* (McGraw-Hill Book Co., Inc., New York, 1958).

R. C. Johnson, *Atomic Spectra* (Methuen & Co., Ltd., London, 1950).

H. A. Bethe and E. E. Salpeter, "Quantum Mechanics of One and Two Electron Systems," in *Handbuch der Physik*, Vol. 35 (Springer Verlag, Berlin, 1957).

Problems

1. Calculate the frequency and wavelength of the radiation which would have been expected to have been induced in the Franck and Hertz experiment when the mercury atoms return to their ground state energy levels. Is an intense spectral line found at about this wavelength in the spectrum of mercury?

2. Suppose an electron is scattered through an angle of 45° halfway between K and G of Fig. 7.1. If the applied voltage is 5.0 volts between K and G, and if the electron undergoes no additional collisions prior to reaching G, what is its kinetic energy when it reaches G? What fraction of its momentum is in a direction perpendicular to the plane of G? What kinetic energy would be associated with this momentum component?

3. Using the assumed functional relationship $R(r) = \rho^l L(\rho) \exp(-\rho)$, in which $\rho = Zr/na$, calculate Eq. 7.17 in Appendix 7.1 from Eq. 7.14, assuming $W = -2\pi^2 me^4 Z^2/\epsilon^2 n^2 h^2$, as specified in Appendix 7.1.

4. By solving the equation $\int_0^\infty |R(r)|^2 r^2 dr = 1$ for the condition $n = 1, l = 0$, show that the normalized constant $a_0 C = 2$ as indicated in Appendix 7.1 for R_{10}.

5. Show as in Problem 4 that the normalized constant $a_0 C$ for R_{20} is $1/\sqrt{2}$.

6. In some texts the term ρ in the solution of $R(r)$ is defined as $\rho = 2Zr/na$. In this case Eqs. 7.17 and 7.18 assume slightly different forms, but the physical interpretation of the results remain the same. Calculate the new Eqs. 7.17 and 7.18 and show from the ratio a_{k+1}/a_k that the physical interpretation does not change.

7. There are 36 electrons in an atom of krypton. Tabulate the quantum numbers associated with each of these electrons, and show from this tabulation that the Pauli exclusion principle is obeyed.

8. Suppose the valence electron of a sodium atom is in the $5s$ level. By what routes may it return to its ground state? Radiations of what wavelengths are emitted in the process?

9. Suppose an atom has two valence electrons, one of which is in an $l = 2$ state, and the other in an $l = 3$ state. Use the vector model to calculate the possible values of the resultant orbital angular momentum quantum number L. What then are the possible magnitudes of the total quantum number J?

10. Using the spectroscopist's energy state notation, tabulate the energy state notation description for each of the possible energy states of Problem 9.

11. In the Bohr model of the hydrogen atom the planetary electron was considered to be revolving around the nucleus in a circular orbit. In this chapter electrons with orbital angular momentum quantum numbers that are smaller than the maximum possible value are considered, according to the planetary model, to penetrate the inner shells of electrons in the atom because they are moving in elliptical orbits. Show that an electron moving under the influence only of the positively charged nucleus in an elliptical orbit with its semimajor axis r_0 has the same total energy, $W = W_K + V$, as an electron moving in a circular orbit of radius r_0. Thus no energy difference would be noted between circular and elliptical orbits for hydrogen and hydrogen-like atoms, except as noted in Problem 12.

12. For circular orbits it was shown that the velocity of the electron in the hydrogen atom was sufficiently small that relativistic effects need not be considered. However, if the electron moves in elliptical orbits, it may have at its distance of closest approach to the nucleus a kinetic energy that is sufficiently large that relativistic effects must be considered. According to one planetary

model that was developed to represent the atom, a $4s$ electron was proposed as moving in an elliptical orbit having a major axis four times its minor axis. Calculate the kinetic energy of an $n = 4$ electron moving in a circular orbit around a hydrogen nucleus, and the kinetic energy at perihelion and at aphelion of the elliptical $4s$ orbit. What change in kinetic energy at perihelion is made by consideration of relativistic effects? Make the same calculations for OVIII.

13. Suppose a sodium atom were stripped of all but a single electron. Using the Bohr model, calculate the energy with which this electron would be bound to the nucleus in its lowest energy level. How much does this energy differ from the actual binding energy of a sodium $1s$ electron? In the neutral sodium atom other electrons help shield the $1s$ electrons so that, on the basis of a Bohr model atom, the effective nuclear charge on this electron is $Z - \sigma$. Calculate σ for the sodium atom.

14. Make the same calculation as in Problem 13, but for the silver atom, and compare the answers with those obtained for sodium.

15. The temperature of a bunsen burner flame is approximately 1550°C. Suppose both sodium atoms and hydrogen atoms exist in a ratio of one sodium atom to 1000 hydrogen atoms in a gaseous form in the flame. Using the Boltzmann distribution, calculate the ratio of the number of sodium atoms in the first excited state to those in the ground state in the flame. Assuming equal probability for an electron to occupy any state, calculate the ratios of the number of hydrogen atoms in the first and second excited states to the number in the ground state at this temperature. Based on these results, what can be said about the color of the flame?

16. Using the energy state notation of Section 7.10, what states would be expected, using the vector model of the atom, to arise from the interactions of a $3d$ and a $4d$ electron? Make the same calculation for two $3d$ electrons.

17. Actually the probability that any two energy levels will be populated in an atom is not equal but is proportional to the number of degenerate energy states at that level. This degeneracy is produced by the fact that the states with different m_j or M_J all have the same energy, leading to the conclusion that there are $2J + 1$ degenerate levels in each atomic energy state. Recalculate Problem 15 on this basis.

18. A photon with an energy of 30,000 ev ejects photoelectrically an electron from the K-shell of an atom of copper. What are the kinetic energy and the momentum of the photoelectron? Suppose the electron is ejected from the atom at an angle of 90° with respect to the direction of motion of the incident photon; what is the momentum, the kinetic energy, and the direction of motion of the ion that remains?

19. Suppose the vacant K-shell of Problem 18 is filled by an electron from the L-shell. What are the wavelengths of the characteristic x-rays that may result from this transition? What energy Auger electrons can be emitted in the process?

20. If the photoelectrons and Auger electrons of Problems 18 and 19 are analyzed by a magnetic spectrometer which has a radius of curvature of 10 cm, at what magnetic fields will the various groups of electrons pass through the spectrometer?

21. From analysis in a magnetic field G. G. Kretschman [*Phys. Rev.* **43**, 417 (1933)] found the ratio e/m for electrons by determining their momenta from the measured Br (in gauss-cm) for photoelectrons ejected by molybdenum K radiation from films of gold, silver, copper, and platinum. He found that for a gold foil the M_{I} electrons had a momentum 402.201 gauss-cm; the M_{II} electrons, 406.240 gauss-cm; the M_{III} electrons, 412.043 gauss-cm, the M_{IV} electrons,

418.439 gauss-cm, and the M_V electrons, 419.741 gauss-cm. For a silver foil he found that the L_I electrons had a momentum of 396.960 gauss-cm, and the L_{III} electrons, 403.537 gauss-cm. Calculate e/m_0, making certain to consider relativistic effects.

Chapter VIII

MOLECULAR STRUCTURE

8.1 What are Molecules? In earlier chapters it has been seen that matter in its normal state consists of only electrons and atomic nuclei. To these perhaps should be added the photon since it is always present because of the constant changes which are occurring in nature. The atomic nuclei and the electrons are held together in the atom by electrostatic attraction of the negative charge on the electron and the positive charge of the nucleus. A very limited number of varieties of atoms (elements) are formed by the combination of the nuclei and their associated electron shells, this number being limited by the number of unit charges, $+e$, that can be put into a single nucleus. There are only 80 stable elements. A total of only 102 varieties have ever been found or produced, the extra 22 being radioactive elements which do not remain unchanged for an indefinite period of time. Many of the 80 stable varieties are quite rare, so that the number of common varieties of atoms is extremely limited.

With such a limited variety of atoms, how can the number of types of materials that are known be almost unlimited? This limitlessness of the varieties of matter results from the extremely large number of ways that atoms can combine to form what are known as molecules. Practically everything that is visible is composed of one or more types of molecule. A water molecule, for example, consists of three atoms, two hydrogen and one oxygen (H_2O). Hydrochloric acid consists of two types of atoms, hydrogen and chlorine (HCl). Carbon, hydrogen, and oxygen may combine in many different ways to form an almost infinite variety of molecules. It is upon this great variety of possible combinations of atoms to form molecules that the science of chemistry is founded. Molecules are held together by electrostatic forces, and it is the nature of these forces and some of the resultant physical phenomena that are discussed in this chapter.

8.2 Ionic Binding. The simplest force holding two atoms together in molecular form is that which results in *ionic*, or *heteropolar*, binding. A diatomic ionic molecule is formed from the electrostatic attraction of a positively charged ion and a negatively charged ion. Although the formation of either positive or negative ions is theoretically possible with any atom, the energy expended or gained during ionization varies considerably from atom to atom. Hence only a very limited number of atoms can easily form ionic molecules.

First consider the formation of negative ions. All electrons in a single subshell (having the same n and l quantum numbers) are bound to an atom with approximately the same force. If there are several electrons in a subshell it is essentially impossible to distinguish one electron in the subshell from any other. Each of these electrons is bound to the atom by the electrostatic attraction of several nuclear charges, and for this reason considerable energy must be expended to remove any one of them. Good examples of such atoms are the inert gases, in which the least tightly bound shell contains six p electrons. In neon, for example, the $2p$ subshell is filled, and the energy required to remove one of the electrons is 21.6 ev. For argon the $3p$ subshell is filled and the binding energy of the least tightly bound electrons is 15.8 ev.

Should an atom in its normal electrically neutral state need only one more electron to complete a closed shell, the extra electron can often be added without too much difficulty. Under many conditions the electron that is added remains with the atom to form a negative ion, even though there is no longer a balance of charge. For this to be true the extra electron must have been placed in a region where it feels a relatively strong attractive electrostatic force. An example of an atom for which only a single electron is required to complete a subshell is chlorine. Neutral chlorine has five $3p$ electrons, so only one more electron need be added to complete the $3p$ subshell. This extra electron actually is held in the Cl^- ion by an attractive force for which the potential energy is 3.72 ev.

The group of atoms known as the alkali atoms have a single valence s-state electron that is very loosely bound because of the electrostatic shielding provided by the more tightly bound electrons. The alkali atom with the lowest atomic number is lithium, for which the $n = 1$ shell is filled and there is but a single $2s$ electron in the $n = 2$ shell. The energy required for ionization of the lithium atom is 5.37 ev. In the sodium atom the $n = 2$ shell is completely filled, and there is a single $3s$ electron for which the binding energy is 5.12 ev. The binding energy for the single $4s$ electron of potassium is 4.318 ev, for the single $5s$ electron of rubidium 4.159 ev, and for the single $6s$ electron of cesium 3.87 ev. Such single valence electrons are therefore relatively easily removed from the atom, leaving a positively charged ion.

If the $3s$ electron is removed from a sodium atom and placed into a chlorine atom, in which its binding energy is 3.72 ev, there is a net energy expenditure of only 1.40 ev. The Na^+ ion and the Cl^- ion are now attracted electrostatically. Since the attractive force is that of a single electronic charge, the potential energy is the same as for the electron-proton system of the hydrogen atom, as given by Eq. 5.5. The ions need approach only to within 1.03×10^{-7} cm of each other for the total energy of the system to be equal to the energy of the free sodium atom and the free chlorine atom.

As the two ions approach each other, it appears that they would get sufficiently close together that the electrons of one ion would occupy the same region of space as electrons of the other ion. However, for those electrons which have the same set of quantum numbers such overlapping of the wave functions would be a violation of the Pauli exclusion principle. Thus there is generated a repulsive force which determines the minimum distance of approach of the two ions. This repulsive force is of much shorter range than the attractive force. As a result, the energy of the system is a minimum at some finite distance of separation between the ions. For NaCl the separation of minimum energy is 2.36 A. The energy of the system at this minimum is -4.16 ev, measured relative to the energy of a free sodium atom and a free chlorine atom. This then is the energy that must be expended to dissociate the two components of the molecule. Even at the separation of minimum energy there is very little overlap of the electron clouds of the Na^+ and Cl^- ions, as is shown in Fig. 8.1. Hence, at normal room temperatures a NaCl molecule can be expected to be a dipole, positively charged at one end and negatively charged at the other end. The positively charged end can attract another Cl^- ion and the negatively charged end another Na^+ ion. Successive addition of ions to the structure leads to a NaCl crystal lattice, as will be discussed in Chapter 9.

It is possible that the discussion of the NaCl molecule gives a better insight into the nature of the Pauli exclusion principle. In the world of atomic dimensions this principle corresponds to the law in the macroscopic world that no two things can occupy the same space at the same time. The laws here, though, are somewhat different. Space in the atomic world consists not only of the three coordinates of distance (x, y, and z in the Cartesian system) but also coordinates of momentum or energy. For example, a Cl^- ion cannot get closer than 2.36 A to a Na^+ ion with all electrons in both systems in the lowest possible energy state, for, if it did, two electrons having the same set of quantum numbers would be sharing the same region in Cartesian space. But, if the energy of the system is increased by raising one or more electrons into higher energy states, the

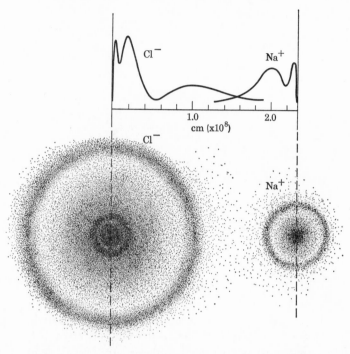

FIG. 8.1. Electron density distributions for the NaCl molecule. At top is radial probability density distribution $r^2|R|^2$, based upon calculations by Pauling [*J. Am. Chem. Soc.* **49**, 765 (1927)]. At the bottom in a plane through the nuclei of the two atoms of the molecule is schematic representation of the electron density distribution. This is a representation of the electron density in each incremental volume, dv, not in each incremental annular ring, $4\pi r^2 dr$, as at the top; hence for s electrons the electron density is a maximum at the center of the atom. The physical size of the atomic nuclei is so small that they could not be seen in this figure.

electrons which could not formerly share the same Cartesian space now have different momentum coordinates and, even though in the same Cartesian space, are no longer in the same space relative to all atomic coordinates. Therefore it is possible to make the ions approach closer together than 2.36 A. However the energy that must be added to the system for the atoms to approach much closer than the equilibrium position very quickly exceeds the binding energy of the system. Thus, even though it is theoretically possible for the two ions to approach each other to a distance considerably less than 2.36 A, the energy required for such an approach is so high that distances of approach only slightly less than the equilibrium distance are generally observed.

The exact nature of the repulsive force is not easily calculated. It is known, however, that it is a much shorter range force than is the force of attraction between the ions. For this reason any mathematical representation of the energy as a function of distance of separation, r, of the atomic nuclei must be a steeply decreasing function for small values of r, gradually rising beyond the separation of minimum energy to approach asymptotically the finite energy that the system has when its two components are separated by an infinite distance. An empirically determined form of this function for diatomic molecules is the Morse equation:

$$V = V_0\{\exp\left[-2(r-r_0)/a\right] -2\exp\left[-(r-r_0)/a\right]\}, \qquad (8.1)$$

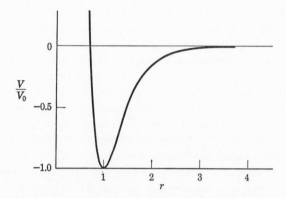

FIG. 8.2. Plot of the Morse function for the potential energy of a diatomic molecular system for the condition $a/r_0 = 0.4$.

in which V_0, r_0, and a are parameters characteristic of the bond. This function is illustrated in Fig. 8.2 for arbitrarily chosen constants. The Morse function appears to provide relatively good fit for most diatomic molecules and is therefore in general use for describing the potential energy of molecular systems.

8.3 Covalent Binding. A somewhat different type of molecular bond may develop when all the individual atoms in the molecular structure possess valence electrons outside a closed shell. This type of binding is called *covalent* or *homopolar*, binding.

An understanding of covalent binding may best be had by considering a simple molecule, such as the Na_2 molecule. A sodium atom has a single $3s$ electron outside the closed neon $n = 2$ shell. Without this electron the Na^+ ion has an effective charge of $+e$ and would then electrostatically repel another Na^+ ion. If the single $3s$ electron is added to one of the Na^+ ions, that atom is neutral and seemingly should not be influenced by an external electrostatic force. But if a Na^+ ion and a sodium atom approach within a few angstroms of each other, the valence electron probability density distribution of the sodium atom overlaps the sphere of influence of the Na^+ ion. When this happens the valence electron can no longer distinguish between the two closed shell cores. It can easily wander back and forth between the two ions and, as a result of these wanderings, the probability density distribution representing the position at which the electron can be found is no longer symmetric about the one sodium atom, but is of larger magnitude in the region between the two ion cores. The electron is thus found most of the time between the two positively charged ions; hence the negatively charged electron acts as an electrostatic bond attracting each ion toward the center of the system. Since the electron belongs part of the time to one ion and part of the time to the other, the force holding the two ions together is often called an *exchange force*.

The system described above is not electrically neutral. Another electron can be added at the same energy level as the first electron, provided that the spin of the second electron is oppositely directed to that of the first electron. The two electrons then appear to be the same except that the spin magnetic quantum number for one of them is $m_s = +\frac{1}{2}$ and for the other $m_s = -\frac{1}{2}$. Since both electrons wander between the fields of both ion cores, it is impossible to say which electron belongs to which core. Instead, it is necessary to say that the system possesses two electrons that act as a covalent or homopolar electrostatic bond that attracts both positively charged ions toward the center of the system.

The limitation on the degree of attraction for this mechanical model is, as it is for ionic binding, the Pauli exclusion principle. As the two ions approach each other, they reach a position at which the core electrons begin to overlap. Since the core electrons in the $n = 2$ shell of one sodium ion have exactly the same sets of quantum numbers as the core electrons in the $n = 2$ shell of the other ion, they cannot share the same region in space. Thus there is a limiting closeness of approach. This leads to an energy system which is a combination of the effects of a longer range attractive force and a shorter range repulsive force. These combine to produce a potential energy for the molecule that varies as a function of the distance of separation of the component atoms in the covalent bond. This potential energy is of the general shape illustrated by the Morse function in Fig. 8.2 with a minimum at the most stable distance of separation between the atoms.

Covalent binding is not limited to atoms having only a single valence electron. The carbon atom, for example, with four valence electrons, is held in molecules by covalent binding. Carbon is the principal ingredient of all organic molecules, which can develop into long chains because of the number of covalent bonds available in a carbon atom. Typical of the type of molecule that can be developed with carbon as a constituent is the

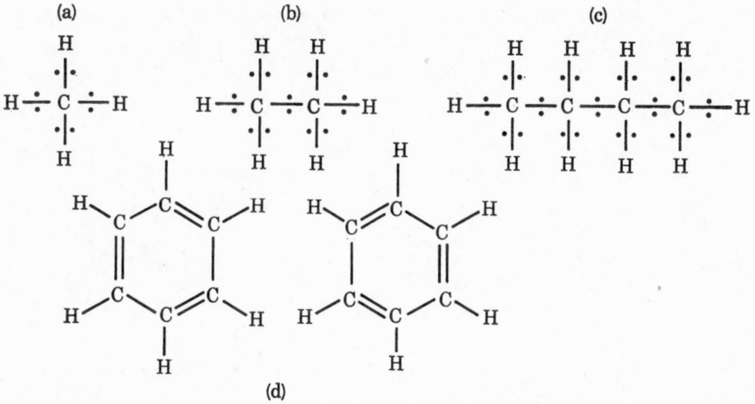

FIG. 8.3. Schematic illustration of covalent bonds in the (a) methane, (b) ethane, and (c) butane molecules, and the ring structure (d) of benzene rings, showing possible location of double bonds.

methane molecule illustrated in Fig. 8.3(a).* The closed shell core for carbon is the $n = 1$ shell. There are four electrons exterior to this shell; thus the carbon ion core presents a charge of $+4e$. Each of these four electrons combines with the electron of one hydrogen atom to form four covalent bonds in the methane molecule, CH_4. If, instead of forming covalent bonds with four hydrogen atoms, the carbon ion core forms only three such bonds, it is possible to begin the growth of a chain-type molecule by forming the fourth covalent bond with another carbon ion core. The result is the ethane molecule, CH_3CH_3, in which the two carbon ion cores are connected by a covalent bond, and each carbon ion core is connected to three hydrogen ions by covalent bonds, as illustrated in Fig. 8.3(b). Further carbon-carbon covalent bonds may be added to form other chain molecules such as butane, $CH_3(CH_2)_2CH_3$, illustrated in Fig. 8.3(c), and even longer chains. An almost infinite number of other molecules is possible using covalent binding to combine not only carbon and hydrogen, but other atoms as well.

8.4 Molecular Energy Levels. The mechanical model of molecular structure discussed in the last two sections gives for a diatomic

*Fig. 8.3 is simply a planar schematic representation of the various molecules. In real molecules, though, the bonds between carbon atoms do not form into simple straight lines, nor are the hydrogen atoms located on exactly opposite sides of the carbon atoms. The angle between two carbon-carbon bonds is about 120° and in the type of molecule illustrated in Fig. 8.3(a), (b), and (c) the molecule forms a sort of staggered chain [see G. Natta and P. Corradini, *Nuovo Cimento Supplement* **15**, 9 (1960)]. If all the bond angles are in the same direction and the same plane, six carbon atoms can form a closed loop, forming what is known as a benzene ring, Fig. 8.3(d). Associated with each carbon atom of the benzene ring is only a single hydrogen atom. The extra valence electrons form what are known as double bonds between three pairs of carbon atoms, the double lines of Fig. 8.3(d).

molecule, such as Na_2, a qualitative description of one type of energy state as a function of distance of separation of the component ions. This type of energy state has a minimum at some finite separation distance and is hence stable. There is also another distinctly different type of energy state for which the minimum energy is at infinite separation distance, hence an unstable state. Perhaps the easiest method for showing the general features of these two types of energy states for a diatomic molecule is to discuss the analogies between the planetary model of the atom and another central force system, such as, for example, a ball on the end of a spring. If the ball is displaced from its equilibrium position, it oscillates in simple harmonic motion. In the planetary model the electrons are considered to revolve around the nucleus in much the same manner as the planets revolve around the sun. For a circular orbit a projection of this motion along any diameter describes simple harmonic motion. This similarity in particle motion makes possible a comparison of these two analogous systems. One system consists of two atoms that have come close enough together to form a molecule. The other system has two masses each tied by identical springs to two fixed positions A and B, as shown in Fig. 8.4, and furthermore are tied together by another spring. When in their equilibrium positions the balls on the springs represent by analogy the atoms of a diatomic molecule at their equilibrium separation. If energy is added to the system there are corresponding displacements from equilibrium. The analogies between a diatomic molecule and the spring system of Fig. 8.4 are limited to the conditions near equilibrium and any results

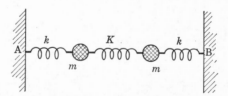

FIG. 8.4.   The spring system used for describing by analogy a diatomic molecule.

obtained from the simple harmonic motions of the springs must be considered only an approximation of the physical situation in the molecule.

If the two masses of the spring system oscillate in phase, they are always separated by a constant distance and there is no change of length of the spring connecting them. Hence the restoring force produced by that spring is always $K = 0$, just as if it were a massless rigid rod. The only restoring forces are those proportional to the spring constants (k) being individually applied to each of the two masses. These produce an energy for the system of kx^2 (one-half of this energy is associated with each mass), where x is the maximum displacement of each mass from its equilibrium position. The frequency of the oscillation is $\nu = (k/m)^{1/2}/2\pi$. An analogous situation occurs when the two electrons oscillate in phase, in which case there is always the equivalent of one electron in the region separating the two ions. This is the lowest energy state.

If the two masses attached to the springs oscillate 180° out of phase, both masses are in the vicinity of the center of the system at the same time and away from the center of the system at the same time. Instead of the center spring moving back and forth as it did in the previous case, it simply expands and contracts and its center remains fixed in space, as do the two ends of the entire system. In addition to the restoring force supplied by the two end springs, an additional force is effected by the center spring. Since only half the spring is effective on each mass, the restoring force constant is $2K$. If each mass has the same displacement as in the previous case, the energy of the system is $(k + 2K)x^2$, and the frequency of oscillation $\nu = [(k + 2K)/m]^{1/2}/2\pi$. This is analogous to the case when both electrons are between the two ions part of the time, but are both on the far side of their respective ions the remainder of the time. The energy of the system must be higher, as for the spring system, since the restoring force of each electron is a combination of the electrostatic attraction of each electron by both ions (no shielding is provided by the other electron), in addition to an electrostatic repulsion between the two ions (no shielding provided by either electron). A diatomic molecule in this energy state is not stable and tends to fly apart, the system having minimum energy when the two atoms are separated by an infinite distance. There is no equivalent action by the spring system, though, unless a nonlinearity is introduced to reduce gradually the force constant K of the middle spring to zero. Therefore the analogy between the two systems breaks down at this point.

The existence of both these types of energy distributions as a function of the distance of separation between the ions can be found by a simple quantum mechanical treatment. As seen by the valence electrons, each of the ions is a potential well having general shape similar to that of the potential well of the hydrogen atom. The energy levels that can be occupied by the system are therefore determined by solving quantum mechanically for the energy levels within the

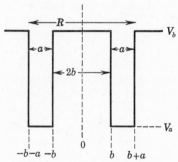

FIG. 8.5. Two rectangular potential wells separated by a rectangular potential barrier.

potential wells To simplify the mathematics, a rectangular one-dimensional potential well is used to represent each ion, as illustrated in Fig. 8.5. Under these conditions many of the features of the solution for the levels in the single rectangular potential well, in Section 6.3, can be brought over to the present problem.

Suppose that $(V_b - V_a) \gg h^2/a^2m$. Then the result for a single potential well is:

$$\tan\{(4a\pi/h)[2m(W - V_a)]^{1/2}\} \approx 0$$

$$\text{and} \quad (4a\pi/h)[2m(W - V_a)]^{1/2} \approx n\pi,$$

where n is an integer. The energy levels near the bottom of the potential well are then at levels such that

$$W - V_a \approx n^2h^2/32ma^2. \tag{8.2}$$

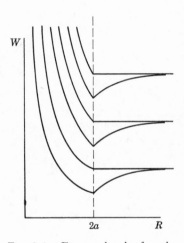

W

$2a$ R

FIG. 8.6. Energy levels for the rectangular potential wells of Fig. 8.5 as a function of distance of separation. For the meaning of R, see Fig. 8.5.

These are the energy levels in each well if the two potential wells are separated by a distance sufficiently great so that there is no interaction through the potential barrier separating the wells; the wells are independent of each other. As the distance of separation of the potential wells is reduced there is penetration of the wave functions through the potential barrier, resulting in an interaction of the wave functions of any one level with the corresponding level in the other potential well. This interaction produces, prior to the merging of the potential wells into a single well, a splitting of each energy level to form a lower and upper level, as illustrated in Fig 8.6. At the instant that the potential wells merge, the density of energy states is twice the density in a single well. Thus there are just twice as many levels in the two wells as in one, such that the total number of energy states remains constant even though the wells may be an infinite distance apart or have just merged. This principle also is valid for molecules, and, as shall be seen later, for larger groupings of atoms, as in solids.

As the wells move closer together after joining, they become what is essentially a narrower single well, and the individual energy levels move to higher energies, as observed in real molecules. Thus the gross features of the potential energy of a molecule is explained by the quantum mechanical treatment of the energy levels of two rectangular potential wells.

This treatment also indicates that the molecular potential energy function applies to excited energy states as well as the ground state. Elaboration of this point as it applies to real molecules is made in Section 8.7.

8.5 Rotational States. One of the degrees of freedom allowable to two objects held together in the manner of a diatomic molecule is rotation about the center of mass of the system. From the mechanics of rigid bodies it is known that the kinetic energy of such rotation is $W_K = \frac{1}{2}I\omega^2$, where I is the moment of inertia of the system* and ω is the angular velocity of rotation. Now the angular momentum of such a system is $I\omega$. But this system is essentially a two body rotating system, as was the hydrogen atom, so the quantum mechanical solution of this problem involves the same general type of Schroedinger equation as did the hydrogen atom problem. For these conditions the angular momentum of the system is $I\omega = [K(K+1)]^{1/2}h/2\pi$, where K is a quantum number that may be zero or any integer.† Thus the energy of the rotating system is $W_K = (h^2/8\pi^2I)$ $[K(K+1)]$, which for the first few energy states has magnitudes 0, $2h^2/8\pi^2I$, $6h^2/8\pi^2I$, $12h^2/8\pi^2I$, etc.

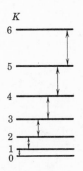

FIG. 8.7. Energy levels of and allowed transitions between rotational states.

Transitions within a single set of rotational levels are allowed according to the selection rule $\Delta K = \pm 1$. Thus, for example, transitions are allowed between $K_i = K$ and $K_f = K - 1$. In this case, the energy of transition is $W = (h^2/8\pi^2I)\,(2K)$. Transitions of this type, either by absorption or by emission of radiation, are illustrated in Fig. 8.7. Pure rotational transitions for molecules require the expenditure of very small quantities of energy. They are therefore observed in the far infrared portion of the spectrum.

8.6 Vibrational States. The separation between atoms in a molecule is not rigidly fixed, as has already been indicated in the discussion of the analogies between the diatomic molecule and the system of springs and

---

*For two objects at the ends of a massless rod, the representation often used for a diatomic molecule, the moment of inertia is $I = m_A r_A{}^2 + m_B r_B{}^2 = (r_A + r_B)^2[M_A M_B/(m_A + m_B)] = \mu r^2$, where m_A and m_B are respectively the masses of the atoms A and B, r_A and r_B are respectively the distances of the atoms A and B from the center of mass. Note that $r = r_A + r_B$, and μ is the reduced mass of the system.

†For the hydrogen atom this quantum number was designated by the letter l. The K used in this section to designate a quantum number is independent of, and should not be confused with, the K used as a spring restoring constant in Section 8.4.

masses in Section 8.4. The application of energy to the system can displace the atoms of a diatomic molecule relative to their equilibrium positions. After displacement the system tries to return to equilibrium, and it oscillates about the equilibrium distance of separation, producing what is known as a *vibrational state* in the molecule.

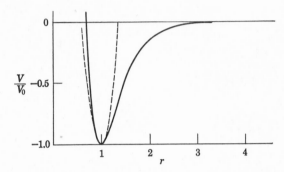

Fig. 8.8.   The Morse potential energy function and the potential energy for a simple harmonic oscillator.

The potential well of a harmonic oscillator, given by the dashed line in Fig. 8.8, approximates at the lower energies the potential of the diatomic molecular system. It was seen in Section 6.6 that the energy of a harmonic oscillator is given by the quantized states $W = h\nu_0(v + \frac{1}{2})$, where $h\nu_0$ is a constant amount of energy and v is a vibrational quantum number (v has only integer values beginning with 0). Thus for a harmonic oscillator the energy levels are equally spaced. Since the lower part of a molecular potential well has a shape reasonably close to that of a harmonic oscillator, the lower vibrational levels of a molecule are very nearly equally spaced. However, the upper part of the molecular potential well opens to considerable width, and the levels are no longer equally spaced, but are much more compactly packed. According to theory, transitions occur in simple harmonic oscillators only if the vibrational quantum number changes are 0 or ± 1. But no molecule is exactly a simple harmonic oscillator, and Δv often has values greater than unity.

The energy required to excite a molecule into a vibrational state is considerably greater than that required to excite it into a rotational state. As a result, a molecule may exist in rotational states at any of the vibrational levels, and radiation is characteristic of transitions between combined vibrational-rotational states. These transitions are observed usually in the near infrared.

8.7 Transitions Between Molecular Energy Levels. In addition to the rotational and vibrational levels, either of the atoms of a diatomic molecule may have one of its electrons raised to an excited state, called

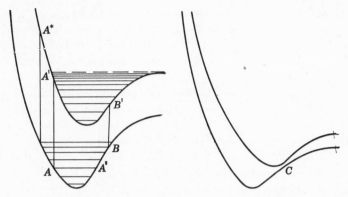

F<small>IG</small>. 8.9.   Illustration of transitions between two electron energy states in a
molecule showing the Franck-Condon principle.

here an *electronic excited state* to distinguish it from rotational and vibrational excited states.   For each electronic energy state there is a new set
of potential energy surfaces for the molecule.   A typical ground state and
first electronic excited state set of potential energy curves is shown in
Fig. 8.9.   The minimum of the molecular potential energy curve for the
excited state usually is displaced from the minimum for the ground state
because of differences in the interaction energies between the electrons
in the two states.   Within each potential energy curve may be found both
vibrational and rotational energy levels.

If the vibrational energy exceeds the binding energy of the system,
there is no effective outer edge to the potential well to prevent the atoms
from flying apart.   On the other hand, if energy is added to the system in
such a way that it excites one atom into an excited electronic energy
state, an energy in excess of the binding energy of the molecular system
in the ground level may be added without the constituent atoms of the
system becoming separated.   Since many transitions between atomic
states are in the visible or ultraviolet portions of the spectrum, and since
vibrational and rotational states can exist in excited electronic states, as
well as in the ground level electronic state, vibrational and rotational
spectral lines can be seen in the visible region of the spectrum if there are
simultaneously transitions between electronic states and between
vibrational and/or rotational states.   The series of spectral lines so
produced are usually called *bands* because they are so thick that they are
not easily resolved and therefore often appear to be a continuous band of
radiation within a small region of the spectrum.   Such spectra are called
band spectra.

In the potential wells of each electronic energy state are found the
discrete energy levels of the vibrational and rotational states.   According

to quantum mechanics, a molecule in a selected vibrational level may have any distance of separation between its constituent atoms. Most probably, though, the distance of separation is found within the confines of the potential well, such as, for example, anywhere along the energy level defined by A and A'' in Fig. 8.9. Under such circumstances the separation spacing oscillates between the two extreme positions within the well at the single energy level. The extra energy above the electronic potential energy curve goes into vibrational kinetic energy.

When a large amount of energy is supplied to the molecule, as by the entry of a photon, a transition between the ground state and the electronic excited state may occur, as in the transition AA' of Fig. 8.9. Such transitions take place almost instantaneously, so that the nuclei do not have an opportunity to change either their interatomic spacing or their momenta. That transitions occur in this manner is known as the *Franck-Condon principle.* Thus all transitions must be represented as vertical lines on the energy diagram. Once the molecule reaches a level A' it may come down to lower levels in the electronic excited state by changes between vibrational levels. Also it will continue vibrations appropriate to the energy level in which it is at the time. At some point, such as B', there may be a transition back to the electronic ground state. Usually, as is illustrated by the transition $B'B$, the photon released in the process is of much lower energy than the energy which went into the transition which raised the molecule to the electronic excited state. It is even possible that the excited and ground state potential energy curves are so close together at some separation distance, such as at C, that the energy of transition may be released as thermal energy, a *radiationless transition.*

In some cases the level A^* to which the molecule is excited is sufficiently high that the molecule is not restrained by a potential barrier as it moves toward its maximum distance of separation. Under these circumstances the molecule dissociates, and the energy in excess of the dissociation energy, V_d, appears as kinetic energy of the two product components.

References

R. C. Johnson, *An Introduction to Molecular Spectra* (Pitman Publishing Corp., New York, 1949).

G. Herzberg, *Spectra of Diatomic Molecules* (D. Van Nostrand Co., Inc., Princeton, N. J., 2nd Ed., 1950).

G. Herzberg, *Infrared and Raman Spectra of Polyatomic Molecules*, (D. Van Nostrand Co., Inc., Princeton, N. J., 1945).

A. R. von Hippel, *Molecular Science and Molecular Engineering* (Technological Press of MIT, Cambridge, Mass., and John Wiley and Sons, Inc., New York, 1958).

F. O. Rice and E. Teller, *The Structure of Matter* (John Wiley and Sons, Inc., New York, 1949).

L. Pauling, *The Nature of the Chemical Bond* (Cornell University Press, Ithaca, New York, 3rd Ed., 1960).
W. Kauzmann, *Quantum Chemistry* (Academic Press, Inc., New York, 1957).
J. C. Slater, *Quantum Theory of Matter* (McGraw-Hill Book Co., Inc., New York, 1951).
G. P. Harnwell and W. E. Stephens, *Atomic Physics* (McGraw-Hill Book Co., Inc., New York, 1955).
E. Cartmell and G. W. A. Fowles, *Valency and Molecular Structure* (Academic Press, Inc., New York, 1956).
C. A. Coulson, *Valence* (Oxford University Press, London, 1952).

Problems

1. Calculate the electrostatic field produced by the sodium ion at the center of the chlorine ion in a NaCl molecule. What force would be exerted on a charge of one coulomb if it were located in an electrostatic field of this strength? If the charge of one coulomb were located on a mass of one gram, what would be the acceleration of this mass by the field?

2. Calculate the energy of the electrostatic attractive force between the two ions of a NaCl molecule at their equilibrium distance of separation. How much does the force of repulsion contribute to the energy of the molecular system in equilibrium? Remember that the energy of attraction in this type of calculation is measured relative to the free Na^+ and Cl^- ions, not relative to the free atoms for which the energy at equilibrium is quoted in the text.

3. For the KCl molecule the equilibrium distance of separation between the two ions is 2.79 A and the minimum of the potential energy curve is 4.98 ev relative to the energy of the free K^+ and Cl^- ions. How much is the energy of repulsion at equilibrium and what is the minimum energy relative to the energy of the free potassium and chlorine atoms?

4. Although it might at first appear that an HCl molecule should also be ionic, this is not the case. At equilibrium the internuclear distance in the HCl molecule is 1.27 A and the minimum of the potential energy curve relative to the energy of the free atoms is 4.43 ev. Calculate at an internuclear separation of 1.27 A the energy of the electrostatic attractive force between an H^+ ion and a Cl^- ion and show that this is larger than the minimum energy of the HCl molecular system.

5. Empirical evidence indicates that in the Morse function for HCl the constant $a = 0.524$ A. Plot the Morse function for HCl and on the same graph plot the energy of the electrostatic attractive force as a function of internuclear separation distance between the H^+ ion and the Cl^- ion.

6. In its most stable state the two atomic nuclei of the H_2^+ molecule ion are separated by a distance of 1.06 A. What is the electrostatic repulsive force between the two nuclei? If, at this separation distance, a single electron is placed midway between the two nuclei, what is the attractive force between the electron and a single nucleus? What is the net force on each nucleus?

7. Calculate the potential energy of the system of Problem 6 by summing the potential energy of each of the three forces. Why does this differ so much from the dissociation energy of 2.65 ev for the hydrogen molecule ion?

8. In its ground state the nuclei of the atoms of a H_2 molecule are separated by a distance of 0.75 A. Suppose the two electrons of the molecule are equidistant from each hydrogen nucleus and also equidistant from a line joining the two nuclei. Calculate the potential energy of the system in which the net force on each particle is zero. Now compare this with the 4.48 ev dissociation energy of the H_2 molecule.

9. What must be the separation distance of the hydrogen nuclei of Problem 7 for the static conditions described therein to result in a potential energy for the system of -4.48 ev?

10. In its most stable state the hydrogen atom holds a single $1s$ electron. The wave function for this electron is $\psi = K \exp(-r)$, where K is a constant (see Appendix 7.1). For the hydrogen molecule, H_2, the wave functions of the individual hydrogen atoms either add, forming a symmetrical wave function, or subtract, forming an antisymmetrical wave function. Plot along a line connecting the nuclei of the two atoms the individual wave functions for each of the hydrogen atoms and the resultant wave functions for the H_2 molecule. Based on the results of Problems 6, 7, 8, and 9 and the knowledge that the electron density distribution is proportional to $|\psi|^2$, determine which wave function represents the stable hydrogen molecule.

11. Based on the results of Problem 10, plot in the plane through the two nuclei of the hydrogen molecule the contours of equal electron probability density distribution. This is analogous to the plots of Fig. 7.4 and 7.5.

12. In Fig. 8.6 each level of an individual rectangular potential well splits into two levels as the wells approach each other. The upper level in each splitting is formed by the antisymmetric wave function and the lower by the symmetric wave function. Plot the wave functions associated with the lowest four energy levels for well separation distance of $R = 4a$, $R = 3a$, $R = 2a$, and $R = a$. Why is it that the wave functions for $R = a$ are identical to the wave functions for an individual well?

13. The separation of the atomic nuclei of a N_2 molecule is 1.09 A in its ground state. What rotational energy levels would be expected for N_2?

14. The spectra arising from molecular rotation generally occur at infrared wavelengths. For example, HCl rotational spectra are observed at wave numbers of $\bar{\nu} = 83.03$, 104.15, 124.30, 145.03, and 165.51 cm^{-1}. Assuming that these represent transitions between rotational levels for which $K > 1$, calculate the moment of inertia of the molecule and the radial separation between the H^+ and Cl^- ions and compare this separation with the value quoted in Problem 4.

15. Besides the Morse function another function that has been used by Born and Mayer to describe the potential energy of ionic molecules has the form

$$V = -e^2/\epsilon r + B \exp(-r/\rho).$$

Calculate the magnitude of the constants B and ρ in this function for the NaCl molecule. Hint: Note that the magnitude of both V and dV/dr are known for the equilibrium condition of the molecule. The potential energy V must be measured relative to the energy of the free Na^+ and Cl^- ions.

Chapter IX

SOLID STATE PHYSICS

9.1 Introduction. In the study of the atom and of the interactions between atoms, there is a merging of the field of physics and the field of chemistry. In fact, many research problems are solved by research teams composed of both chemists and physicists. For this reason this chapter relates some of the most significant properties of solids, as Chapter 8 did for molecules, without any specific attempt to separate physics from chemistry.

Matter may exist as either a gas, a liquid, or a solid. Under terrestrial conditions, because of the force of gravity, both gases and liquids must be confined by some sort of container. Individual molecules of both gases and liquids are constantly in motion relative to each other. On the other hand, matter is considered to be solid if its surface may be defined without the use of an external container.* In the atomic scheme of things a substance is solid if its atoms retain the same set of neighboring atoms over long periods of time. The detailed nature of the location of individual atoms in a solid and the forces that hold them there is quite varied. For this reason the subject matter of solid state physics is quite extensive and is currently the subject of many research investigations. In the limited space available in this chapter, it will be possible to discuss only the bare fundamentals of this area of physics.

9.2 Crystals. Crystals are one of three general types of solids, the other two being glasses and polymers. A *perfect crystal* is composed of identical structural units put together in a regular repetitive pattern over an infinite number of steps. No real crystal though is perfect; not only is it finite in extent but also it possesses throughout its structure a limited number of flaws and impurities. To present as elementary a discussion as possible, the crystal is discussed in this chapter as if it has no flaws or

---

*For present purposes, this definition is satisfactory, but some substances classified as solids according to it are really highly viscous liquids (e.g., "molasses in January"). To avoid ambiguity, many physicists use the terms *crystalline state*, *glassy state*, and *high polymer* to distinguish among three categories that we here group together as *solids*. The distinction will be made clear in Sections 9.10-9.11.

impurities except those that are purposely introduced. First a mechanical or chemical picture of the crystalline structure is presented, followed by quantum mechanical or energy level representation. For the fundamental discussion presented here, the forces holding a crystal together are divided into four types, ionic, covalent, metallic, and Van der Waals. Frequently it is difficult, or impossible, to say that the forces within a real crystal are any single one of these types, for they often consist of some combination of or are intermediate between two or more types.

(a) *Ionic Crystals.* Ionic crystals are held together by the same type of coulomb force as ionic molecules (see Section 8.2). A NaCl molecule, for example, appears to be a dipole, charged positively at the sodium end and negatively at the chlorine end. The Na^+ ion thus may attract other Cl^- ions, and vice versa. In a NaCl crystal, then, Na^+ ions and Cl^- ions are alternately arranged in a three-dimensional array with each Na^+ ion in the crystal being surrounded by six *nearest neighbor* Cl^- ions, and each Cl^- ion by six nearest neighbor Na^+ ions, as illustrated in Fig. 9.1. Within this regular array there is an ion of opposite electrical charge between any two ions of the same kind.

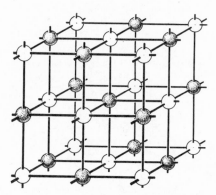

FIG. 9.1. The NaCl crystal lattice. The Na^+ ions and Cl^- ions are alternately spaced in a cubic array as indicated by the alternately shaded and unshaded spheres.

(b) *Covalent Crystals.* A covalent crystal consists of a regular array of atoms in which individual ions, created by the sharing of the valence electrons, are held together by covalent binding. An example is the diamond crystal structure, illustrated in Fig. 9.2. Each carbon atom in the diamond crystal has four $n = 2$ electrons which it shares with four neighboring carbon ions and is thus bound to these four neighbors by covalent binding. In each bond, two electrons, one from each of two neighboring ions, are constantly being exchanged by the ions, just as for covalent binding in molecules. The electrons are confined to fixed

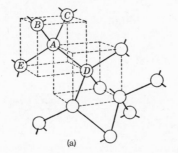

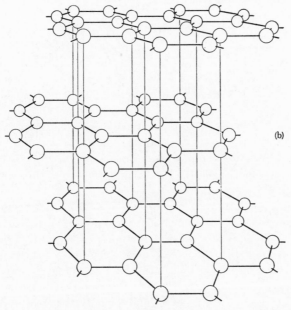

FIG. 9.2. (a) The diamond lattice. The carbon atom *A*, at the center of the cube enclosed by the dashed lines, is connected by four covalent bonds to atoms *B*, *C*, *D* and *E* at alternate corners of the cube. (b) The graphite lattice. The thinner lines represent the Van der Waals bonding between parallel planes of extended benzene rings.

regions of the crystal but the electron density in these regions is limited; the result is that no net transfer of charge is possible and a covalent crystal is a good electrical insulator.

(c) *Metallic Crystals.* There is a third important type of crystal, the metallic crystal, which has no direct counterpart in molecular structure. A force similar to the covalent bond holds the metal crystal together but the electrons are not paired and do not provide well-defined linkage between specified ions.

As an example, consider sodium. The two atoms in a sodium molecule are held together by the covalent bond of the two $3s$ valence electrons. But suppose one or more additional sodium atoms are brought into the immediate vicinity of the original two atoms, as must be done if a solid is to be formed. Sodium forms into a body centered cubic crystal, but in this form there are an insufficient number of electrons to provide covalent binding between each neighboring pair of ions. It is still possible, though, to picture the metallic crystal as a structure of positively charged ions held together by the valence electrons, but, because of an electron deficiency for covalent binding, the positioning of the connecting electrons, is not always perfectly clear. A picture of the metallic solid might therefore be a lattice of positively charged ions embedded in a sea of electrons or in an *electron gas*. Because there are a smaller number of electrons than are needed to form covalent bonds, the electrons are free to migrate through the crystalline structure; hence the metallic crystal is a good electrical conductor.

(d) *Van der Waals Forces.* An attractive force, much weaker than the other three just discussed, can exist between atoms and molecules, even in the absence of valence electrons. Within an atom the motions of each electron establish a dipole field, and the combined effect of the movement of all the electrons of an atom, even for the inert gases, is a weak, randomly fluctuating, dipole field, $\mathbf{E}$. In a neighboring atom this field induces a dipole moment (see Section 2.6). Because the magnitude of the dipole moment is proportional to the amount of displacement $\Delta l/2$ of the atomic charge q from its equilibrium position, the dipole moment is of magnitude $\mu = \alpha E$, in which α is a constant of polarization for the atom. The energy associated with this interaction is classically proportional to $\mathbf{E}^2$. At any instant the radial diminution of the strength of a dipole field follows an r^{-3} function, so the Van der Waals energy between two atoms or molecules diminishes as an r^{-6} function of distance of separation.

9.3 The Carbon Crystal Lattice. Some atoms form two or more different types of crystal lattices, depending on the conditions of formation. The different crystalline forms usually have quite different external appearances and also different electrical, thermal, and other physical properties. As an illustrative example, diamond and graphite are two basic solid forms of carbon. The diamond crystal has already been mentioned; all its four valence electrons are used for covalent binding to the four nearest carbon atom neighbors, producing in the process a relatively good insulator.

On the other hand, in the graphite crystal only three of the carbon atoms are tied to nearest neighbors by covalent bonds. The atoms are disposed in a series of planes of extended benzene rings, as shown in

Fig. 9.2 [see also Fig. 8.3(d)]. The crystal is built by stacking layers of parallel planes, displaced with respect to each other. Bonding between layers in graphite is provided by Van der Waals forces, and is consequently weak in comparison to the bonding in any single layer. Just as in the benzene ring, there are three double bonds in each of the extended rings. If an electrostatic field is applied, these double bonds can shift in the plane of the extended rings, producing in the process an electric current.

9.4 Electron Energy Bands. The preceding discussion has been concerned with the predominant forces that hold solids together. From this some mechanical and electrical properties of crystals have been deduced. In this section attention is turned to a description of the energy states available to the crystal electrons, the magnitude and spacing of which can be determined only by quantum mechanical methods. In a crystal there is a series of potential wells, one at each positively charged nucleus. The same problems are encountered in attempting to plot the potential surface for this series of energy depressions as for the potential surface of a single atom (see Section 6.2). To plot energy as a function of position requires three coordinates of position and one of energy. Since there are only two spatial dimensions on the surface of the page, only a one-dimensional, cross-sectional view of the potential energy surface for a crystal can be plotted in Fig. 9.3.

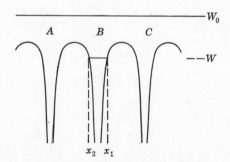

FIG. 9.3. The potential energy distribution within a crystal lattice. The potential wells of individual atoms are located at A, B, and C. The energy W_0 is the ground state energy for an electron in a vacuum.

Because, according to the laws of quantum mechanics, an atomic size particle, such as an electron, does not encounter a sharp, impenetrable boundary at the potential surface, it is not necessary that an electron at energy W in the system illustrated in Fig. 9.3 be confined to the region between x_1 and x_2, but under certain conditions the electron may penetrate the region to the right of x_1 or to the left of x_2. If there were only a single nucleus in the vicinity, the electron could go only a short distance before it would be forced to return to the region of the potential well, for the function, $|\psi|^2$, which describes the probability of existence, decreases exponentially to the right of x_1 and to the left of x_2. But in a crystal the electron is under the influence of many potential wells. Since it can penetrate a potential barrier, there is a finite probability that a particular electron might just as easily be in well A or in well C as in well B.

When sufficiently far apart to be independent of one another, as in a gas, the one or more types of identical atoms that form a crystal have exactly the same sets of energy levels. But if the distance of separation between two identical atoms is reduced, the wave functions of electrons at the same energy levels in each atom interfere, as discussed in Section 8.4 for the two potential wells forming a diatomic molecule. The smaller the distance of separation, the greater the magnitude of that part of the electronic wave function that extends into the potential well of a neighboring atom. Under these circumstances an electron belonging to one atom is influenced by other nuclei in the vicinity. This interference between the wave functions of individual electrons in the same energy state in neighboring atoms causes a separation of the possible energy levels of these electrons. For any uniform spacing of atoms within an array, the maximum separation of energy levels for a single electronic energy state is approximately the same regardless of the number of atoms in the array. Thus, if the magnitude of the energy level splitting is known for two atoms physically separated by a distance equal to the crystal lattice spacing, the addition of other atoms to the array does not increase the maximum energy level splitting, but simply adds to the number of energy levels in the intervening energy region between the maximum and minimum levels. For any crystal there are just as many energy levels as there are levels in all the individual atoms of the crystal. As a result, between the maximum and minimum levels of a particular atomic state the level spacing in a crystal of finite size is so compact that individual levels cannot be distinguished and the region of allowed energy levels appears to be continuous. If, for example, the assumption is made that there are 10^{22} sodium atoms in a crystal, then there are 2×10^{22} energy levels in the $3s$ band, one for each possible $3s$ atomic energy state. The nature of the width of these bands as a function of distance of separation of the atoms is seen in Fig. 9.4 for the specific case of sodium. The width of the band of allowed energies increases with decreasing distances of separation between nuclear potential wells. The upper and lower energy edges of each band have shapes similar to the two types of energy states discussed in Section 8.4 for the corresponding molecular electronic state. Because of the influence of effects described

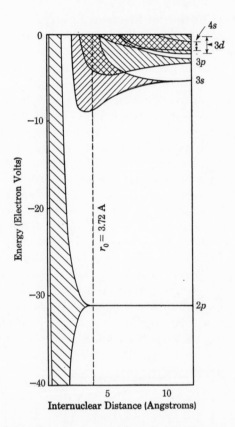

FIG. 9.4.   Plot of the allowed energy regions for a sodium crystal as a function of separation distance between sodium nuclei. [Based on J. C. Slater, *Phys. Rev.* **45**, 794 (1934), and *Rev. Mod. Phys.* **6**, 209 (1934)]

by the Pauli exclusion principle, the energy of the lower energy edge increases very rapidly at close nuclear approach, just as in the case of molecular energy levels. Outer electron shells show a widening at larger separation distances because they feel much stronger influence from neighboring nuclei than the more tightly bound shells. It can be noted that for sodium the $3s$ and $3p$ bands overlap at all separation distances of less than $r = 6.3$ A. At the atomic spacing in the normal sodium crystal (the dashed line at $r_0 = 3.72$ A), there is essentially a continuum of energy levels above $W = -8.5$ ev. Hence, within the sodium crystal, electrons with quantum number $n = 3$ have a continuum of allowed energy states. Electrons within the more tightly bound $n = 1$ and $n = 2$ shells are still strongly under the influence of an individual parent nucleus and are confined to a much smaller energy spacing.

9.5 Fermi Distribution of Electron Energies. Those discussions which have referred to the electrons in a metal as a sea of electrons, or an electron gas, must be tempered by one very important limitation. Unlike the situation in a real gas, the number of energy levels available, and the number of electrons that can occupy each energy level are limited. If the energies of the electrons that exist within the confines of a metal were distributed in the same way as the energies of the atoms and molecules in the gas of a planetary atmosphere (hence obeying the Boltzmann energy distribution, Eq. 1.9), the mean kinetic energy of the electrons at room temperature would be $W_K = \frac{3}{2}kT \approx 0.04$ ev. But this obviously cannot be true for there simply are not enough energy levels adequately close to the bottom of the valence energy band to accommodate all of these electrons. The energy states are distributed in sodium metal, for example, such that, if all electrons are in the lowest possible energy states, all available levels are filled up to 3.1 ev above the bottom of the 3s energy band. This situation occurs only at absolute zero (0° K). A distribution describing this situation is the graphical representation illustrated in Fig. 9.5 by the curve marked $T = 0°$ K of a plot of the percentage of energy states that are filled in any energy interval dW as a function of energy W. At absolute zero all levels are filled below the energy W_F, known as the *Fermi brim*, and all states are empty above W_F.

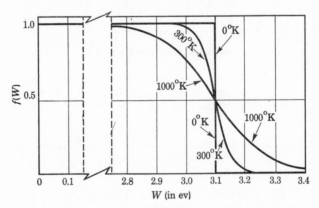

Fɪɢ. 9.5. Plot of the Fermi function, $f(W)$, as a function of energy for 0°K, 300°K, and 1000°K, assuming a Fermi brim at 3.1 ev. Note the break in the energy scale between 0.1 ev and 2.8 ev.

Now, if the temperature of the metal is raised above absolute zero, some of the electrons will be given additional kinetic energy and a few will be raised to energy levels above the Fermi brim. For the usually attainable terrestrial temperatures, though, only a very small percentage of the total number of electrons are raised to these levels. At energies a few tenths of an electron volt above the Fermi brim and higher, the density of possible energy states is so high and the number of electrons so small that each electron can occupy essentially any energy level and is effectively independent of all other electrons. For these energies the electron distribution as a function of energy would be expected to obey the Boltzmann distribution, Eq. 1.9.

An equation which fits these two extreme conditions is:

$$f(W) = \{\exp[(W - W_F)/kT] + 1\}^{-1}. \qquad (9.1)$$

That this equation describes the physical situation just discussed may be seen by first plotting the equation for absolute zero, $T = 0°$ K, for which, if $W < W_F$, the exponential function is exp $(-\infty)$ and $f(W) = 1$, and, if $W > W_F$, the exponential function is exp (∞) and $f(W)$ is 0.

Now consider the situation for temperatures above absolute zero, $T > 0°$ K. When a band is partially filled, as for sodium, only a very small fraction of an electron volt is required to raise an electron from an energy state just below the Fermi brim to an energy state just above the brim. A small amount of thermal energy can relatively easily elevate electrons into these states. Thus the distribution of electrons in the allowed energy states changes as a function of temperature. Suppose for example a material with a partially filled band is at some finite temperature T. It is found that, even at finite temperatures, for energies $W \ll W_F$ the Fermi factor $f(W)$ is still very nearly unity. At the energy W_F of the Fermi brim, the Fermi factor $f(W) = \frac{1}{2}$ since exp $[(W - W_F)/kT] = 1$. At energies $W \gg W_F$, the quantity exp $[(W - W_F)/kT] \to \infty$ and the Fermi factor $f(W) \to 0$. In the intermediate energy region the exact Fermi factor is a continuous function between these values. The Fermi factor, $f(W)$, for three temperatures is shown in Fig. 9.5. This distribution is independent of the atomic number of the material under consideration and is valid for any partially filled band.

The Fermi function, $f(W)$, describes the distribution of electrons within a set of quantum states that are uniformly distributed in energy. For a real metal, though, the relative density of quantum states as a function of energy level, $S(W)$, is not constant but varies with energy as, for example, the typical s state distribution illustrated in Fig. 9.6(a). Thus the distribution of electrons in any energy band is a function of both the distribution of quantum states, $S(W)$, and the Fermi energy distribution, $f(W)$. The resultant electron distribution as a function of energy, $N(W)dW$, is formed from these two functions, as shown in Fig. 9.6(c), and is expressed mathematically by

$$N(W)dW = S(W)f(W)dW = S(W)$$
$$\{\exp[(W - W_F)/kT] + 1\}^{-1}dW. \qquad (9.2)$$

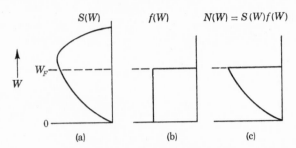

Fig. 9.6. Plots of the density of quantum states, $S(W)$, for a hypothetical energy band in a solid; of the Fermi function, $f(W)$, at absolute zero; and of the resulting electron density distribution, $N(W)$.

The function $S(W)dW$ for a free electron gas confined to a metal cube of volume $V = a^3$ can be calculated using the wave properties of the electrons. This calculation is similar to the calculation of the distribution of frequencies made n Appendix 4.1 for the equilibrium density of electromagnetic radiation in an enclosure. From Eq. 4.9 the number of possible electron frequencies in the metal cube is

$$S(\nu) = (4\pi a^3/3C^3)\nu^3, \tag{4.9}$$

where C in this case is the wave phase velocity of the electron. But the frequency of an electron is $\nu = C/\lambda = Cp/h$, so in momentum space

$$S(p) = (4\pi a^3/3h^3)p^3, \tag{9.3}$$

and the number of possible states in the range of momenta between p and $p + dp$ is

$$dS(p) = (4\pi a^3 p^2/h^3)dp = (4\pi V p^2/h^3)dp. \tag{9.4}$$

Since the kinetic energy $W_K = p^2/2m$ and $dW_K = p\,dp/m$,

$$\frac{dS(W_K)}{dW_K} = \frac{8\pi a^3 (2m^3)^{1/2} W_K^{1/2}}{h^3}, \tag{9.5}$$

the distribution of electron energies, $dN(W_K)/dW_K$, is

$$\frac{dN(W_K)}{dW_K} = \frac{8\pi a^3 (2m^3)^{1/2}}{h^3} \frac{W_K^{1/2}}{\exp\left[(W_K - W_F)/kT\right] + 1}. \tag{9.6}$$

This is the distribution of electron kinetic energies in a *Fermi gas*. In a real solid, though, the electrons do not form an ideal Fermi gas of free electrons but are at least partially bound to the atomic nuclei. The net result is that the electrons are confined to energy bands, and the electron density $S(W)$ diminishes at the upper energies of the band, similar to the distribution in Fig. 9.6(a).* In many metals, such as sodium, the electrons fill only the lower part of the band, and in this region the electron density can still be approximated by the equation for a Fermi gas.

Even for relatively high temperatures, the distribution of electron kinetic energies in a Fermi gas is much higher than the corresponding distribution of electron energies in a Maxwell-Boltzmann gas. For comparison the two types of distributions are shown in Fig. 9.7 for a temperature of 6000° K, very nearly the temperature at the surface of

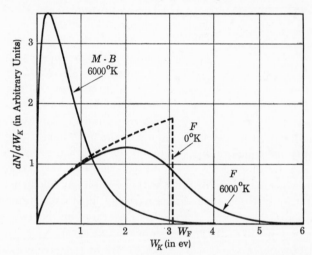

Fig. 9.7. Plots of the Fermi distribution (F) of electron energies and the Maxwell-Boltzmann distribution (M-B) of electron energies at 6000°K. For comparison the Fermi distribution at 0°K, the dashed line, is also plotted.

the sun. For a low temperature, such as room temperature, the Fermi-type distribution drops much more abruptly at W_F as indicated by the dashed line, and the Maxwell-Boltzmann distribution is concentrated at extremely low energies (so low the distribution would form an extremely high spike barely above $W = 0$). Because the electron kinetic energies in a Fermi distribution are all so great compared to the equivalent kinetic energies of a Maxwell-Boltzmann gas, a change in the thermal temperature of a metal produces only a negligibly small change in the mean kinetic energy of the electrons.

9.6 Electrical Insulators and Conductors. The discussion in Section 9.5 assumes that the Fermi brim exists within a solid at some

*The distribution of electrons as a function of their energy in the bands of real solids has been determined experimentally by precision x-ray spectroscopy [see H. W. B. Skinner, *Trans. Roy. Soc.* (London) **A239**, 95 (1940), and *Reports on Progress in Physics* **5**, 257 (1939)] and by the energy distributions of photoelectrons emitted by selected crystals [see H. Philipp, E. Taft, and L. Apker, *Phys. Rev.* **120**, 49 (1960)].

energy level intermediate between the top and bottom of an energy band.

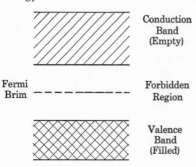

Conduction Band (Empty)

Fermi Brim — — — — — — **Forbidden Region**

Valence Band (Filled)

FIG. 9.8. Typical energy bands for an insulator, showing location of the Fermi brim in the forbidden region between bands.

This is true only for those materials which have electrical properties that cause them to be called conductors. There are many crystalline substances in which, at absolute zero, one energy band is completely filled and the next higher band is empty. These substances are electrical insulators. For them it is necessary to assume the Fermi brim at an energy halfway between the top of the filled (or valence) band and the bottom of the empty (or conduction) band, as illustrated in Fig. 9.8. An electron must acquire sufficient energy to jump all the way from the top of the filled band to the bottom of the empty band before any change in the electrical properties of the material can be observed.

To show what makes a substance with a completely filled energy band an insulator and a substance with a partially filled energy band a conductor, a short discussion of the electron states in the two types of crystals is perhaps in order at this time.

The motion of an electron through a crystal is restricted by forces described by the Pauli exclusion principle. If every atom in a crystal has a filled valence shell, no additional electron can be added to any single atom without an energy increase sufficient to move the extra electron to a higher energy shell. Under these circumstances an electron can move from one atom to another without change of energy only if another electron moves in the reverse direction, or if there is some combination of electron movement that results in no net transfer of charge. Because there can be no net transfer of charge, the crystal has large-scale properties which make it an insulating or dielectric type of material. For the crystal to be nonconducting, it is not necessary for each atom to have had a completed shell prior to its being made a part of the crystal, but only that a complete shell be formed through the affinity of neighboring atoms. For example, the NaCl crystal consists of an array of Na^+ ions and Cl^- ions. The transfer of one electron from sodium to chlorine fills the $3p$ subshell of chlorine. There remains behind a completed $2p$ subshell in the sodium, but there are no electrons in the $n = 3$ shells of sodium. The empty $3s$ subshell of sodium and $3d$ and $4s$ subshells of chlorine are all at much higher energy levels than the filled subshells, so there is no possibility of measurable electron motion without excitation of electrons to much higher energies. Thus, the NaCl crystal is an insulator.

Conduction bands are those that are unfilled at absolute zero. They may be either partially filled, as discussed below, or empty, as discussed above for the empty shells of NaCl. Since it is generally true that nature seeks the lowest energy state, electrons tend to occupy the lowest levels of a partially filled band, as illustrated in Fig. 9.9. For example in

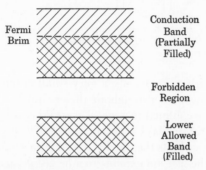

FIG. 9.9. Typical energy bands for a conducting medium, showing location of Fermi Brim in conduction band.

the crystal composed of 10^{22} atoms of sodium mentioned in Section 9.4, there are 2×10^{22} energy levels in the $3s$ band but only 10^{22} $3s$ electrons. In such a band there are empty energy levels that are only infinitesimally small fractions of an electron volt above occupied levels. Therefore only an extremely small amount of energy is required to raise one of the electrons to a higher level in which it may move to some other region of the crystal without the requirement of a reverse motion by another electron. Thus there can be a measurable net transport of electronic charge in the material. This results in a net measurable electric current.

In the mechanical model of a metallic crystal [see Section 9.2(c)], the valence electrons were pictured as not being distinctly associated with any single atom, with the result that the crystal lattice was considered to be composed of a regularly spaced series of positive ions and a sea of negative electrons. A similar conclusion can now be reached by means of the quantum mechanical energy diagram for a metallic crystal. Individual atoms in a metallic crystal are sufficiently close together that the peak value of the potential surface is depressed considerably from the energy required for an electron to escape from a single atom. Thus, it is possible, as illustrated in Fig. 9.10, for an electron in a conduction band to have no barrier between atoms. It must then be concluded that the valence electrons, such as the $3s$ electrons of sodium, are always within the potential wells of more than one nucleus. The electrons thus have

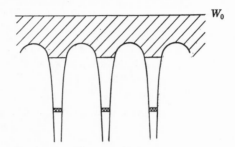

FIG. 9.10. Typical allowed energy bands in array of potential wells of a crystal lattice.

either no potential barrier or only a very small potential barrier to prevent their free movement throughout the crystal.

The electrons are confined to a metal crystal because the last ion at the surface of the metal displays a potential well which on the surface side appears about the same as the potential well for a single atom. Thus, the potential well of the last ion extends to a height greater than the level of the electron energies in the conduction band. Electrons then cannot escape from the metal unless energy is added. This is discussed in more detail in the next chapter.

Under appropriate circumstances a single type of element may exist in crystalline form either as a conductor or as an insulator. For example, sodium is a conductor when formed into a solid of nothing but sodium atoms, but when combined with chlorine as an ionic crystal, the crystal formed is an insulator. For sodium metal, the highest energy band in which electrons are found, the $3s$ band, is not filled. Thus the highest energy electrons in the band are essentially free electrons and are able to roam throughout the solid. On the other hand, the highest occupied energy band in the sodium chloride crystal is completely filled, and a rather large energy, 9.6 ev, must be added to the electrons at the top of this band to get them into the lowest energy levels of the next highest unfilled (conduction) band in which they are free to roam through the solid. The difference between conductors and insulators is largely a matter of the energy required to excite the valence electrons of the material.

9.7 Semiconductors. The name semiconductor has been applied to a type of solid in which the highest occupied electron energy state consists of a filled valence band but for which the energy gap between the filled valence band and the lowest empty conduction band is very small. The type of material usually called a *semiconductor* is neither a good conductor nor a good insulator. While it is true that at very low temperatures a semiconductor is a nonconductor, since its highest occupied band of energy levels is filled, only a small rise in temperature is needed to excite thermally some of the electrons into an unfilled energy band. In the most commonly used semiconductors, this unfilled energy band is about one electron volt above the top of the highest filled band. This situation is intermediate between the continuous series of levels available to the electrons in a conductor, and the requirement for an energy transition of several electron volts to lift an electron to an empty level in a good insulator. For example, the energy difference between the top of the last filled band and the bottom of the lowest empty band is 0.72 ev in germanium and 1.09 ev in silicon, compared to 9.4 ev in KCl, and 9.6 ev in NaCl. Germanium and silicon in their pure state are known as *intrinsic semiconductors*. Although they have the same lattice structure and type of covalent bonding as diamond, their energy gaps are much smaller than the 7.2 ev gap between energy bands in diamond. Diamond actually is a relatively good insulator.

The electrical properties of semiconductors, such as silicon, may be further influenced by the existence of certain types of impurities, such as phosphorus, boron, arsenic, or antimony, in amounts sometimes no greater than 1 impurity atom to 10^6 semiconductor atoms. The atoms which have this remarkable influence possess either three or five valence electrons, compared to the four valence electrons of silicon, or germanium. Thus, if an impurity atom is placed into a silicon lattice, it is surrounded by either one too few or one too many electrons to complete all the covalent bonds with its neighbors.

To illustrate the situation, consider first a phosphorus impurity with its five valence electrons. The extra electron, which does not combine with an atom from one of the neighboring silicon atoms, is relatively weakly bound; thus only a very small amount of energy must be added to set the electron free. The motion of this almost free electron is somewhat similar to the motion of the single electron in the hydrogen atom. According to this picture, the electron is under the influence of a single positive charge, but it is in a medium with a rather high relative permittivity ($\epsilon = 12$ for silicon, and 16 for germanium). If the Bohr model is used to picture the motion of the electron in silicon, the radius of an electron in the $n = 1$ shell is 12 times the radius of the same electron in the hydrogen atom and its binding energy is $1/144$ times its binding energy in the hydrogen atom. Based on this reasoning, the binding energy of the electron is calculated to be only 0.09 ev (experimentally it is even lower, 0.05 ev). For germanium the Bohr model calculation gives an electron binding energy of about 0.05 ev, and the experimentally observed energy is between 0.01 and 0.02 ev.

In the silicon energy level diagram the impurity electron of phosphorus appears, as in Fig. 9.11, only 0.05 ev below the bottom of the vacant conduction band. The phosphorus atom to which this electron belongs is called a *donor atom* because, when ionized, it gives an electron to the conduction band. The combination of silicon with *donor impurities*, such as phosphorus with its five valence electrons, results in what is known as *n-type* silicon because it contains a negatively charged carrier.

On the other hand, a boron impurity has only three valence electrons. In this case one additional electron is needed for the completion of all covalent bonds. Each trivalent atom gives rise to a vacant electron level just above the filled band, also shown in Fig. 9.11. In this case an electron from the filled valence band may be raised to the empty level with

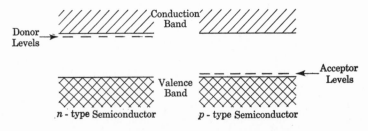

FIG. 9.11.   Energy bands of semiconductors.

the expenditure of only a very small energy, for example 0.05 ev for a boron impurity in silicon. This leaves behind a vacancy, or *hole*, in the filled band, which may successively be filled by neighboring electrons, resulting in the illusion of a moving positive charge. The boron or other trivalent atom is called an *acceptor* because of the ease with which it may absorb an electron from the filled band. Silicon or germanium with impurities, such as boron, with three valence electrons are called *p-type* semiconductors because they contain a positively charged carrier.

At absolute zero, the Fermi brim of an impurity semiconductor is centered between the donor levels and the conduction band for a donor-type semiconductor, and between the filled band and the acceptor levels for an acceptor-type semiconductor. This location for the Fermi brim exists because, at temperatures just above $T = 0°$ K, the only electrons that are observed to attain sufficient energy to be raised to a higher energy level are those electrons in donor levels which are raised to the conduction band, or electrons from the filled band which are raised to acceptor levels. At these low temperatures the relative number of electrons in the filled band which acquire enough energy to reach the conduction band cannot be experimentally measured. As the temperature increases, though, the donor levels tend to become depleted and a larger fraction of the electrons in the upper levels of the filled band acquire energies sufficient to lift them into the conduction band. The filled band electrons, therefore, exert an influence on the conduction properties of the medium. This means that, as the temperature of the solid rises, the level of the Fermi brim changes from a position above the donor level for *n*-type semiconductors, or below the acceptor level for *p*-type semiconductors, to a position closer to an energy midway between the filled band and the conduction band, which is the position of the Fermi brim in an intrinsic semiconductor. This transition in the energy of the Fermi brim as a function of temperature is illustrated in Fig. 9.12.

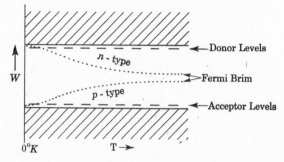

FIG. 9.12. Illustration of the changing energy level of the Fermi brim as a function of temperature for *n*-type and *p*-type impurity semiconductors.

9.8 *p-n* Junctions. If an *n*-type and a *p*-type semiconductor are fused together, the junction is a good rectifier of electron current.* It also is the basis for the transistor. The *p-n junction* is chosen for a relatively detailed treatment because it not only illustrates some of the fundamental principles of the energy level structure of semiconductors, but also shows one case of their practical importance.

Near the fused surface layer the electrons in the donor levels of the *n*-type region are influenced by the vacant acceptor levels in the *p*-type region. As a result of this influence there is a tendency for some of the donor level electrons near the surface to migrate into vacant acceptor levels near the surface. As a result of this transport of charge across the surface there is a net positive electrostatic charge developed on the *n*-type side of the surface and a net negative electrostatic charge developed on the *p*-type side of the surface. The potential developed by the electrostatic charge raises the electron energy bands on the *p*-type side of the surface relative to the energy bands on the *n*-type side of the

*No attempt is made to explain the experimental methods used in fusing together a *p*-type and an *n*-type semiconductor. If a more detailed knowledge of these techniques is desired, the reader is referred to the solid state physics books listed in the references at the end of this chapter.

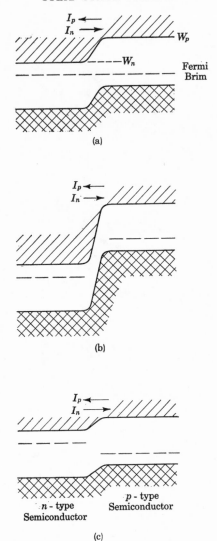

Fig. 9.13. Electron energy levels at a *p-n* junction for (a) no applied voltage, (b) a negative voltage applied to the *p*-type region, and (c) a positive voltage applied to the *p*-type region.

surface until the Fermi brim is at the same level on both sides. This is illustrated in the energy level diagram of Fig. 9.13(a).

At normal room temperatures, when no voltage is applied between the two sides of the junction, the electron current I_p, moving from the *p* to *n* regions just balances the current moving in the opposite direction, I_n. That these two currents are equal may be understood relatively easily by considering the energy requirements of the system. The Fermi distribution equation tells us that in the *p*-type semiconductor the number of electrons N_p in an incremental region of energy at an energy W_p in the conduction band is very nearly $N_p dW = S(W_p)dW \exp[-(W_p - W_F)/kT]$, since $W_p - W_F \gg kT$. These electrons in the conduction band are distributed uniformly over the volume of the *p*-type semiconductor. Since they are not bound to a single atom, they diffuse through this volume; and during the process of diffusion, a fraction of the total approach the surface region between the two types of impurity semiconductors. When an electron in the conduction band of a *p*-type semiconductor approaches the surface region, it may easily move into the *n*-type region because the potential energy of the bottom of the *n*-type conduction band is lower than the bottom of the *p*-type conduction band. Thus, there is a current of electrons I_p from the *p*-type semiconductor through the surface region into the *n*-type semiconductor.

On the other hand, an electron at the bottom of the conduction band in the *n*-type semiconductor, on approaching the surface region, finds a potential barrier blocking its passage into the *p*-type semiconductor. To overcome this barrier requires the expenditure of a quantity of energy $W = W_p - W_n$. Again using the Fermi function, the number of electrons capable of crossing the barrier at some energy W_p is approximately $N_p = N_n[S(W_p)/S(W_n)] \exp[-(W_p - W_n)/kt]$. The quantity N_n is the number of electrons with an energy W_n corresponding to the bottom of the conduction band on the *n*-type side of the junction, which, related to the energy W_F of the Fermi brim, is very nearly $N_n dW = S(W_n)dW \exp[-(W_n - W_F)/kT]$. Substituting this value of N_n into the equation for N_p gives

$$
\begin{aligned}
N_p dW &= S(W_p)dW \exp[-(W_n - W_F)/kT] \exp[-(W_p - W_n)/kT] \\
&= S(W_p)dW \exp[-(W_p - W_F)/kT],
\end{aligned} \tag{9.7}
$$

which is exactly the same number of electrons that were found to be at an energy W_p in the *p*-type semiconductor. This is really not unexpected, since the energy levels W_p are at the same height above the Fermi brim on both sides of the junction and the same electron density would then be expected at this level in both cases. The rate of electron diffusion to the *p-n* surface from the *n*-type side of the junction would therefore be expected to be the same as the rate of diffusion from the *p*-type side. The electron currents moving in each direction across the junction are thus equal, $I_n = I_p$.

A very similar analysis may be made of the current created by the apparent motion of the holes which remain in the valence band as a result of electrons having been lifted out of that band either into acceptor levels or into the conduction band. The resultant is a zero net current of holes across the surface region when no voltage is applied between the two types of semiconductors.

Now suppose that a negative voltage is applied to the p-type region relative to the voltage on the n-type region. Since these are energy levels for the negative charged electrons, the potential of the n-type region is lowered relative to the potential of the p-type region, as illustrated in Fig. 9.13(b). If the applied voltage is V, all electron energy levels in the p-type semiconductor are higher by an amount eV relative to the n-type levels, but there is no change in the relative position of the individual levels within the p-type region. Thus electrons that are raised to a level W_p in the conduction band of the p-type semiconductor are still above the Fermi brim energy by an amount $W_p - W_F$, with the result that the same distribution of electron densities is found in the conduction band of the p-type semiconductor as for the case of no voltage gradient across the p-n junction, and the current from the p-type crystal to the n-type crystal is the same as before. Likewise, since the relative level positions entirely within the n-type semiconductor are not changed, the number of electrons, N_n, that are raised to the bottom of the conduction band from donor levels or from the valence band is the same as if there were no applied voltage. However, when any of these electrons diffuse to the junction surface, they encounter a potential barrier that is higher than the barrier that existed with no applied voltage and the energy difference $W_p - W_n$ is now larger than in the previous case. Therefore, a smaller percentage of the electrons in the n-type crystal are now able to cross the barrier into the conduction band of the p-type semiconductor. This leads to a smaller electron current I_n, with the result that there is a net current $I = I_p - I_n$ crossing the surface. This current has an upper limit I_p.

The potential energy diagram for a reversal of the applied voltage across the p-n junction is illustrated in Fig. 9.13(c). The number of electrons, N_p and N_n, raised to the bottom of their respective conduction bands is still the same, but now the energy difference $W_p - W_n$ is greatly reduced such that the total energy required to bring electrons from the n-type semiconductor region across the p-n surface into the conduction band of the p-type semiconductor is less than the energy required to bring them from the acceptor levels or the valence band of the p-type semiconductor. As a result there is a net electron current $I = I_n - I_p$ which may become quite large. A plot of the net current across the p-n junction as a function of applied voltage is shown in Fig. 9.14.

9.9 Glass. Besides crystals there are two other types of substance which, according to the definition of a solid presented in Section 9.1, must be so classified. They are the glasses and the polymers.

If a liquid can be cooled sufficiently rapidly that it solidifies without crystallization, the solid so formed is a glass. In the process of solidification there is no discontinuous change, as in crystallization, but the material becomes rigid through a progressive increase in its viscosity. This nature of glasses may easily be seen by watching a glassblower at work. There is no defined temperature at which glass changes from the solid to the liquid phase; but as the glass is heated, it becomes less rigid and can be molded into almost any desired shape. A glass appears to be some sort of state intermediate between solid and liquid phase, possessing the rigid character of solids and the amorphous disordered atomic structure of liquids.

The currently existing picture of the atomic structure of a glass is a random, but continuous, network of molecular bonds. The extent to which order exists in this network is not well known at the present time. X-ray diffraction has shown that there exists a preferred lattice distance between any atom and its nearest neighbors. On the other hand, the separation between an atom and slightly more distant neighboring atoms does not show the regularity that exists in a crystal. The probability of finding another atom at any given distance from a selected atom is determined solely by the volume available, not by any characteristic structure. Various structures have been proposed to account for the experimental observations. One such proposal assumes that glass consists of a series of tiny crystalline domains any one of which has been able to grow through only a few layers before it encounters another small crystalline domain. The result is a set of rather randomly oriented bonds between atoms at the edges of the domains. Other hypotheses include the random network of polygonal rings and a series of irregular hexagonal meshes, both illustrated in Fig. 9.15.

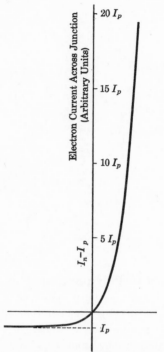

Voltage Across Junction (Arbitrary Units)

Fig. 9.14. Current across p-n junction as function of voltage applied to p-type region.

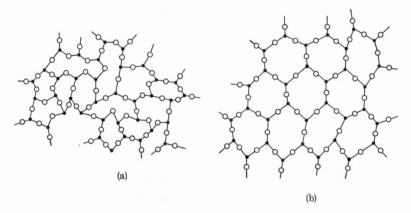

(a)

(b)

FIG. 9.15. Two proposed schematic representations of a flattened two-dimensional cross sectional atomic array in amorphous silicon oxide. A fourth bond from each silicon atom (solid circles) connects with other oxygen atoms lying either above or below this array.

9.10 Polymers. The final type of solid to be considered in this chapter is the polymer, a substance made up of chains of atoms held together by covalent bonds, some of which (high polymers) are quite long molecules composed of a series of similar component parts. These solids range from a glassy-type substance to a rubbery-type substance with appropriate intermediate steps. To a first approximation it is possible to think of some of these solids as held together simply by the entanglement of the chain molecules among themselves. The covalent bonds holding a single chain molecule together are stronger than the bonds between different molecules, so it is not possible for one molecule to break through another. Actually there is some binding between molecules, produced by the Van der Waals forces. The core of most polymeric structures is the carbon atom, but it is also possible to replace carbon with other atoms such as silicon which displays similar chemical properties as carbon.

The four covalent chemical bonds of carbon make possible a wide variety of molecular chains. Sometimes, as in the case of propane, there is a fixed finite length to the chain with three hydrogen atoms closing the chain at each end. In other cases, such as benzene, the molecule forms a closed ring. This structure limits the finite size of the molecule. In some cases, though, the molecule is composed of a whole series of repetitive basic units and may be of almost any length. Polyisoprene (natural rubber), polyethylene, and polystyrene are such molecules. The basic units of two of these molecules are shown in Fig. 9.16. Occasionally, as in benzene and ethylene, a double chemical covalent bond exists between two of the carbon atoms.

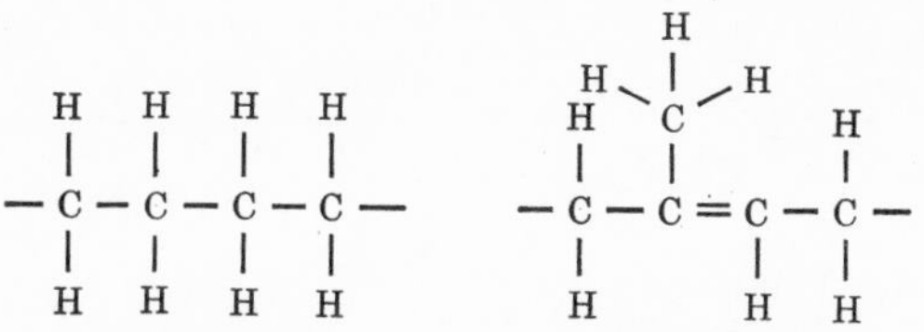

FIG. 9.16.   Basic molecular units for two polymeric substances.

The long chain molecules form polymers of very high molecular weight; hence they are called *high polymers*. High polymer molecules have no unique number of basic units, but instead the number of units is distributed about some statistical mean. For natural rubber the average number of individual isoprene units in a molecule is 5000; hence a mean molecular weight for a single molecule of rubber is about 350,000 AMU. A material made up of this type may be thought of as a series of long chain molecules entangled together to form a solid material. But, if this is the total picture, one chain molecule can gradually slip past its neighbor such that the substance can have a permanent change of shape. If there is nothing to prevent this slippage from continuing, the material slowly flows as does a liquid. In fact, many of the properties of polymers are similar to liquids. That there are similar properties is evidenced by the fact that the deformation of natural rubber takes place substantially without change in volume, as does a liquid when it flows. The individual units of a long chain molecule undergo thermal motions just as do the smaller molecules of liquids. But instead of being able to move independently of each other, these units are limited in their motion because they are bound together in a chain.

At this point it is necessary to ask what distinguishes an elastic high polymer, such as rubber, from a liquid. What prevents the free slippage of one molecule across surrounding molecules? As well as the Van der Waals forces, such slippage may also be prevented by chemical cross-links (bonds) between molecules at a few points along their lengths. This causes a slight change in individual molecular units at a few points along the chain and produces a three-dimensional network of interconnected chains. The process by means of which the necessary cross-linking is introduced in rubber is normally called vulcanization. To preserve the necessary elasticity the cross-linking must not appreciably interfere with the thermal motions of the individual units for it is this motion which produces the elasticity that pulls the elastic substance back into shape after elongation.

To have elasticity, cross-linking is not absolutely necessary, for natural rubber prior to vulcanization does show some elasticity, but cross-linking is necessary for a permanent retention of shape. The physical forces caused by the entanglement of the individual molecules among themselves often holds the material together for extended periods of time, and flow appears only after prolonged stressing of the material.

References

F. Seitz, *The Modern Theory of Solids* (McGraw-Hill Book Co., Inc., New York, 1940).

C. Kittel, *Introduction to Solid State Physics* (John Wiley and Sons, Inc., New York, 2nd Ed., 1956).

A. J. Dekker, *Solid State Physics* (Prentice-Hall, Inc., Englewood Cliffs, N. J., 1957).

F. O. Rice and E. Teller, *The Structure of Matter* (John Wiley and Sons, Inc., New York, 1949).

R. L. Sproull, *Modern Physics* (John Wiley and Sons, Inc., New York, 1956).

C. Zwikker, *Physical Properties of Solid Materials* (Pergamon Press, Ltd., London, 1954).

W. Shockley, *Electrons and Holes in Semiconductors* (D. Van Nostrand Co. Inc., Princeton, N. J., 1950).

W. Ehrenberg, *Electric Conduction in Semiconductors and Metals* (Oxford University Press, London, 1958).

N. B. Hannay, *Semiconductors* (Reinhold Publishing Corp., New York, 1959).

J. N. Shive, *The Properties, Physics, and Design of Semiconductor Devices* (D. Van Nostrand Co., Inc., Princeton, N. J., 1959).

G. O. Jones, *Glass* (Methuen & Co., Ltd., London, 1956).

L. R. G. Treloar, *The Physics of Rubber Elasticity* (Oxford University Press, London, 2nd Ed., 1958).

F. W. Billmeyer, Jr., *Textbook of Polymer Chemistry* (Interscience Publishers, Inc., New York, 1957).

H. Melville, *Big Molecules* (The Macmillan Co., New York, 1958).

H. S. Green, *The Molecular Theory of Fluids* (North Holland Publishing Co., Amsterdam, 1952).

N. F. Mott and R. W. Gurney, *Electronic Processes in Ionic Crystals* (Oxford University Press, London, 1948).

J. D. Bernal, "The Structure of Liquids," *Scientific American* **203**, No. 2, 125 (1960).

J. M. Ziman, *Electrons and Phonons* (Oxford University Press, London, 1960).

Problems

1. In a NaCl molecule two adjacent ions are separated by 2.36 A. If this were the separation of the ions in solid NaCl, what would be the density of solid NaCl? In solid NaCl the spacing between Na^+ and Cl^- ions is 2.81 A. Calculate from this information the density of solid NaCl and compare with handbook values.

2. The density of KCl is 1.984 gm/cm³. If it is assumed that the spacing between ions in a crystal is a measure of the size of the ions, which is larger, the Na^+ ion or the K^+ ion, and what is the magnitude of the radial difference?

3. The potential energy that holds a single ion in an ionic crystal results from the electrostatic forces between ions. This energy may be represented by $\alpha e^2/r$, where r is the spacing between ions and α is a constant, known as the *Madelung* *constant.* This constant is determined by summing the potential energies of the interactions between individual ions, just as the potential energies were summed for electrons and ions in Problems 6 and 7 of Chapter 8; hence the Madelung constant is a function of the geometrical arrangement of ions in a crystal. Show that, for the one-dimensional case of alternate positive and negative ions, separated along a line by a constant distance r_0, the Madelung constant is 2 ln 2. Note that the factor ln 2 results from the series of terms arising from the effects of ions on one side of the ion for which the potential energy is being calculated. The factor 2 results from the fact that ions are distributed along a line in two opposite directions.

4. Show that for a cubic array of alternate positive and negative ions, such as the NaCl crystal, the Madelung constant is 1.75. This problem is solved most simply by dividing the space around one ion in the NaCl crystal into spherical shells. The effect of all ions equidistant from the central ion can then be treated simultaneously.

5. Using the Madelung constant from Problem 4, calculate the energy with which each ion is bound to the NaCl crystal, assuming that only the effects of the electrostatic forces produce this binding. The total energy that must be expended to separate a NaCl crystal into its component ions, also known as the heat of formation, is experimentally found to be 183 kilocalories/mole. If the heat of formation is assumed to be formed from the electrostatic forces of Problem 4 and an unknown repulsive force, what is the magnitude of the energy associated with the unknown repulsive force? Note that the heat of formation per ion is the heat of formation per mole divided by N_0, not $2N_0$, since forces are between ion pairs and the effects of each ion pair can be considered only once.

6. Generally it is assumed that the potential energy curve for a crystal lattice can be expressed by a form $V = -\alpha e^2/\epsilon r + A/r^n$, where A and n are constants for any single crystal. Calculate the magnitude of n and A for NaCl. The same hint is applicable here as for Problem 15, Chapter 8.

7. Sodium metal forms a body centered cubic crystal. The distance between the sodium atom at the center of the cube and the atom at each of the eight corners is 3.715 A. By means of the free electron theory for metals show that the Fermi brim for sodium metal is 3.1 ev. Hint: For a volume $V = a^3$, calculate the number of valence electrons (one per atom) having energies between 0 and W_F by integrating Eq. 9.6 between these energy limits. Assume $T = 0°K$. Solve the integrated equation for W_F after substituting the appropriate valence electron density.

8. For the free electron theory of metals, and assuming a Fermi brim of 3.1 ev, what percent of the electrons would be expected to be within an energy interval having a width of 0.01 ev in the region immediately above 3.2 ev? Calculate for metal temperatures of 290° K (room temperature), 500° K, 1000° K, and 5000° K.

9. Make the same calculations as in Problem 8 for the 0.01 ev energy interval immediately above 3.5 ev, above 4.0 ev, and above 4.5 ev.

10. What would the percentages in Problems 8 and 9 have been if the electrons had obeyed the Maxwell-Boltzmann energy distribution?

11. If, when a phosphorus atom is placed into a germanium crystal as an impurity, the fifth valence electron in phosphorus is assumed to revolve around the P^+ ion according to the Bohr model, what is the radius of the $n = 1$ orbit? Of the $n = 4$ orbit? Locate these orbits relative to the neighboring germanium atoms.

12. Suppose the density of energy states in the conduction band of pure germanium is determined by the free electron theory, Eq. 9.6. How many electrons will there be in the 0.01 ev energy interval immediately above the bottom of the conduction band for a temperature of 290° K? For a temperature of 1000° K? Of 2500° K? Of 5000° K? Of 10° K?

13. For the same conditions as in Problem 12, how many electrons are in the 0.01 ev energy interval 0.5 ev above the bottom of the conduction band?

14. Make the same calculations as in Problems 12 and 13 for diamond.

15. Suppose impurity atoms which form a donor level 0.02 ev below the bottom of the conduction band are added to germanium in the ratio of one part to 10^5. What contribution do these energy states make to the number of electrons calculated to be in the 0.01 ev energy intervals of Problems 12 and 13?

16. At 290° K calculate the ratio I_p/I_n and the difference $I_p - I_n$ at a *p-n* junction for an applied voltage of $+0.1$ volt and of -0.1 volt.

Chapter X

ELECTRON EMISSION FROM SOLIDS

10.1 The Electron Potential Energy Barrier at the Surface of a Solid. If an electron in the conduction band approaches the surface from the interior of a solid, it encounters a potential barrier. This is experimentally evident from the observation that electron emission in easily measurable quantities is not observed at room temperature even when electrons in measurable quantities are free to move in the conduction band throughout the volume of the solid. For an electron near a metal-vacuum surface, the potential energy curve along a line perpendicular to the surface, and passing through the centers of a series of atoms in the metal, is shown in Fig. 10.1. At depths of only two or three atomic layers from the surface, there is the same series of depressed potential barriers between atoms as for atoms deep in the interior. At the surface, though, the potential energy curve rises to a considerably higher energy.

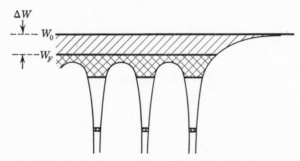

FIG. 10.1. Electron potential energy near the edge of a metal. Potential wells are at atomic nuclei. Shaded regions represent allowed electron energy levels below the free electron energy, W_0. The energy of the Fermi brim is W_F.

Within a few angstroms of the last atom at the surface, where an electron is very strongly influenced by a single potential well, the potential energy function closely resembles that of a single atom. However, within a distance of about 10 A from the last atom at the surface of a metal, no single individual atom strongly influences the potential energy function

177

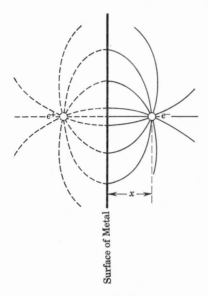

Surface of Metal

FIG. 10.2. Schematic illustration of the method of images for determining the potential energy of an electron near a metal surface. Solid lines of force are outside the metal and are continued as dashed lines to the conjectured image charge inside the metal.

for an electron. Instead, the force on the electron may best be described as that arising from the effects of the field induced because of the interaction of the electron charge and a conducting plane at the surface of the metal. The field so produced is the same as one resulting from a charge of equal magnitude but opposite polarity an equal distance behind the surface as the electron is in front of the surface. Such a situation is illustrated in Fig. 10.2. The forces so produced on the external electron are usually called image forces. The electrostatic field at the electron is $-e/\epsilon(2x)^2$, the force on the electron is $-e^2/4\epsilon x^2$, and the potential energy is $-e^2/4\epsilon x$, in which x is the perpendicular distance from the electron to the surface of the metal.

For all solids the Fermi brim lies well below the ionization energy of the individual atoms. Thus, if electrons are to escape from the surface of a metal in appreciable quantities, either energy must be added to the interior of the metal, or the barrier at the surface must be modified in such a way that the energy of electrons just outside the surface is lower than the Fermi brim. A number of experimental methods have been used to attain the desired goal. Four of these methods, resulting in thermionic emission, field emission, photoelectric emission, and secondary electron emission, are discussed in this chapter.

10.2 Thermionic Emission. In the conduction band of a metal the distribution of electron energies, Eq. 9.6, is temperature dependent. For any temperature above absolute zero there is a finite probability of finding in the conduction band an electron with an energy $W > W_F + \Delta W$, where ΔW, usually called the *work function*, is the difference between the energy of the Fermi brim and the energy W_0 of the surface potential barrier (see Fig. 10.1). Thus, even at room temperature, the electron energy distribution in the conduction band is such that there is a finite probability that a few electrons will diffuse to the surface and escape. It is this type of escape from the surface that is called thermionic emission. As the temperature of a metal increases, the number of electrons in energy levels above the Fermi brim increases (see Fig. 9.5) with the result that the higher the temperature, the larger the number of electrons that possess the required energy to escape.

Only electrons having energies $W > W_0$ can possibly escape, but the mere possession of this amount of energy is not sufficient to guarantee escape. To understand the reason why energy considerations alone are insufficient to determine the probability of escape, a review of the concept of electron energy inside the metal is required. An energy level diagram, such as Fig. 10.1, simply attempts to picture one dimensionally something that is really a three-dimensional pattern. If the electrons possess enough energy not to be trapped by a single positive ion, they move in a field in which there are no general gradients but only local gradients around individual ions. Also, if the conduction electrons in a metal are treated as a gas of Fermi electrons in a lattice of positive ions, as in Section 9.5, any energy that is added to these electrons must be kinetic energy. There must then be a measurable momentum associated with each electron. At the surface of the metal there is a perpendicular potential gradient which pulls electrons in the direction of the metal ions. There is no gradient parallel to the surface. Thus for an electron inside the metal to be able to escape it must have a momentum component in the direction perpendicular to the surface of sufficient magnitude that the portion of the kinetic energy associated with this component of momentum exceeds the energy of the barrier. For example, in Fig. 10.3, an electron can escape only if it has a kinetic energy inside the metal $W_K =$

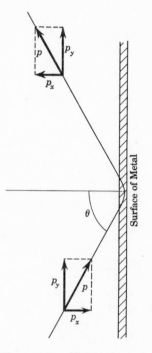

FIG. 10.3. Illustration of the change in momentum of an electron by reflection at the surface of a solid. The surface is shown as an extended region rather than a line because the position of the surface cannot be well defined, for it lies somewhere on the rising potential energy curve to the right of the outermost potential well of Fig. 10.1.

$(p_x^2 + p_y^2 + p_z^2)/2m$ such that $p_x^2/2m \geq W_0$. Hence electrons that encounter the surface at an angle may possibly not escape even though their total energy is sufficient.

Because of quantum mechanical effects not even all those electrons for which $p_x^2/2m > W_0$ are able to cross the surface to the vacuum outside a metal, for some of those electrons that encounter a step barrier, even though above the highest potential energy on either side of the step, are reflected and thus return to the interior of the metal (see Problem 1). Although the actual potential surface of a metal is not a step function, it is sufficiently steep that it gives some reflection of electrons. The magnitude of this reflection, though, is less than would be given by a step potential.

Using the information now available, it is possible to determine a relationship between the physical description of a metal and the number of electrons emitted into a vacuum from the surface of that metal. If inside the metal an electron approaches the surface with a kinetic energy $W_K = p^2/2m = (p_x^2 + p_y^2 + p_z^2)/2m$, and assuming that $p_x^2/2m = W_{Kx}$, it is necessary that $W_K \geq W_{Kx} \geq W_0$ and $\cos\theta \geq (W_0/W_K)^{1/2}$ for the electron to escape. Within the energy interval dW_K, the number of electrons, $dN_\theta(W_K)$, coming from inside the metal that strike a unit area of surface at an angle between θ and $\theta + d\theta$ is

$$\frac{dN_\theta(W_K)}{dW_K} = \frac{dN(W_K)}{dW_K} \frac{v}{V} \frac{d\Omega}{4\pi} \qquad (10.1)$$

where $dN(W_K)/dW_K$ is taken from Eq. 9.6, $V(= a^3$ in Eq. 9.6) is the volume of the metal, v is the speed with which the electrons are moving, and $d\Omega = 2\pi \sin\theta \, d\theta$ is the total solid angle from which electrons are incident. The $d\Omega/4\pi$ term is required because the factor $dN(W_K)/dW_K$ gives the number moving in all directions, not just within the $d\Omega$ solid angle of acceptance. The multiplication by v is for the same reason as v was introduced into Eq. 1.17 to give Eq. 1.17a, the number of molecules passing through a surface.

When a beam having unit cross sectional area intersects a surface at an angle θ, it covers a total surface area of $1/\cos\theta$. Thus Eq. 10.1 must be multiplied by $\cos\theta$ for dN_θ to represent the number of electrons escaping from unit cross sectional area. The electron current is then

$$I = e \int \cos\theta \, dN_\theta(W_K)$$

$$= \frac{8\pi m e}{h^3} \int_{W_0}^{\infty} W_K \exp\left[-(W_K - W_F)/kT\right]$$

$$dW_K \int_0^{\cos^{-1}(W_0/W_K)^{1/2}} \sin\theta \cos\theta \, d\theta, \qquad (10.2)$$

where the assumption is made that all kinetic energies are sufficiently small that $W_K = \frac{1}{2}mv^2$, and the term $+1$ is omitted from the denominator of Eq. 9.6 because $W_K - W_F \gg kT$. Now if $W_K = W_0 + \Delta W_K$ $= W_F + \Delta W + \Delta W_K$,

$$I = \frac{4\pi me}{h^3} \exp\left(-\Delta W / kT\right) \int_0^\infty \Delta W_K \exp\left(-\Delta W_K / kT\right) d(\Delta W_K)$$

$$= \frac{4\pi me}{h^3} (kT)^2 \exp\left(-\Delta W / kT\right). \tag{10.3}$$

If, to complete the equation, r, the reflection coefficient at the surface, is introduced,

$$I = A(1 - r)T^2 \exp\left(-\Delta W / kT\right), \tag{10.4}$$

where $A = 4\pi emk^2 / h^3 = 120$ amp cm^{-2} degrees^{-2}. This expression for the current thermionically emitted from a surface is known as the *Richardson-Dushman equation*.

Because of the potential barrier at the surface, electrons that escape have smaller kinetic energies after leaving a metal than they had inside the metal. The electron kinetic energy inside the metal is the total electron energy above the bottom of the conduction band. To barely escape in the x-direction, in which case the x-component of the electron velocity outside the metal is zero, the x-component of velocity inside the metal must be $p_x^2 / 2m = W_0$. In crossing the surface the y- and z-components of velocity remain unchanged. All the loss in electron kinetic energy occurs in the x-component of velocity such that the kinetic energy outside the surface is

$$(p_{x0}^2 + p_y^2 + p_z^2)/2m = (p_x^2 + p_y^2 + p_z^2)/2m - W_0. \tag{10.5}$$

As a result of this reduction in velocity as electrons cross the surface, there is general pile-up of electrons just outside the metal, producing what is known as a *space charge*. The existence of the negative space charge just outside the surface of the metal causes an effective increase in

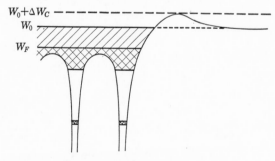

FIG. 10.4.   Illustration of the effects of space charge on the electron potential energy near the surface of a metal.

the potential barrier, as seen in Fig. 10.4. The build-up of space charge eventually reaches an equilibrium condition for which just as many electrons find their way away from the space charge region as are emitted from the metal surface. At equilibrium the potential barrier is effectively raised to a height $W = W_0 + \Delta W_C$ and only those electrons that have energies higher than this barrier escape from the metal.

The adsorption of a monolayer of atoms of a different type onto the surface of a pure metal can change quite markedly the work function of the surface. Perhaps the best known examples of this are the thoriated tungsten surfaces that are used as cathodes in many electronic vacuum tubes. In this case a monolayer of thorium atoms, for which the exact electron ionization potential is unknown but is somewhere between 4 and 5.5 ev, is adsorbed onto the surface of a piece of tungsten metal, for which the work function is 4.52 ev. The thorium layer reduces the work function of the tungsten surface to 2.63 ev. On the other hand, a layer of oxygen atoms, with an ionization potential of approximately 13.6 ev, adsorbed onto a tungsten metal surface raises the work function of the surface to 9.1 ev.

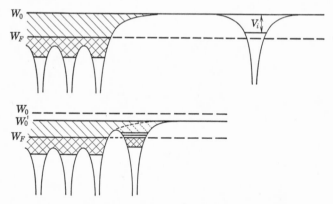

FIG. 10.5. A layer of atoms, such as thorium, for which the ionization energy V_i is less than, or not much greater than, the work function, $\Delta W = W_0 - W_F$, of a metal, adsorbed onto the metal surface results in a lowering of the work function from W_0 to W_0'.

Using the energy band scheme of Fig. 10.5, a qualitative explanation can be given for the reduction of the work function for a metal surface covered by a surface monolayer of atoms. When the thorium atom is at a distance of several atomic layers from the tungsten surface, as in the upper diagram of Fig. 10.5, its valence electrons are in discrete energy states. If a surface monolayer of thorium atoms is attached to a tungsten surface, the interaction between the wave functions of the atoms in the two-dimensional surface lattice of thorium and of the atoms in the metal induces a broadening into energy bands of the less-tightly bound energy levels of the thorium monolayer, as illustrated in the lower diagram of Fig. 10.5. If the ionization potential V_i of the monolayer atoms is less than or only slightly greater than the work function ΔW of the pure metal surface, the energy band induced in the monolayer extends both above and below the Fermi brim of the metal. By itself the Fermi brim of the monolayer would then be at a higher energy than the Fermi brim of the metal. An interchange of electrons between the surface atoms and the metal is now possible because these electrons can tunnel through the separating potential barrier, and, as discussed in connection with the p-n junction, there is a general rearrangement of atomic energy levels to bring the Fermi brim of the entire system to the same energy level.

Because of the loss of electrons from the higher filled energy states in the monolayer to the lower unfilled energy states in the metal, a dipole is created, with the thorium atoms being the positive charge of the dipole. This lowers the potential energy just outside the final tungsten atom at the surface of the metal, and thereby allows an electron to escape from this surface with less kinetic energy than for a pure tungsten surface. This dipole, with its positive pole outward, allows the lower kinetic energy electrons to escape to a sufficiently large distance from the metal surface that they are influenced only by the image forces and, along with the generally higher Fermi brim for the surface monolayer, lowers the work function of the surface, as illustrated in Fig. 10.5.

In case an atom has an ionization potential considerably greater than the work function of the metal, as illustrated in Fig. 10.6, the highest

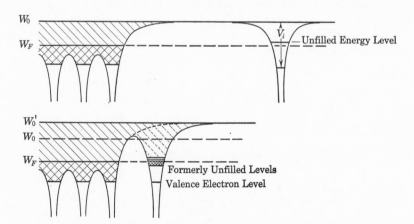

FIG. 10.6. A layer of atoms, such as oxygen, for which the ionization energy V_i is considerably greater than the work function of a metal, and which has an affinity for one or more additional valence electrons, raises the work function from W_0 to W_0' when adsorbed onto the metal surface.

energy electrons of this atom remain so deep in the potential well, even after they have been attached as a part of a monolayer that none of these electrons can be transferred to the metal. It may even be that the atom has an affinity for an additional electron, as in the case of chlorine in the discussion of the NaCl molecule. Oxygen is one such atom. The attachment of an additional electron to form a negative ion always occurs in a higher energy level than the level of the valence electrons, as illustrated in the upper part of Fig. 10.6. If the energy levels of the adsorbed atoms produce energy bands sufficiently wide that they overlap the energy of the Fermi brim of the metal, some of the electrons of the metal will tunnel through the barrier to form negative ions. This negative charge exterior to the surface of the metal produces a negative space charge, which raises the potential barrier of the metal surface, as illustrated in Fig. 10.6, and hence the work function of the metal.

In considering electron emission from a surface, it is necessary to remember that, even though an electron in a solid has a kinetic energy component of sufficient magnitude to escape, there is no automatic guarantee that it will escape. The electron must possess the appropriate properties at the actual time that it reaches the surface. Electrons far in the interior of the solid must diffuse to the surface. In the diffusion process they encounter many other electrons and many ions. In the ensuing collisions with these electrons and ions, there is a continuing interchange of energy. Therefore there may be many electrons in the interior of a solid, the energy of which at the moment lies well above the surface potential barrier, but which, because of collisions with other electrons and with ions, never reach the surface to escape.

10.3 Field Emission. If a strong positive electrostatic field is applied in the vicinity of the surface of a solid, there is a marked change in the characteristics of the potential barrier at the surface, and an increase in the electron current density emitted from the surface. Electrons so emitted are said to have undergone *field emission*.

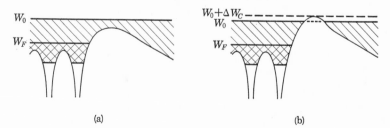

Fig. 10.7. (a) The potential energy for an electron near a metal-vacuum surface when a weak electric field exists near the surface; and (b) the modification of (a) as a result of the effects of space charge.

The application of a small electrostatic field in the vicinity of the surface has the effect of lowering the potential barrier outside the surface, as in curve (a) of Fig. 10.7. If the field gradient is not extremely large the barrier is not lowered sufficiently to increase greatly the number of electrons that cross the barrier. This is the situation in most electronic vacuum tubes. In these tubes electrons are emitted thermionically from the cathode and accelerated toward the anode by an electric field having a relatively small field gradient. A negative space charge is often observed near the cathode under these circumstances, with the result that the potential is modified to curve (b) of Fig. 10.7. Larger positive voltages increase the field gradients and lower the top of the barrier, hence provide the opportunity for a larger number of electrons to escape.

However, even with the fairly large potential gradients that are applied in many electronic vacuum tubes, the condition known as field emission does not exist. If the applied electric field simply has modified the potential to the extent that electrons can more easily cross the top of the potential barrier, the change in emission current is relatively small. It is only when the field gradients become so large that the rapid decrease in potential outside the metal produces a thin potential barrier, as in Fig. 10.8, that the field emission process becomes important. Under these circumstances, because of quantum mechanical effects, even electrons below the Fermi brim have an opportunity to penetrate the barrier. This opportunity did not exist under the conditions of no applied field, or even when a field of medium strength existed, for the barrier was simply too thick. To a first approximation, the field emission current is $I = BE^2 \exp(-u/E)$, in which E is

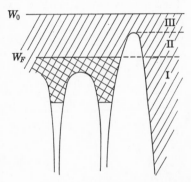

Fig. 10.8. The potential energy for an electron near a metal-vacuum surface if a strong electric field is applied near the surface. In this case electrons may be emitted by field emission from below the Fermi brim through the potential barrier into region I.

the field strength at the surface and B and u are constants for a single type of surface but depend on the work function of the material. To get measurable emission currents, fields in excess of 10^6 volts/cm are usually required.

If a large field gradient is applied near the surface of a metal, the rate of surface emission of electrons is usually governed by a combined field emission — thermionic emission process, known as T-F emission. To illustrate this consider the potential energy curve of Fig. 10.8. Even at

$T = 0\,°\mathrm{K}$, the potential energy surface a few atomic layers outside the metal falls below the Fermi brim energy. Thus the electrons below the Fermi brim (region I) possess a finite probability of penetrating the potential barrier. Electron emission at these energies is true field emission. For finite temperatures some electrons possess energies in excess of the energy at the top of the potential barrier (region III). Electron emission from the metal surface at these energies is true thermionic emission. It is in the intermediate energy region (region II) that the combined *thermionic-field* (T-F) *emission* occurs. The emission itself is a barrier penetration process and hence is field emission; but if there were no thermal energy to get the electrons into this region of the thinner potential barrier, there could be no such emission.

10.4 Photoelectric Emission. The photoelectric process has been discussed twice previously in Sections 4.3 and 7.13. The first of these discussions was a rather gross coverage of the photoelectric ejection of an electron from a metal surface. This phenomenon is discussed in more detail in this section. The second of the previous discussions was concerned primarily with the photoelectric removal of the more tightly bound electrons from the atom. Because the energy levels deep in each atomic potential well show no appreciable broadening in a solid, the discussion in Section 7.13 of photoelectric interactions involving these relatively tightly bound electrons is just as applicable to a solid as to a free atom. Therefore, there will be no further discussion here of photoelectric interactions with the more tightly bound electrons, but only discussion of the processes that occur when there is an interaction that photoelectrically removes an electron from the valence or conduction bands of the solid.

It should be noted that Eq. 4.2 assumes a distinct, well-defined threshold for the photoelectric process. This is true only if the surface from which there is photoelectric emission is at absolute zero, in which case all electrons in the metal have energies below the Fermi brim. For any temperature $T > 0\,°\mathrm{K}$, some of the electrons are raised by thermal energies to available energy levels above the Fermi brim.

This may be shown by an experiment which indicates that a few of the photoelectrons have kinetic energies $W_K > h\nu - \Delta W$. If a voltage V is applied across the electrodes of the photoelectric cell of Fig. 4.3 the current through the cell is found to be a function of the magnitude of the applied voltage. With a sufficiently high voltage on the anode of the cell in Fig. 4.3, but one that is still very low compared to the voltages required for field emission, all electrons that are ejected from the cathode by monochromatic radiation of constant intensity move across the cell and are measured as part of the photoelectron current. This is called the *saturation current.* As the voltage across the cell is reduced there is some minimum value of the voltage, V_s, illustrated in Fig. 10.9 at which the saturation current can be observed. At lower voltages there is a reduction in the photoelectron current. The current continues to be finite and definitely measurable for no applied voltage and even for small negative voltages, because the incident photons eject electrons from the surface of the cathode with finite kinetic energies. However, if the incident radiation is monochromatic, the current is expected by the theory presented in Section 4.3 to become zero at an applied voltage $V_0 = -(h\nu - \Delta W)/e$, in the manner indicated by the dashed line in Fig. 10.9, and to have zero magnitude for all applied voltages $V < -(h\nu - \Delta W)/e$. Ex-

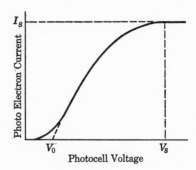

FIG. 10.9. Photoelectron current as a function of voltage across the photocell of Fig. 4.3. If all electrons within the metal cathode of the photocell are below the Fermi brim, which is the case if $T = 0°K$, the threshold for photoelectron emission is at V_0. Because of the existence of electrons in energy levels above the Fermi brim for temperatures above absolute zero, the photoelectron current approaches zero asymptotically at a voltage below V_0.

perimentally, though, it is observed that, for any finite temperature, $T > 0°K$, the current does not become zero at V_0, but approaches zero asymptotically below V_0, the solid line in Fig. 10.9. Another type of experiment shows a similar result. If a series of different monochromatic radiations are used to illuminate the cathode of the photoelectric cell, it is observed that, for $T > 0°K$, some electrons are emitted even for radiations for which $h\nu < \Delta W$.

Both of these experimentally observed effects result from the interaction of the incident photons with electrons in energy states above the Fermi brim. Of course, the higher the temperature of the surface the larger the number of electrons in energy states above the Fermi brim, and the greater the probability for finding electrons that have been photoelectrically ejected from energy levels above the Fermi brim. At room temperature, the number of electrons in these energy levels is exceedingly small, so Eq. 4.2 is at least a good first approximation to what is observed at room temperatures.

Incident photons may interact with electrons that are distributed throughout the allowed energy bands of the solid. Since the character of this electron energy distribution is temperature dependent, any theory of photoelectron emission must include a temperature factor. When an incident photon is photoelectrically absorbed it adds to some electron in the solid an amount of energy $W = h\nu$. Electrons that originally were in levels as low as $W = W_0 - h\nu$ thus may escape from the solid. To obtain appreciable photoelectron currents, photon energies in excess of the photoelectric threshold of Eq. 4.2, $h\nu > h\nu_0 = \Delta W$, must be used. These photons interact with electrons that are below the Fermi brim as well as with those above the Fermi brim. It is therefore not possible to assume that, for electrons photoelectrically emitted from a surface, $W_K - W_F \gg kT$, with the result that it is no longer valid to assume the simplification in the denominator of the Fermi function, $f(W)$, that was used in deriving the Richardson-Dushman equation for the electron current thermionically emitted from a surface. Thus integration of the Fermi function to derive the magnitude of the photoelectron current is much more difficult than the relatively simple integrations made in Eqs. 10.2 and 10.3. Fowler has performed the integration, however, through use of a series expansion from which a series of integrations is made.* The result is an expression for the photoelectric current from a metal surface given by $I = \alpha A T^2 \phi(x)$, in which A is the same as in the Richardson-Dushman equation for thermionic emission, and α is a factor of proportionality between the number of electrons that escape from the surface after absorption of the energy of an incident photon and the number that escape as a result of thermionic emission. The factor α is a function both of the type of surface and of the energy of the incident radiation. The factor $\phi(x)$ is the series:

$$\phi(x) = \{ \exp(x) - \exp(2x)/2^2 + \exp(3x)/3^2 - \dots \} \text{ for } x \leq 0,$$
$$\phi(x) = \{\pi^2/6 + x^2/2 -$$
$$[\exp(-x) - \exp(-2x)/2^2 + \exp(-3x)/3^2 - \dots]\} \text{ for } x \geq 0, \quad (10.6)$$

and $x = (h\nu - \Delta W)/kT$. For thermionic emission, $h\nu = 0$, and only the series can exist for which $x \leq 0$. Also for thermionic emission ΔW is sufficiently large compared to kT that the higher order exponentials are negligibly small compared to $\exp(-\Delta W/kT)$, with the result that the term $\phi(x)$ reduces to $\exp(-\Delta W/kT)$, the final term in the Richardson-Dushman equation, Eq. 10.4.

The Fowler equations indicate that at $T = 0°$ K the threshold for photoelectric emission is indeed the energy ΔW, for $I = 0$ whenever $x \leq 0$, but $I = \alpha A(h\nu - \Delta W)^2/2k^2$ whenever $x > 0$. However, for any temperature $T > 0°$ K the photoelectron emission current has finite magnitude, even for photon energies $h\nu < \Delta W$.

Generally the Fowler theory for photoelectron emission can best be compared with experimental observations if the equation is divided by T^2 and the equation set into logarithmic form, thus

$$\ln(I/T^2) = \ln(\alpha A) - \ln \phi(x). \quad (10.7)$$

*R. H. Fowler, *Phys. Rev.* **38**, 45 (1931).

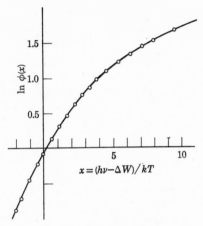

F_{IG}. 10.10.   Fowler plot of photoelectron emission from a calcium surface at 298.4°K. [From N. C. Jamison and R. J. Cashman, *Phys. Rev.* **50**, 624 (1936)]

The Fowler function ln $\phi(x)$ is plotted as a function of x in Fig. 10.10, the solid line. Experimentally, if the photoelectron current I emitted by a surface at a temperature T is adjusted vertically by an amount ln (αA), the experimental observations should coincide with the theoretical predictions. That they do can be seen by the nearness of fit of the circles in Fig. 10.10, which are the experimental observations made by Jamison and Cashman of the photoelectron emission current from a calcium surface at 298.4° K. Note in particular that there is a finite and measurable photoelectron current for $h\nu < \Delta W$ (or $x < 0$), which was considered in Section 4.3 to be below the photoelectric threshold. Note too, because this plot is made on a logarithmic scale, that at the temperature of this surface, essentially room temperature, the current for $x < 0$ is extremely small compared to the current for $x > 0$ and that it diminishes extremely rapidly with decreasing photon energies. Photoelectron currents for $x < 0$ are observable only because, at temperatures $T > 0°$ K, a few electrons are distributed in metals, such as calcium, in the energy levels above the Fermi brim.

Photoelectron emission is possible from surfaces of both metals and nonmetals, but there are distinct differences in the observed currents. The retarding voltage V_0 required to reduce the photoelectron current to negligibly small magnitude is an experimentally determinable quantity which can best show the difference in the photoelectric process in metals on the one hand, and in insulators or semiconductors on the other. At absolute zero, in the latter two types of solids, electrons completely fill the valence band. Above this there is an energy gap in which no electron states are found. The next allowed energy state is at some finite energy,

W_g, above the top of the valence band, at the bottom of the conduction band. The Fermi brim, which determines the magnitude of the work function of the material, is located midway between the top of the valence band and the bottom of the conduction band, as has been illustrated in Fig. 9.9. At low temperature, such as room temperature, the number of electrons in the conduction band is extremely small. To observe measurable photoelectron currents at these temperatures, electrons in an insulator must be given more energy to escape photo-electrically from the surface than electrons in a conductor with the same work function. This additional energy is $W_g/2$, half the width of the energy gap, and is required because the highest energy electrons in the valence band have an energy $W_g/2$ below the Fermi brim. Thus, for two materials, one a metal, and the other an insulator or semiconductor, the stopping voltage V_0 for the semiconductor or insulator is less than the stopping voltage for the metal by an amount $W_g/2$. This is illustrated for two such materials in Fig. 10.11.

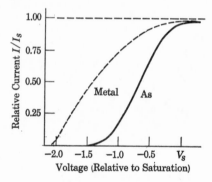

FIG. 10.11. Photoelectron current as a function of voltage across a photo-electric cell for a metal cathode and for a semiconductor cathode, in this case arsenic, with the same work function, 4.66 ev, and for a temperature of 300°K. [From E. Taft and L. Apker, *Phys. Rev.* **75**, 1181 (1949)]

10.5 Secondary Electron Emission. The photon of the photo-electric process is simply one means of getting energy into a solid to excite its electrons into higher energy states. An electron beam incident upon the solid can also provide the required energy. However, the kinet-ic energy of an incident electron is dissipated through a series of Coulomb interactions with the atoms of the solid, not in a single destructive process as is that of the photon. In each Coulomb interaction an electron in the solid is raised to some higher energy level. If one of these electrons is given enough energy to reach a level above the surface potential barrier and if its momentum is directed toward a surface, it may escape from the

solid. After escape this electron is called a secondary electron and the
process is called secondary electron emission. Since, in each Coulomb
interaction with an atom in the solid the primary electron loses only a
part of its kinetic energy, it is possible to have several such interactions
in which atomic electrons are raised to sufficiently high energy levels to
allow escape from the surface. Then, too, it is possible that no interaction gives sufficient energy to a secondary electron to allow it to escape
from the surface. In either case secondary electrons are produced within
the interior of the solid, and these electrons move through the solid in the
conduction band until they either escape or lose their energy by some
appropriate process and fall back into a lower energy level. A secondary
electron that has been raised to an energy level above the surface potential barrier may never reach the surface because of interactions with
other electrons and with atoms in the solid prior to reaching the surface.
The consequent loss of energy by the secondary electron brings it to a
level below the potential barrier.

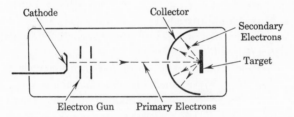

FIG. 10.12. Experimental arrangement for measuring secondary electron
emission.

If an experiment of the type illustrated in Fig. 10.12 is performed, the
yield δ of secondary electrons can be measured. In this case yield is
defined as the ratio of the number of secondary electrons emitted from
the target surface to the number of primary electrons incident on the
target surface, $\delta = N_s/N_p$. The collector of Fig. 10.12 captures all
electrons emitted from the surface of the target. Such collection includes
not only the true secondary electrons that have been produced by the
processes described in the last paragraph, but also primary electrons that
have entered the solid and have been scattered through large angles with
subsequent re-escape from the surface. These two groups can be distinguished to some extent because the distribution of the kinetic energies
of the electrons emitted from the surface generally has two peaks, as
shown in Fig. 10.13. The sharp higher energy peak is at the same energy
as the incident primary electrons and is produced by elastically scattered
primaries. The broader low energy peak is produced by the true secondaries that have diffused from the surface of the solid. The energies of

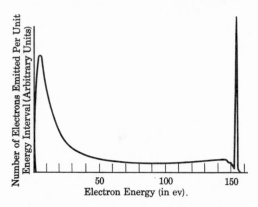

FIG. 10.13. Secondary electron emission current from a copper target as a function of secondary electron energy for an incident beam of 155 ev electrons. [From E. Rudberg, *Phys. Rev.* **50**, 138 (1936)].

these electrons are distributed in a manner resembling, but not quite the same as, a Maxwellian distribution of velocities. The intermediate energy region is composed of a composite of secondary electrons and inelastically scattered primary electrons.

The secondary electron yield as a function of primary electron energy, illustrated in Fig. 10.14 for magnesium oxide, has the same general shape for all materials. This shape can be explained qualitatively by a relatively simple consideration of the processes that are occurring. The initial rise for low energy primary electrons can be explained simply by the increase in the number of secondary electrons that are produced. Each collision between the primary electron and one of the atoms in the

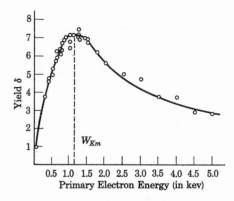

FIG. 10.14. Secondary electron emission yield from a MgO surface as a function of incident electron energy. [From J. B. Johnson and K. G. McKay, *Phys. Rev.* **91**, 582 (1953)].

material results in a loss of energy, the average loss being about 30 ev per collision. Thus higher energy incident electrons have more energy to release and therefore produce more secondary electrons. The more secondary electrons that are produced the greater the probability that a secondary electron can escape.

To explain the drop in the yield curve at higher energies, further consideration of the ionization process must be made. The rate at which ionization is produced by an electron traveling through matter is amost constant as long as the electron is moving at relativistic speeds, but increases rather markedly when the electron has been slowed near the end of its path. This comes about because the ability of the passing electron to produce ionization in an atom depends on the time that the electron spends in the vicinity of the atom. An electron moving at relativistic speeds spends approximately the same amount of time in the vicinity of each atom along its path, but as its speed decreases the time spent in the vicinity of individual atoms increases. Thus at relativistic energies the probability of ionization is very nearly constant, but increases as the speed decreases.

For four different incident energies the ionization probability and the consequent loss of kinetic energy by the electrons are shown as a function of path position in Fig. 10.15. Secondary electrons generally have rather low kinetic energies which are distributed about some mean value. If the

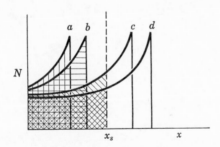

FIG. 10.15. Ionization as a function of distance from the surface of a solid for incident electrons of four different energies. The depth x_s is the mean maximum depth below the surface from which secondary electrons can escape. Electrons c and d produce some secondaries that cannot escape from the surface.

position x_s is a rough measure of the maximum depth from which secondary electrons can escape from the surface of the solid, the number that escape will be approximately proportional to the number that are produced in the region between the surface and x_s. For primary electrons a and b that are stopped prior to penetration to a depth x_s, the number of electrons that are produced in the region of possible escape is proportional to the total kinetic energy of the primary electron; hence the number of secondary electrons is directly proportional to the kinetic energy of the primary electrons. However, if an electron penetrates to a depth greater than x_s, such as electrons c and d, only those secondary electrons produced in the shaded areas can escape. The maximum number of secondary electrons that can escape are produced when the primary electron has an incident kinetic energy of just the right magnitude to stop it at x_s.

For those electrons that penetrate beyond x_s the amount of ionization produced in the region between the surface and x_s diminishes slightly with increasing primary electron kinetic energy. This results in the observed decrease in Fig. 10.14 of the yield δ at energies greater than W_{Km} and the gradual flattening of the curve at higher energies. Classical considerations show that the kinetic energy of a primary electron at any point along its path can be given by the equation $W_K^2 = W_{Kp}^2 - ax$, where a is a constant depending on the density of the material, and W_{Kp} is the kinetic energy with which the electron enters the surface. This equation states that the kinetic energy of the electron decreases rapidly near the end of the path, as shown in Fig. 10.16. The ionization produced is proportional to the loss of kinetic energy per unit path length, hence becomes much larger near the end of the path. These considerations are in agreement with the results shown in Figs. 10.14 and 10.15.

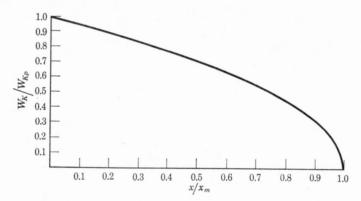

FIG. 10.16.   Plot of the function $W_K^2 = W_{Kp}^2 - ax$.

Experimental analysis shows that most of the secondary electrons are emitted in a direction perpendicular to the surface of the solid. At other angles the number is directly proportional to $\cos \theta$, where θ is the angle of emission relative to the direction perpendicular to the surface. Two theories have been proposed to explain the cosine distribution of secondary electrons emergent from the surface of a solid. Most probably both contribute to the effect. First of all it is only the momentum component perpendicular to the surface that contributes to the ability of the electron to escape, as discussed in Section 10.2. The perpendicular component is $p_x = p \cos \theta$, where p is the total momentum of the electron. The second contributing factor is related to the fact that the range r_0 of the secondary electron is independent of direction of travel through the solid. Hence an electron moving at an angle θ with respect to the normal to the surface cannot go through as great a layer of material before it is stopped as it could if it is moving perpendicular to the surface. As a result the secondary electrons that escape at any angle θ with respect to the normal to the surface can be produced only within the layer of thickness $r_0 \cos \theta$.

References

C. Herring and M. H. Nichols, "Thermionic Emission," *Rev. Mod. Phys.* **21**, 185 (1949).

L. P. Smith, "Thermionic Emission," in *Handbook of Physics*, edited by E. U. Condon and H. Odishaw (McGraw-Hill Book Co., Inc., New York, 1959), pp. **8**-74ff.

R. J. Maurer, "Photoelectric Effect," in *Handbook of Physics* edited by E. U. Condon and H. Odishaw (McGraw-Hill Book Co., Inc., New York, 1959), pp. **8**-66ff.

A. L. Hughes and L. A. DuBridge, *Photoelectric Phenomena* (McGraw-Hill Book Co., Inc., New York, 1932).

W. P. Dyke and W. W. Dolan, "Field Emission," in *Advances in Electronics and Electron Physics*, Vol. 6 (Academic Press, Inc., New York, 1956), pp. 90-187.

K. G. McKay, "Secondary Electron Emission," in *Advances in Electronics*, Vol. 1 (Academic Press, Inc., New York, 1948), pp. 65-130.

A. J. Dekker, "Secondary Electron Emission," in *Solid State Physics*, Vol. 6 (Academic Press, Inc. New York, 1958), pp. 251-311.

H. Bruining, *Physics and Applications of Secondary Electron Emission* (McGraw-Hill Book Co., Inc., New York, 1954).

O. Hachenberg and W. Brauer, "Secondary Electron Emission from Solids," in *Advances in Electronics and Electron Physics*, Vol. 11 (Academic Press, Inc., New York, 1959), pp. 413-499.

S. Flügge, *Handbuch der Physik*, Vol. 21 (Springer-Verlag, Berlin, 1956).

Problems

1. To approximate the effect of the change in the potential energy at the surface of a metal, a step function, such as that discussed in Problem 11, Chapter 6, is sometimes used. This approximation shows the principles involved even though it does not give accurate answers for any real metal. Suppose the depth of the potential barrier V_0 is 6 ev. Assume a one-dimensional problem in which electrons approach the step function in the x-direction from inside the metal. Calculate what fraction of these electrons will penetrate into the vacuum outside the metal, the quantity $1 - r$ of Eq. 10.4, if the electron kinetic energy inside the metal is 7 ev. If it is 8 ev. If it is 12 ev.

2. If, instead of approaching the potential barrier from a perpendicular direction as in the one-dimensional case of Problem 1, an electron approaches a potential barrier from some angle θ, as illustrated in Fig. 10.2, a limited analogy may be made with the approach of electromagnetic radiation toward the edge of a medium from inside the medium. One similarity is that there is a critical angle of incidence, θ_c, such that for all angles of incidence $\theta > \theta_c$, there is total reflection at the surface. Suppose an electron approaches the step barrier of Problem 1, 6 ev in depth, from inside at some angle θ. What is the minimum angle of incidence, θ_c, at which total reflection occurs for an electron with kinetic energy inside the metal of 7 ev? Of 8 ev? Of 12 ev?

3. The potential change at the edge of a real metal is not a single step function, but a function that changes continuously over a finite distance. To show some of the difficulties that arise in calculating the transmission coefficient across the edge of a real metal consider the two-step function of Fig. 10.17. Calculate in one dimension the transmission probability for an electron that has kinetic energy

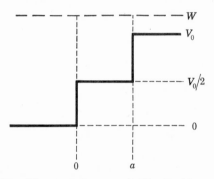

FIG. 10.17.   The two-step potential for Problems 3 and 4.

inside the metal, $W > V_0$. Make a plot of transmission probability as a function of the distance between steps to show that this is a regularly varying function.

4. Suppose the barrier of Problem 3 consists of two equal steps, each 3 ev in depth, and suppose an electron has a kinetic energy of 8 ev inside the metal. What is the transmission coefficient for a distance of 0.55 A between the steps? Of 1.1 A between the steps? Of 5.5 A between the steps?

5. The work function of tungsten is 4.52 ev. Assuming that the reflection coefficient is zero, what thermionically emitted current density, expressed both in amperes cm^{-2} and in electrons cm^{-2} sec^{-1}, are expected for a tungsten surface at 290° K (room temperature)? For a tungsten surface at 1000° K and at 3000° K? For tungsten the reflection coefficient is approximately 0.5. What change does this make in the current density calculated above?

6. A surface layer of thorium on tungsten reduces the work function to 2.63 ev. What is the ratio of the current density from a thorium-coated tungsten filament to that from a pure tungsten filament at the three temperatures of Problem 5? Assume no change in r.

7. A layer of oxygen raises the work function of tungsten to 9.1 ev. What is the ratio of the current density from an oxygen coated tungsten filament to that from a pure tungsten filament at the three temperatures of Problem 5? Again assume no change in r.

8. If an electric field is applied to the region outside the surface of a metal, the force exerted upon an electron is $-eE$ and the potential energy of the electron is $-eEx$, in which $x = 0$ at the surface of the metal. Assuming that the only other contributor to the potential energy of the electron is the image force and that no space charge is developed, what is the magnitude of the maximum potential barrier relative to W_0 for a field of 100 volts/cm and how far from the surface is this maximum located? Make the same calculation for fields of 10^4 volts/cm and 10^6 volts/cm.

9. What would be the thickness of the potential barrier for tungsten at the level of the Fermi brim for the three applied electric fields of Problem 8? Again assume no space charge.

10. For field emission the relationship between the current and the field is approximately $d \, [\log_{10}(I/E^2)]/d(1/E) = -2.96 \times 10^7 (\Delta W)^{3/2}$, where ΔW is in electron volts. Calculate the magnitude of the constant u in the equation for I on page 185.

11. For a particular tungsten field emitter ($\Delta W = 4.5$ ev) it is observed that with a field of 2.5×10^7 volts/cm there is a field emission current density of 1 amp/cm^2. What is the current density for the same emitter for a field of 1.0×10^7 volts/cm, and for a field of 7.5×10^7 volts/cm?

12. In a more exact expression than that given in the text, the exponential portion of the equation for current emitted by the field emission process is $\exp \{u[1 - 14 \times 10^{-8}E/(\Delta W)^2]/E\}$, where E is in volts/cm and ΔW is in ev. For tungsten, what field strength is required before this correction produces a 10 percent change in field emission current?

13. Assume that α and A are constants in the Fowler equation for photoelectron emission. What is the ratio of photoelectric currents between a tungsten surface at $T = 300°$ K and a surface at $T = 1000°$ K, assuming the incident photons have an energy of 10 ev? Assuming the incident photons have an energy of 3 ev?

14. According to Sternglass (see p. 279 of Dekker's paper on secondary electron emission in references) the secondary electron yield is $\delta/\delta_m = (W_K/W_{Km}) \exp [2(1 - W_K/W_{Km})^{1/2}]$, where δ_m is the maximum yield and W_{Km} is the incident electron energy at which δ_m is found. Plot this curve and compare it with the experimental results of Fig. 10.14.

Chapter XI

NUCLEAR PROPERTIES AND NUCLEAR REACTIONS

11.1 Atomic Mass. In earlier chapters there have been many discussions which have assumed that almost all the mass of the atom is concentrated in a tiny nucleus at its center. Such discussions include Rutherford scattering, the Bohr model of the hydrogen atom, and the general discussions of atomic and molecular structure and of solid state physics. In all these cases no regard has been given to the specific structure of the atomic nucleus nor to its actual measured mass, except for an average mass as may be determined by chemical means; it has been assumed simply to be a heavy, positively charged, object. Because the interpretation of precision measurements of atomic mass require the introduction of some details of nuclear structure, discussions of such precision measurements of atomic mass have been deferred to this chapter.

The removal of one or more electrons from an atom results in a positively charged ion. This ion is subject to a force if placed into an electric field, and, if it is already in motion, is also subject to a force if placed into a magnetic field. It is through use of these forces that precision measurements of atomic masses are usually made. The instrument used for making them is called a *mass spectrometer*, illustrated in Fig. 11.1(a), or a *mass spectrograph*, illustrated in Fig. 11.1(b). The basic principles of both are the same except that in the former a focused beam of ions having a single mass is passed through a fixed slit and detected electrically, and in the latter a range of masses is detected simultaneously, usually by means of a photographic plate. In all such instruments ions are produced in an *ion source* and accelerated by an electrostatic field to a measurable kinetic energy. In many instruments, where really precision measurements are to be made, a more refined energy selection is made as the charged ions pass between the circularly shaped electrodes of an *electrostatic analyzer*. Finally mass selection is made by separation of the ions into momentum groups in a *magnetic analyzer*.

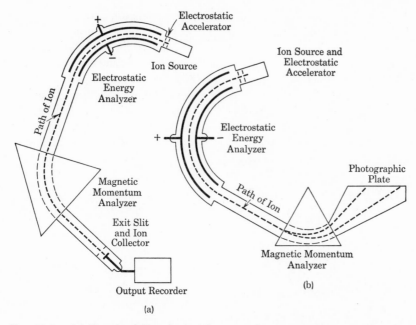

FIG. 11.1.   (a) Sketch of the principal features of a mass spectrometer [based on
A. O. Nier and T. R. Roberts, *Phys. Rev.* **81**, 507 (1951)]; (b) sketch of the
principal features of a mass spectrograph [based on K. T. Bainbridge and E. B.
Jordan, *Phys. Rev.* **50**, 282 (1936), and K. Ogata and H. Matsuda *Phys. Rev.* **89**,
27 (1953)].

The electrostatic anlyzer is based on the principle that a centripetal
force Mv^2/r_1 is required to maintain a particle having mass M moving
with a velocity **v** in a circular path with radius r_1. The force exerted on a
particle having charge q by an electric field **E** is $q\mathbf{E}$. Hence, if the electric
field between the electrodes of the electrostatic analyzer is directed
radially inward and is of magnitude E, the equations describing the
motion of ions in a circular path midway between these electrodes is
$Eq = Mv^2/r_1$, and, if the ion is moving at less than relativistic speeds, its
kinetic energy is defined by the equation $W_K = Mv^2/2 = Eqr_1/2$. For
all ions the charge q is some multiple of the electronic charge e, depending
on the degree of ionization of the atom for which the mass is being
measured.

In the magnetic analysis a centripetal force is applied in a direction
perpendicular to both the direction of the motion of the ion and the
direction of the magnetic flux density **B**. The magnitude of this force
is qvB, such that the radius of curvature, r_2, through which the ion
moves is defined by the equation $qvB = Mv^2/r_2$. The known or measurable
quantities q, r_2, and B thus define the momentum of the ion: $Mv = qBr_2$.

By eliminating the velocity from the energy and momentum equations, the mass of the ion is determined: $M = qB^2r_2^2/Er_1$. For a single setting of the spectrometer, E, B, r_1, and r_2 are constant; the only variables are m and q. If a family of singly charged ions ($q = +e$) are considered, the mass of the ion may be uniquely determined from the settings of B and E. The mass determined by this type of magnetic analysis is that of the ion. Because it is the mass of the whole, neutral atom that is desired, the mass of one electron (or more than one electron if the ion has been charged to an amount greater than $+e$ by the removal of more than a single electron) must be added to the experimentally determined mass.

11.2 Isotopes. Very soon after the atomic nature of matter was established, the average masses of the various types of atoms were determined by chemical means. It is on the basis of such chemical determinations that the chemical atomic weights given in Appendix 1.2 have been found. Suppose now that, instead of using chemical methods, a mass spectrometer is used to measure atomic mass. The results are usually surprisingly different. For example, a mass spectrometric analysis of the simplest of all atoms, hydrogen, reveals that the proton, which remains when an electron is stripped from an atom of hydrogen, has a mass of 1.67245×10^{-24} gram, 1836 times the mass of the electron, and very nearly the atomic mass for hydrogen as determined by chemical means. But these results are not universally true for all hydrogen ions; instead, a very small number of the hydrogen ions, about 0.015 percent of them, are found to have a mass just slightly less than double the mass of the proton. Because there is only one electron in the structure of the hydrogen atom, the positively charged hydrogen ion is a bare nucleus. Apparently then there are two types of hydrogen nuclei, one of which has a mass approximately twice that of the other.

It is now known that the reason for the existence of two different masses for hydrogen nuclei stems from the existence of two different types of particles in atomic nuclei. One of these particles, the proton, which is the nucleus of most hydrogen atoms, carries an electrical charge $+e$, but the other, the neutron, is electrically neutral. All atomic nuclei are composed of these two types of particles. For example, the alpha particle, mentioned in Chapter 1 in connection with Rutherford scattering, is a helium nucleus. It has a mass almost four times the mass of the proton but a charge only twice the proton charge, so it consists of two protons and two neutrons. The heavier hydrogen nucleus consists of one proton and one neutron and, since it is composed of two nuclear particles, it is often called a deuteron.

Two atoms that have identical nuclear charge but different masses, such as the two types of hydrogen atoms, are said to be two *isotopes* of a single element. All isotopes of any one type of element have essentially identical chemical properties and hence form the same types of molecules, because chemical properties are determined by the number of electrons in the atom, which in turn is controlled by the nuclear charge. Many elements have more than one isotope. The maximum number of isotopes observed in any single naturally occurring element is found in tin, for which there are ten isotopes.

To distinguish isotopes it is customary to give the number of nuclear particles in a nucleus, the *mass number*, as a superscript to the right of the chemical symbol for that nucleus. Thus a hydrogen atom which has only a single proton as its nucleus is designated as H^1, and a deuterium atom is designated as H^2.

11.3 The Physical Atomic Mass Unit.

In nuclear physics the atomic mass unit (AMU) is defined in a slightly different manner from the chemical definition given in Section 1.2. By that definition, the *chemical mass unit*, one AMU, is $1/16$ the mean mass of one atom of naturally occurring oxygen. But it is now known that naturally occurring oxygen consists of three isotopes, O^{16}, O^{17}, and O^{18}. The currently acceptable atomic mass unit among nuclear physicists and chemists, the *physical atomic mass unit*, is exactly equal to $1/16$ the mass of the oxygen isotope O^{16}, which consists of 8 protons, 8 neutrons, and 8 electrons. When placed in this scale, mass spectrometric analysis shows that the mass of a proton is 1.007593 AMU. The mass of the isotope of neutral hydrogen for which the proton is the nucleus is 1.008142 AMU — greater than the mass of the proton by one electron mass. Since 99.76 percent of naturally occurring oxygen is O^{16}, the difference between 1 AMU in the chemical and physical systems is very small. All subsequent discussions of atomic mass in this book will be in terms of the physical system.

11.4 Mass Defect and Binding Energy.

Although the same number of nuclear particles exist in the constituent atoms of two different types of molecules, the masses of these two molecular types always are found to differ when measured precisely using mass spectrographic means. An example is shown in Fig. 11.2 for singly ionized $(N^{14})_2$, $C^{12}O^{16}$, and $(C^{12})_2 (H^1)_4$ molecules. It is apparent from this figure that the mass of two N^{14} atoms is greater than the sum of the masses of a C^{12} atom and an O^{16} atom, even though both groups contain a total of 14 protons, 14 neutrons, and 14 electrons. The sum of the masses of two C^{12} atoms and four H^1 atoms, with 16 protons, 12 neutrons, and 16 electrons, is greater than either of the other two molecular combinations, but is still con-

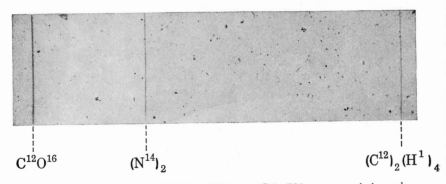

$$C^{12}O^{16} \qquad (N^{14})_2 \qquad\qquad\qquad (C^{12})_2(H^1)_4$$

FIG. 11.2.   The mass triplet $C^{12}O^{16} - (N^{14})_2 - (C^{12})_2(H^1)_4$, as recorded on the photographic plate of a mass spectrograph. (Courtesy of Professor K. Ogata, University of Osaka, Osaka, Japan.) Groups with smaller radii of curvature, hence lower mass, are recorded nearest the left side of the plate.

siderably less than the sum of the masses of 14 electrons and 28 nuclear particles (neutrons and protons).

A study of the experimental photodisintegration of the deuteron (H^2) provides a clue toward a simple understanding of the reason for this mass difference and also provides a measure of the mass of the neutron. If a beam of x-rays is directed at deuterium (a gas composed of deuterons), no interaction of the x-rays with the deuterium nuclei is observed until individual x-ray photons have energies greater than 2.225 Mev. Above this energy protons are observed to emerge from the deuterium. What has occurred above this energy is a nuclear photoelectric effect in which a photon incident upon a deuteron has split the deuteron into its constituent parts, a proton and a neutron.

Since an incident photon energy of 2.225 Mev is required to initiate this nuclear photoelectric effect, it must be concluded that the *binding energy* by which the constitutent parts of the deuteron are held together is 2.225 Mev. This is then the binding energy of the neutron to the proton in the deuterium nucleus. Relativity theory has shown that mass is a form of energy. The binding energy that holds the neutron and the proton together as a deuteron shows up as a reduction in the mass of the deuteron below the masses of its constituent parts by a mass increment equivalent to 2.225 Mev. The total binding energy for larger atoms is then the energy equivalent of the difference between the mass of the atom and the sum of the masses of all its component parts and is usually expressed either in units of Mev or of AMU.

Another related quantity is the *mass defect*, defined as the difference Δ between the number of nuclear particles in the nucleus A and the atomic mass M, in AMU. The *mass excess* is $-\Delta = M - A$. Thus for O^{16}

$\Delta = 0$, and for all other atoms Δ is different from zero but may be either positive or negative.

11.5 Mass of the Neutron. Since the neutron has no charge, its mass cannot be determined by magnetic analysis, so some other means must be used. The mass of the deuterium atom has been measured by magnetic analysis to be $M_D = 2.014735$ AMU, and the mass of the single proton hydrogen atom (M_H) is 1.008142 AMU. From this information it is possible to calculate the mass of the neutron (M_n). Since the deuteron consists of a proton and a neutron held together with an energy of 2.225 Mev (1 Mev = 1.07500×10^{-3} AMU), the neutron mass M_n is

$$M_n = M_D - M_H + 2.225 \text{ Mev}$$

$$= (2.014735 - 1.008142 + 0.002390) \text{ AMU}$$

$$= 1.008983 \text{ AMU.} \tag{11.1}$$

Thus, the rest mass of the neutron is slightly greater than that of the proton. A consequence of this mass difference is that the neutron cannot exist as a free, stable, independent particle (see Problem 5, Chapter 12).

11.6 The Nuclear Potential Well and the Radius of the Nucleus. Since a large number of protons and neutrons can be held together in the small nuclear volume, there must be a strong attractive force between nuclear particles. This force must be stronger than the coulomb repulsive force produced by the positive electrical charge on the protons. If this were not so, any nucleus containing more than one proton would necessarily fly apart, from the effect of the force produced by one proton charge on the others. The strong nuclear attractive force produces some sort of potential well for one nuclear particle in the immediate vicinity of another nuclear particle or group of nuclear particles that have been combined into a single nucleus.

In the study of Rutherford scattering it was seen that, if a charged nuclear particle, such as a proton or an alpha particle, approaches a nucleus, it encounters a rising potential energy surface that is produced by the effect of the coulomb repulsive force between the two particles. This potential surface continues to rise only to a finite maximum for at some measurable distance of separation the strong attractive force which holds nuclear particles together becomes stronger than the coulomb repulsive force. A cross sectional view of the nuclear potential surface encountered by a charged incident nuclear particle is illustrated in Fig. 11.3(a). If the incident nuclear particle approaches sufficiently close to be influenced by the short range attractive force of the target nucleus, it may fall into the potential well and become a part of the target nucleus. This, of course, forms a new nucleus with different charge and mass.

Because a neutron carries no electric charge, the potential surface created for it by a target nucleus does not rise above the zero level, but has the general shape illustrated in Fig. 11.3(b). Thus the neutron does not need a large kinetic energy to enter the immediate vicinity of a

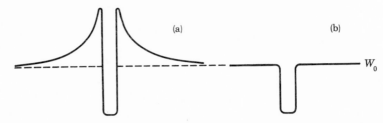

Fig. 11.3.   Cross sectional view of the nuclear potential energy surface for (a) an incident proton, and (b) an incident neutron.

target nucleus and even a very slowly moving neutron will eventually encounter a nuclear potential well and be captured. On the other hand, because of the extremely small diameter of the nuclear potential well, a neutron may wander a considerable distance before it comes within range of the strong attractive forces of a nucleus and is captured by the nucleus. Because of its wave characteristics a moving neutron may also be reflected from the edges of a nuclear potential well, as discussed in connection with Problem 11, Chapter 6.

The radial distance at which an incident nuclear particle first encounters the strong nuclear forces is usually considered to define the radial dimensions of the nucleus. This assumption is valid only because the nuclear forces have extremely short range, a fact that also allows the nucleus to be considered to be a tightly packed incompressible fluid of nuclear particles (neutrons and protons). The nuclear volume is then $V = \frac{4}{3}\pi R^3 = \frac{4}{3}\pi R_0^3 A$, directly proportional to its mass number A. Although there is some fluctuation from nucleus to nucleus, a relatively commonly accepted value for R_0, the radius of an individual nucleon in the incompressible fluid, is 1.33×10^{-13} cm, such that the nuclear radius is $R = (1.33 \times 10^{-13})A^{1/3}$ cm.

11.7 Nuclear Reactions. When an external nuclear particle interacts with an atomic nucleus, the resulting process is usually called a nuclear reaction. In such reactions a compound nucleus is temporarily formed by the merging of the incident particle a with the target nucleus X. The compound nucleus lasts only a very short time before splitting into a product nucleus Y and one or more nuclear particles b. Such reactions are generally expressed either by the equation $X + a \rightarrow Y + b$ or by the symbolic representation $X(a,b)Y$. If, on the other hand, the incident particle is simply scattered, the representation can usually be simplified into the form $X(a,a')X$ or $X(a,a')X^*$, in which X^* means that the scattering nucleus is left in an excited state (if the scattering is inelastic).

As an example of a nuclear reaction, suppose a deuteron comes within the range of the nuclear forces of a C^{12} nucleus and, as a result of the ensuing interaction, an atom of C^{13} is formed and a proton is emitted. This reaction can be written either in the form $C^{12} + H^2 \rightarrow C^{13} + H^1$ or in the form $C^{12}(d,p)C^{13}$. (Note that d and p are used for the deuteron and proton, respectively, in the second form of the equation, whereas the isotopic symbolism is used in the former representation, even though incident deuteron and emitted proton are usually ionized and hence are not really an H^2 or an H^1 atom, respectively.)

There is almost never an exact energy balance in a nuclear reaction. Reactions may be either *exoergic* or *endoergic*, depending on whether energy is released by the reaction, or energy must be supplied from the outside in order to make the reaction take place. The formulation which is commonly used to express a nuclear reaction in such a way that it has energy balance is

$$C^{12} + H^2 \rightarrow C^{13} + H^1 + Q, \tag{11.2}$$

where Q is the nuclear energy change that takes place as a result of the reaction. The Q value of a reaction is customarily obtained by adding the rest mass or rest energy of each side of the equation, usually in units either of AMU or of Mev. Thus for this reaction:

Mass of C^{12}	12.00390 AMU	Mass of C^{13}	13.00755 AMU
Mass of H^2	2.01472 AMU	Mass of H^1	1.00814 AMU
Total	14.01862 AMU	Total	14.01569 AMU

There is a larger total rest mass by 0.00293 AMU on the left side of the equation than on the right side, so the Q value is positive and the reaction is exoergic. Some or all of the surplus energy is nearly always carried away as kinetic energy in the product nuclear particles, although in many reactions the resultant nucleus may also be left in an excited state, as discussed in Section 11.8.

Another very similar reaction is that in which a neutron is captured. An example of this type of reaction is $C^{12} + n \rightarrow C^{13}$. The mass balance for this equation is:

Mass of C^{12}	12.00390 AMU	Mass of C^{13}	13.00755 AMU
Mass of n	1.00898 AMU		
Total	13.01288 AMU	Total	13.00755 AMU

Again the reaction is exoergic, this time by 0.00533 AMU. In this case some energy can be carried away as kinetic energy of the C^{13} atom. However, when a neutron is captured without the emission of another nuclear particle, energy and momentum are usually conserved by the emission of a photon; hence this type of reaction is often called *radiative neutron capture* and the photons are called *capture gamma-rays*. Thus, this reaction is commonly written in the form $C^{12}(n,\gamma)C^{13}$, γ in this case being the symbol for a photon emitted by a nucleus.

To illustrate an endoergic type of reaction, consider the situation when a deuteron is incident on C^{12}, and an alpha particle is emitted. This reaction may be written either as $C^{12} + H^2 \rightarrow B^{10} + He^4$, or as $C^{12}(d,\alpha)B^{10}$. Here the mass balance is:

Mass of C^{12}	12.00390 AMU	Mass of B^{10}	10.01617 AMU
Mass of H^2	2.01472 AMU	Mass of He^4	4.00391 AMU
Total	14.01862 AMU	Total	14.02008 AMU

Thus in this case $Q = -0.00146$ AMU, and energy must be added to the system to make the reaction take place. This energy must come from the kinetic energy of the incident nuclear particle, the deuteron in this case.

Another endoergic reaction is the photodisintegration of the deutron, the reaction $H^2(\gamma,n)H^1$, which was considered earlier. Since 2.225 Mev is required to make the reaction occur, its Q value is -2.225 Mev (-0.002390 AMU).

In all nuclear reactions it is necessary to conserve both energy and momentum. The equations that express the momentum and energy transfer must be developed in a manner similar to the conservation equations for the Compton effect. In nuclear reactions, though, both kinetic and rest energy must be inserted into the energy equation. Thus, if the target nucleus is initially at rest, the energy equation is:

$$M_X c^2 + M_a c^2 + W_{Ka} = M_Y c^2 + W_{KY} + M_b c^2 + W_{Kb}, \quad (11.3)$$

where W_K is the kinetic energy of the subscript particle and a, b, X, and Y refer to the same particles as at the beginning of this section.

From this equation it may be seen that the Q value for the reaction,

$$Q = (M_X + M_a - M_Y - M_b)c^2 = W_{KY} + W_{Kb} - W_{Ka}, \quad (11.4)$$

may be expressed in terms of the kinetic energies of the particles as well as the rest energies. Since the resultant nucleus of a nuclear reaction may be rather massive, its kinetic energy and momentum may be quite small and difficult to measure. Therefore it is customary to eliminate W_{KY} from the equations of motion. The resulting Q value for the equation is

$$Q = W_{Kb}(1 + M_b/M_Y) - W_{Ka}(1 - M_a/M_Y) \\ - (W_{Ka}W_{Kb}M_a M_b)^{1/2}(2\cos\theta/M_Y) \quad (11.5)$$

in which θ is the angle of emission of the nuclear particle b relative to the incident direction of motion of the particle a.

Generally an incident charged particle must have a kinetic energy greater than the potential barrier if it is to enter the target nucleus. On rare occasions the incident particle can penetrate the nuclear potential barrier, but for many nuclear reactions the experimentally observed threshold is not so much a function of the Q value of the reaction as the height of the potential barrier. Thus, even for the exoergic case, the probability that a nuclear reaction can take place is often very low for incident particles having small kinetic energy.

To escape from the compound nucleus, a charged particle must either return over the nuclear potential barrier or tunnel through the barrier. Once it does escape, though, it is accelerated by the electrostatic force produced from the interaction between the charge on the resultant nucleus and the charge on the emitted nuclear particle. Here, too, even for exoergic nuclear reactions, there is often a low probability of occurrence if the kinetic energy of the incident particle is small, for the emitted charged nuclear particle may simply not have enough energy to go over the top of the potential barrier, and the probability of barrier penetration is very small. As an example of the effect of barrier height, consider the two exoergic nuclear reactions $N^{14}(n,p)C^{14}$ and $Ni^{58}(n,p)Co^{58}$, the Q values for both of which are about 0.61 Mev. But the barrier height of the C^{14} nucleus is 2.8 Mev while the barrier height of the Co^{58} nucleus is 7.0 Mev. As a result, the proton can penetrate the barrier in the former case much more readily than in the latter case, and the cross section for thermal neutron (neutrons with room temperature kinetic energy) induced reactions of the former type are about 350,000 times more probable than similar reactions of the latter type.

11.8 Excited States in Nuclear Reactions. Within the potential wells of almost all nuclei there exist discrete energy levels above the ground state level. Because of the existence of these higher energy levels, nuclear reactions can leave a resultant nucleus in an excited state. If a nuclear reaction ends with a nucleus in an excited energy level, the magnitude of the Q value for the reaction is reduced by an amount equal to the height above the ground state of the energy level in which the resultant nucleus is found after the reaction is completed. As an example of a nucleus in which excited states have been experimentally observed, a partial energy level diagram for Li^6 is illustrated in Fig. 11.4. The energy of these levels have been determined from the momentum of the alpha particles emitted by the $Be^9(p,\alpha)Li^6$ reaction. Protons with a kinetic energy of 7.25 Mev from an electrostatic generator were used to bombard a beryllium target. The compound nucleus resulting from the capture of

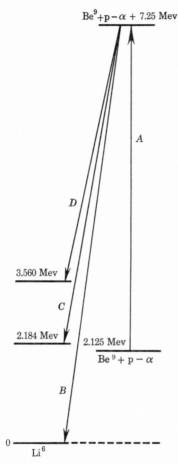

$Be^9+p-\alpha + 7.25$ Mev

A

D

3.560 Mev

C

2.184 Mev

2.125 Mev

$Be^9 + p - \alpha$

B

0

Li^6

Fig. 11.4.   Partial energy level diagram for Li^6.

the proton in the Be^9 nucleus forms an atom approximately 8.37 Mev above the ground state of Li^6, from which Li^6 can be formed only if the compound nucleus emits an alpha particle. Kinetic energy is divided between the alpha particle and the resulting Li^6 ion, the amount of kinetic energy going to each particle depending on the energy level in which the Li^6 nucleus is left after the reaction is completed. If the resultant nucleus is left in an excited state, such as transitions *C* and *D* of Fig. 11.4, the alpha particle and Li^6 ion carry away less kinetic energy than if the Li^6 nucleus is left in the ground state, as in transition *B* in Fig. 11.4 (see Problem 16).

The momentum of an alpha particle emitted by a reaction may be determined by magnetic analysis, using a system similar to that used for mass analysis. Instead of analyzing a beam of particles with equal kinetic energies into different mass groups, the uniform magnetic field is used to separate a beam of particles, all having the same mass, into different velocity groups. Each alpha particle that enters the magnetic field traverses a path which has a radius of curvature directly proportional to its momentum. The different alpha particle momentum groups from the $Be^9(p,\alpha)Li^6$ reaction are shown in Fig. 11.5, along with an indication of the radius of curvature of the trajectory of the alpha particles. In this analysis the magnetic spectrometer records the number of alpha particles following paths within a small range of radii between r and $r + \Delta r$. Based on a knowledge of the magnitude of the magnetic flux density and the radius of curvature of the particle path, the force equation for a charged particle passing through a magnetic field can be used to determine the momentum of the alpha particle. Other ions in addition to the alpha particle may also be formed. For example, in Fig. 11.5 a peak attributed to triply charged Li^6 is shown. If there were impurity atoms, they too would

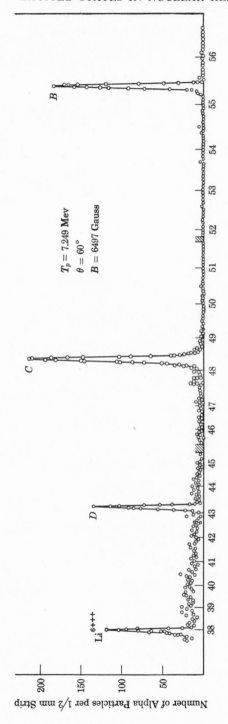

FIG. 11.5. Alpha particle groups as recorded on a photographic plate in a magnetic analyzer from the Be⁹ (p, α)Li⁶ reaction. Groups B, C, and D result from the corresponding transitions in Fig. 11.4. [C. P. Browne and C. K. Bockelman *Phys. Rev.* **105**, 1301 (1957)]. The group marked Li⁶⁺⁺⁺ is a group of triply charged Li⁶ ions.

undergo nuclear reactions and nuclear particles and ions from these reactions would also be observed.

11.9 Multiparticle Reactions. The nuclear reactions thus far discussed have been limited to reactions in which there has been only a single product nuclear particle. Except for simplicity, there has been no reason for limiting nuclear reactions in this way. If the energy of the incident particle is sufficiently high, two or more individual nuclear particles may be boiled out of the compound nucleus during the course of the reaction. For some incident energies, the release of two or more particles is more probable than the release of a single particle. As an example the relative cross sections for three types of proton-induced reactions on copper are shown in Fig. 11.6, these being the $Cu^{63}(p,n)Zn^{63}$, the $Cu^{63}(p,pn)Cu^{62}$ and the $Cu^{63}(p,2n)Zn^{62}$ reactions. In the latter two

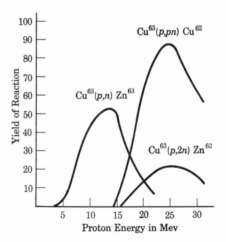

Fig. 11.6.   Relative yields of three different proton reactions on Cu^{63}, shown as a function of incident proton energy. [S. N. Ghoshal, *Phys. Rev.* **80**, 939 (1950)]

reactions there are two emitted nuclear particles; and, as can be seen from Fig. 11.6, such reactions compete more favorably at the higher incident proton kinetic energies.

If the incident proton has very high kinetic energies (greater than 100 Mev), reactions are possible in which many nuclear particles are separated from the compound nucleus. This type of reaction is usually called *spallation*.

11.10 The Fission Process. A special type of nuclear reaction that is highly exoergic for nuclei near the upper end of the periodic table of elements is *fission*, a process in which a nucleus splits into two nearly equal parts. Although it is theoretically possible, if enough energy is added, for any nucleus to fission, the process is of practical significance only when a nucleus near the upper end of the periodic table splits into two nuclei near the center of the periodic table. This process can and does occasionally occur spontaneously, but it is usually initiated by some incident radiation, such as a photon or a neutron. The initiator most commonly used in applications of nuclear fission is the neutron. For example, if a thermal neutron* penetrates the nucleus of a U^{235} atom and

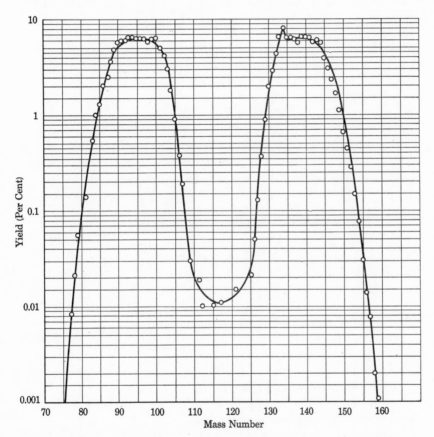

FIG. 11.7. The fission yield for $U^{235} + n$(thermal). Values for individual isotopes based on data from S. Katcoff, *Nucleonics* 16, No. 4, 78(1958); curve from R. C. Bolles and N. E. Ballou, USNRDL — 456 (30 August 1956).

*It is customary to call any neutron that has come to thermal equilibrium with its surroundings a thermal neutron. The kinetic energies of such neutrons are distributed in accordance with the Maxwell-Boltzmann distribution. For calculational purposes a thermal neutron at room temperature is usually considered to have a kinetic energy of about 0.025 ev.

is captured, either a radiative capture (n,γ) reaction is observed, or the compound nucleus fissions into two large nuclear fragments. There are no unique nuclear products of the fission reaction. The masses of the fragments are usually unequal. For thermal neutron fissioning of U^{235} a light group of fission products centers near mass number 95 and a heavy group near mass number 140, as shown by the distribution of nuclear yields in Fig. 11.7. In almost all fission processes, a few neutrons, usually two or three, as well as some gamma radiations, are released at the instant of fission. A fission reaction for U^{235} can be represented by the equation:

$$U^{235} + n \rightarrow U^{236} \rightarrow Z_L + Z_H + xn,$$

in which x is an integer representing the number of neutrons released during the fission process, Z_L is the light fission product and Z_H the heavy fission product. Since the charge number for uranium is 92, the sum of the resulting charge numbers $Z_L + Z_H = 92$. Also the total number of nuclear particles must be conserved, so $A_L + A_H + x = 236$.

The nuclear yield from the fission of U^{235} is plotted in Fig. 11.7 in terms of mass numbers. This does not mean, though, that all fission processes in which one of the product nuclei has mass number 140, for example, lead immediately to the same isotope. The total fission yield of mass 140 isotopes is 6.10 percent, but this yield is divided in the following manner: I^{140}, 0.84%; Xe^{140}, 2.49%; Cs^{140}, 2.23%; and Ba^{140}, 0.54%. Which isotope is formed at the time of fission depends on the way the U^{236} nucleus splits, and how many prompt neutrons are emitted. For example, the reaction might be

$$n + U^{235} \rightarrow U^{236} \rightarrow Xe^{140} + Sr^{94} + 2n.$$

The energy released in the process will be calculated in the next chapter. The reason for the delay in this calculation is that both Xe^{140} and Sr^{94} and most other isotopes formed directly by fission are radioactive isotopes. The overall process can be more easily understood following a discussion of radioactive nuclei.

In addition to U^{235}, several other nuclei undergo fission following absorption of a thermal neutron. All these nuclei are at the upper end of the periodic table, the best known being U^{233} and Pu^{239}, since these two isotopes and U^{235} have both large thermal neutron fission cross sections and are very stable against alpha particle decay. Additional discussion of the fission process is found in Section 12.10.

11.11 Scattering of Nuclear Particles. As mentioned earlier, if the particle emitted by a nuclear reaction is of the same type as the particle that entered, the reaction is considered to be some sort of scattering process. Unlike the Rutherford type of scattering, in which charged nuclear particles are deflected by the coulomb field before they reach the surface of the scattering nucleus, the nuclear reaction type of scattering occurs after the incident nuclear particle reaches this surface. Scattering from the nucleus does not produce the same angular distribution of scattered particles as the Rutherford coulomb scattering and hence has often been called *anomalous scattering*. The incident nuclear particle may be elastically scattered, with no kinetic energy loss by the system, an $X(a,a')X$ reaction, or it may be inelastically scattered, in which case some energy is transferred to the target nucleus in a form other than kinetic energy, an $X(a,a')X^*$ reaction.

Elastic scattering from the nucleus may be of two types: either the incident nuclear particle is reflected at the edge of the potential well by the effect of the relatively abrupt change in potential or, if the energy of the incident particle corresponds closely to an energy level in the compound nucleus, the particle may actually enter the nucleus and then be reemitted with its original kinetic energy. The former type of scattering is called *nuclear potential scattering* and the latter *nuclear resonance scattering*.

In inelastic scattering the target nucleus is left in an excited energy state. This energy shows up in the resultant nucleus as an increase in rest mass, the magnitude of which just equals the equivalent loss in kinetic energy by the system. The excited nucleus usually returns to its ground state by releasing the surplus energy as a photon. This is analogous to the release of energy by the atom when one of its electrons undergoes a transition from a higher energy state to a lower energy state.

11.12 Nuclear Spin. Nuclear particles, as well as electrons (see Section 2.6), have characteristic spin quantum numbers. The existence of nuclear spin was first postulated on the basis of observations of hyperfine structure in atomic spectra. A spectrum is said to have *hyperfine structure* if, with very good resolution, its atomic spectral lines (which appear to be single line, at lower resolution), can be shown to be composed of a number of closely spaced components, the separation between components being some small fraction of an angstrom.

With atoms for which there is more than one isotope, it is possible to have a form of hyperfine structure that results from reduced mass effects on the Rydberg constant. However, the hyperfine structure discussed here is limited to that caused by the interaction of the nuclear spin magnetic moment with the magnetic moments of the orbital electrons. Such hyperfine structure is observed even in atoms having only a single isotope. The nature of hyperfine structure can be explained by recalling the Zeeman effect already discussed in Section 7.12. The spinning nucleus sets up a small magnetic field which then provides a preferential direction upon which the magnetic moments of the atomic energy states may be oriented. Nuclear spin is quantized and its magnitude is given by a *nuclear spin quantum number*, I, such that the spin angular momentum of a nucleus is $I^*h/2\pi = [I(I+1)]^{1/2}h/2\pi$. This quantum number may be combined with the total quantum number, J, of the atom in accordance with the vector model to give a resultant angular momentum $F^*h/2\pi = [F(F+1)]^{1/2}h/2\pi$, where F is an integer or half-integer determined by the vector summation of the I and J quantum vectors. Following the usual rules for vector addition discussed in Section 7.9, the number of states in a designated energy level resulting from a given I and a given J is either $2I+1$ or $2J+1$, whichever is smaller. This determines the number of values of F and thus the amount of splitting of a designated level.

What are experimentally observed are, of course, the spectral lines that result from transitions between appropriate energy levels. Allowed transitions for the quantum number F are the same as for the quantum number J, that is, $\Delta F = 0, \pm 1$, with no $0 \rightarrow 0$ transition allowed. As an example of the way the hyperfine structure that results from the effects of nuclear spin appears in the visible spectrum, consider the case of sodium. There is one stable isotope of sodium, Na^{23}, which has a nuclear spin of $\frac{3}{2}$. The vector model thus says that the $^2S_{1/2}$ ground state of sodium splits into two levels for which $F = 1$ and 2, respectively, as

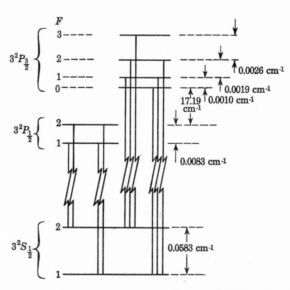

FIG. 11.8. The hyperfine structure energy levels of Na^{23}. [Based on L. P. Granath and C. M. Van Atta, *Phys. Rev.* **44**, 935 (1933)]

illustrated in Fig. 11.8. The $^2P_{1/2}$ state also splits into two levels with the same two values for the F quantum number as for the $^2S_{1/2}$ state, but the $^2P_{3/2}$ state splits into four levels for which $F = 0, 1, 2,$ and 3. The transitions shown in Fig. 11.8 are allowed. The magnitude of the splitting of the levels produced by the effects of nuclear spin is extremely small. Hence the yellow lines in the spectrum of atomic sodium appear as just two spectral lines unless a spectrometer with extremely good resolution is used. Supposedly, though, a spectrometer with sufficiently good resolution should resolve the spectral line at 5896 A into four very closely spaced components, and the line at 5890 A into six very closely spaced components. Because of the spacing of the energy levels, optical spectrometers split the line at 5896 A into two groups of two lines each and the line at 5890 A into two groups of three lines each. Even the best optical spectrometers have not been able to resolve the more closely spaced lines, but only to show the existence of two groups in each of the sodium yellow lines. The intensity of each group is approximately that expected from the combined intensity of the two or three components of which it is comprised.

The best resolution of spectral lines usually can be attained if the magnitude of the experimentally observed photon energy, $h\nu$, is reasonably close to the energy interval to be measured. The use of the visible or near visible regions of the electromagnetic radiation spectrum to measure hyperfine structure does not fit this requirement, for the energies of visible photons are many orders of magnitude greater than the energy difference between hyperfine structure levels. It must be indicated, though, that many excellent pieces of research on hyperfine structure have been conducted using the visible radiations as the means of observation. For the measurement of the effects of nuclear spin, utilization of the Zeeman effect and of the principles of the Stern-Gerlach experiment have provided a means for applying lower energy radiations to the problem. In the particular form of the experiment to be discussed here, an atomic beam passes through a magnetic field that is divided into three

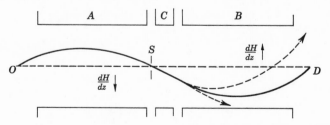

FIG. 11.9. Cross sectional schematic illustration of atomic beam apparatus for measuring nuclear spin. The vertical dimensions are greatly exaggerated relative to the horizontal dimensions.

parts. The pole faces of magnets A and B in the spectrometer diagrammed in Fig. 11.9 are both shaped to produce inhomogeneous magnetic fields. The direction of the two fields are the same but the directions of their gradients are opposite. The field between the pole faces of magnet C is uniform. To determine the effect of this combination of magnetic fields on an atomic beam, suppose that the beam consists of potassium atoms. If magnets A and B produce equal effects, each atom is deflected through one curvilinear path in the region between the pole faces of magnet A and is refocused through a path of reverse curvature in the field of magnet B, such that it reaches the detector D.

The nuclear spin of K^{39} is $\frac{3}{2}$, the same as for Na^{23}. The electronic structure of the valence electrons of these two atoms is also the same except that the single valence electron for sodium is a $3s$ electron, whereas for potassium it is a $4s$ electron. Thus for K^{39} the $^2S_{1/2}$ ground state would be expected to split into an $F = 1$ level and an $F = 2$ level, just as it did for Na^{23}. If a weak homogeneous magnetic field is applied between the pole faces of magnet C, there is a Zeeman splitting of the $F = 2$ level of K^{39} into five levels, each associated with a magnetic quantum number, as shown in Fig. 11.10. In the same magnetic field the $F = 1$ level splits into three magnetic levels. The introduction of the magnetic field produces a Zeeman splitting of the K^{39} energy levels but it has no effect on the intensity of the atomic beam reaching the detector D, for each atom retains a magnetic moment characteristic of the state it had when it left the region of magnet A and is simply refocused by magnet B.

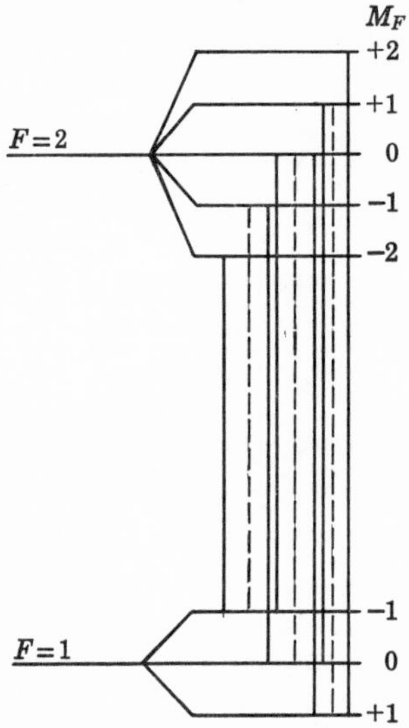

On the other hand, if a radio-frequency field is superposed on the steady field of magnet C, the region between the pole faces of the magnet is flooded with quanta of electromagnetic radiation with energies $h\nu$ characteristic of the frequency of the applied oscillating field. If the frequency of the oscillating field is adjusted such that $h\nu = \Delta W = W_1 - W_2$, where W_1 and W_2 are two of the hyperfine structure energy levels between which transitions are allowed ($\Delta F = 0, \pm 1; \Delta M_F = 0, \pm 1$), as shown in Fig. 11.10, then absorption of radiation or induced emission of radiation

Fig. 11.10. Zeeman energy levels of K^{39} as induced by magnetic moment of nucleus. The $\Delta M_F = 0$ transitions are shown by dashed lines and the $\Delta M_F = \pm 1$ transitions are indicated by the solid lines.

is possible, with a resulting change in the magnetic moment of the atom traversing the spectrometer. As a result, the force exerted upon the atom by the magnet B is different from the force exerted by the magnet A, and the atom is not refocused to the detector D, but passes through an arc with inappropriate curvature to be detected, as for example the dashed lines of Fig. 11.9.

For K^{39} the resonance effect of the characteristic frequencies produces a series of minima when the spectrum of the number of particles detected by D is plotted as a function of the frequency applied in the region between the pole faces of magnet C. The four minima shown in Fig. 11.11 for K^{39} arise only because of the removal from the beam of those

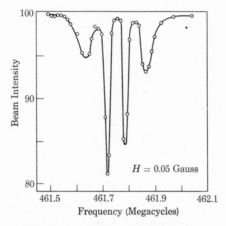

FIG. 11.11. Spectrum for K^{39} as determined in atomic beam spectrometer of Fig. 11.9 for solid-line transitions of Fig. 11.10. [P. Kusch, S. Millman, and I. Rabi *Phys. Rev.* **57**, 765 (1940)]

atoms which have undergone changes in magnetic quantum number of $\Delta M_F = \pm 1$. These are the solid-line transitions of Fig. 11.10. The existence of these transitions without the dashed-line transitions, $\Delta M_F = 0$, is peculiar to this experiment, and is caused by the nature of the oscillating magnetic field. The observed spectrum, though, corresponds to that predicted by theory, and confirms the existence of nuclear spin.

References

In addition to the references listed below, three publications which appear annually and contain many excellent reviews of research in nuclear physics are: *Progress in Nuclear Physics* (Pergamon Press, New York and London); *Progress in Nuclear Energy, Series I, Physics and Mathematics* (Pergamon Press, New York and London); and *Annual Review of Nuclear Science* (Annual Reviews, Inc., Palo Alto, California)

D. Halliday, *Introductory Nuclear Physics* (John Wiley and Sons, Inc., New York, 2nd Ed., 1955).

R. D. Evans, *The Atomic Nucleus* (McGraw-Hill Book Co., Inc., New York, 1955).

I. Kaplan, *Nuclear Physics* (Addison-Wesley Publishing Co., Inc., Reading, Mass., 1955).

A. E. S. Green, *Nuclear Physics* (McGraw-Hill Book Co., Inc., New York, 1955).

E. Segre, *Experimental Nuclear Physics*, Vols. I and II (John Wiley and Sons, Inc., New York, 1953).

L. R. B. Elton, *Introductory Nuclear Theory* (Interscience Publishers, Inc., New York, 1959).

F. Ajzenberg-Selove, *Nuclear Spectroscopy* (Academic Press, Inc., New York and London, 1960).

L. F. Curtiss, *Introduction to Neutron Physics* (D. Van Nostrand Co., Inc., Princeton, N. J., 1959).

K. B. Mather and P. Swan, *Nuclear Scattering* (Cambridge University Press, London, 1958).

L. Landau and Ya. Smorodinsky, *Nuclear Theory* (Plenum Press, Inc., New York, 1959).

H. Kopfermann, *Nuclear Moments* (Academic Press, Inc., New York, 1958).

S. Flügge, *Handbuch der Physik*, Vols. 38-45 (Springer-Verlag, Berlin, 1957-1960).

D. J. Hughes, *Neutron Cross Sections* (Pergamon Press, New York, 1957).

H. E. Duckworth, *Mass Spectroscopy* (Cambridge University Press, London, 1958).

Problems

1. Calculate the density of nuclear matter in tons per cubic millimeter. From how large a cube must water be compressed to form 1 cm^3 of matter having a density equal to that of nuclear matter?

2. In naturally occurring oxygen, O^{16} is 99.7575 percent abundant; O^{17}, 0.0392 percent; and O^{18}, 0.2033 percent. Calculate the ratio of 1 AMU in the chemical system to 1 AMU in the physical system.

3. What is the mass defect of He^4? Of C^{12}? Of Na^{23} (the only stable isotope of sodium)?

4. What is the total nuclear binding energy for each of the isotopes of Problem 3? What is the binding energy per nucleon for each of these isotopes?

5. Suppose two protons are brought together until they are separated by a distance of 3×10^{-13} cm, a distance comparable to separations of nuclear particles within the atomic nucleus. What electrostatic force is exerted on one because of the existence of the other? What repulsive potential energy must be overcome in order to hold these particles at this distance from each other?

6. The radius of the nucleus of an atom is often defined by the equation $R = R_0 A^{1/3}$, as discussed in Section 11.6. If R is considered to be the distance from the center of the nucleus to the position of the top of the potential barrier, what kinetic energy must an incident proton have in order to go over the potential barrier and hence to penetrate into the nucleus of Al^{27}? Of Zn^{64}? Of Au^{197}?

7. Make the same calculation as in Problem 6 but for an incident alpha particle.

8. The mass of Al^{27} is 26.990071 AMU, and of Al^{28} in its ground state 27.990760 AMU. Suppose a thermal neutron (0.025 ev) is absorbed by an Al^{27} nucleus.

How much gamma-ray energy must be released to bring the Al^{28} nucleus to its ground state?

9. The mass of Na^{24} in its ground state is 23.998568 AMU. Suppose a fast neutron is incident upon an Al^{27} nucleus, and an alpha particle is emitted by the compound nucleus, an (n, α) reaction. Considering only the balance of energy, what is the minimum neutron energy at which this reaction can take place? What energy must the alpha particle have to escape across the top of the potential barrier of the Na^{24} nucleus? If the incident neutron for the $Al^{27}(n,\alpha)Na^{24}$ reaction has a kinetic energy of 10 Mev, and the alpha particle escapes at an angle of 30° with respect to the direction of motion of the incident neutron, set up the equations for the conservation of energy and of momentum for the reaction, and solve for the energy of the escaping alpha particle, and of the Na^{24} atom, assuming that the Na^{24} atom that escapes is in its ground state. What is the Q value for this reaction?

10. Assuming that a neutron is scattered by a nucleus only upon actual physical contact with the edge of the nucleus, calculate the mean free path of a neutron diffusing through iron. Assume that this is multicrystalline iron such that on an average the iron atoms can be assumed to be randomly distributed.

11. Prior to the discovery of the neutron it was assumed that the atomic nucleus consists of protons and electrons. However, because of its wave properties, an excessive amount of energy is required to confine an electron within a region as small as the atomic nucleus. Calculate the kinetic energy of an electron for which the wavelength is equal to the diameter of the sodium nucleus.

12. What is the kinetic energy of a proton having a wavelength equal to the diameter of a sodium nucleus? Is this reasonable?

13. Part of the proof of the existence of the neutron consisted of showing the unreasonable nature of any other type of assumption. For example, it was found that the highly penetrating uncharged radiations resulting when polonium alpha particles were incident on boron, now known to result from an (α, n) reaction, could eject protons from an hydrogenous material with kinetic energies as high as 5 Mev. The only known process by which such protons could be so ejected by a photon would be a Compton type of interaction between the photon and the proton. Calculate the minimum photon energy required to eject a 5 Mev proton by such a process. Calculate the minimum kinetic energy of a neutron that ejects such a proton by an elastic collision.

14. Chadwick [*Proc. Roy. Soc.* **A136,** 696 (1932)] found that the uncharged radiation of Problem 13 ejected nitrogen nuclei with kinetic energies of about 1.2 Mev from a volume of nitrogen. What photon energy is required for the Compton ejection of a N^{14} nucleus with this kinetic energy? What neutron kinetic energy is needed to eject this nucleus from an elastic collision?

15. Show from the equations for the conservation of energy and the conservation of momentum that Eq. 11.5 is correct.

16. The mass of H^1 is 1.008146 AMU, of He^4, 4.003876 AMU, of Li^6, 6.017039 AMU and of Be^9, 9.015051 AMU [Everling, Konig, Mattauch, and Wapstra, *Nuclear Physics*, **15,** 34 (1960)]. Show from these masses that the $Be^9 + p - \alpha$ level of Fig. 11.4 is 2.125 Mev above the ground state energy level of Li^6.

17. From the observed alpha-particle momenta, as determined in gauss-cm from Fig. 11.5, calculate the energy of the emitted alpha particles. Make the same calculation for the Li^{6+++} ions. Why does the sum of these energies not add to the transition energies C, D, or E of Fig. 11.4? At what angle would a Li^{6+++} ion be emitted for each of the alpha particles for which the momentum is measured in Fig. 11.5?

Chapter XII

RADIOACTIVITY

12.1 Radioactive Decay of Atomic Nuclei. In Chapter 11 individual atomic nuclei were treated as having fixed properties that change only if the nucleus is acted upon by an external influence, as in a nuclear reaction. Because these nuclei, when left to themselves, retain the same physical properties over an indefinite period of time, they are called *stable nuclei*. Not all nuclei, though, are stable, for some possess the ability to transform spontaneously into another nucleus with different charge and mass, emitting in the process appropriate radiation. This process of spontaneous transformation is called *radioactive decay*. If a particular nuclear species is radioactive, the rate at which it is transformed into a nuclear species of a different type is expressed by a *decay constant* λ. This constant simply states the probability that a radioactive nucleus will decay and may be used to determine the relative number of nuclei of a given type that will undergo a radioactive transformation in unit time.

Suppose, for example, that there are N radioactive nuclei of a single species for which the decay constant is λ. The rate at which the number of radioactive nuclei is changing is then the product of the probability of decay and the number of nuclei available for decay, $dN/dt = -\lambda N$. The rate of change is negative since the number of radioactive nuclei is decreasing. This equation simply states that the larger the number of radioactive nuclei in existence, the larger the number that would be expected to decay in a given interval of time, and the number that do decay is directly proportional to the number present.

If there are initially N_0 radioactive nuclei, then after a time t, the number N_t that remain may be found by integrating the radioactive decay equation between the appropriate limits:

$$\int_{N_0}^{N_t} dN/N = \int_{0}^{t} -\lambda dt, \qquad (12.1)$$

the solution for which is $\ln N_t - \ln N_0 = -\lambda t$, or $N_t = N_0 \exp(-\lambda t)$.

The most commonly used method for expressing the rate of decay of a given species of radioactive nuclei is that of expressing the *half-life* of the species, the time $t_{1/2}$ required to reduce by one-half the number of radioactive nuclei in a given sample. After one half-life $N_t = \frac{1}{2}N_0$, exp $(-\lambda t_{1/2}) = \frac{1}{2}$; hence the decay constant is $\lambda = 0.693/t_{1/2}$. If the probability λ that a radioactive nuclear species will decay in unit time is small, that species has a long half-life, and the chance is high that an individual nucleus will remain in its original form for a long time. For nuclei with large probability of decay, the half-life is short. These equations have been verified experimentally. A typical decay curve for radioactive Na^{24} is shown in Fig. 12.1(a). This figure actually plots the rate of decay of the radioactive species. However, the rate of decay dN/dt and the number of radioactive nuclei N that are present at any time t are given by the same type of exponential equation, the two equations differing only by a multiplicative factor λ. Such exponential curves become straight lines when plotted on semilogarithmic paper in

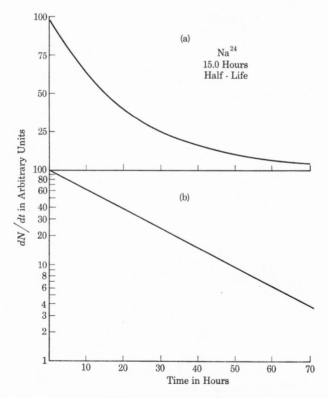

FIG. 12.1.   Rate of decay, dN/dt, of 15.0 hour half-life radioactive Na^{24} plotted (a) on linear scale and (b) on logarithmic scale.

the manner of Fig. 12.1(b). The straight line makes the determination of the half-life of a radioactive nucleus from experimental data relatively easy.

The radiations emitted by radioactive nuclei were initially named α, β, and γ radiations for, at the time of their discovery (1896 and subsequent years), it was not very clear what they were. As time progressed it was determined that the α particle is identical to a helium nucleus, the β particle is an electron, and, as indicated in Section 11.7 in connection with the (n,γ) type of nuclear reaction, a γ ray is a high energy photon. The names α, β, and γ radiation have remained, though, to identify these nuclear radiations.

Because energy must always be conserved, radioactive decay is possible only if the rest energy of the final (*daughter*) nucleus is less than the rest energy of the initial (*parent*) nucleus by an amount greater than the rest energy of the emitted alpha or beta particle. Energy in excess of this amount appears as kinetic energy, or as other radiations.

12.2 Alpha Particle Decay. Decay of a radioactive nucleus by alpha particle emission may be most simply considered as the splitting of the parent nucleus into two parts, the smaller of which is a helium nucleus. Energy conservation requires the mass of the parent atom to be greater than the sum of the masses of the daughter atom and of a helium atom. Any excess energy in the process is carried away as kinetic energy by the alpha particle and the daughter nucleus; thus the energy equation is $M_1 = M_2 + M_a + W_{K2} + W_{Ka}$, where M_1 is the rest energy of the radioactive atom, M_2 the rest energy of the product atom, M_a the rest energy of the helium atom, W_{K2} the kinetic energy of the product atom, and W_{Ka} the kinetic energy of the alpha particle after decay.

An example of an atom from which alpha particle decay is energetically possible is Th^{230}, which has a mass of 230.1043 AMU (physical). Alpha particle decay leads to Ra^{226} which has a mass of 226.0954 AMU. The difference between the masses of these two atoms is 4.0089 AMU, greater than the mass of a helium atom, 4.00386 AMU. Thus Th^{230} may decay by alpha particle emission into Ra^{226}. On the other hand, the mass of O^{16} is 16.00000 AMU and the mass of C^{12} is 12.00385 AMU. This mass difference is 3.99615 AMU, less than the mass of helium atom. Thus it is simply energetically impossible for O^{16} to decay by alpha particle emission. Except for a very few cases, all alpha particle emitting radioactive isotopes are at the extreme upper end of the periodic table, $Z \geq 83$.

For a better understanding of alpha particle decay, consider the potential energy of a system comprising a daughter nucleus and an alpha particle, described as a function of the distance of separation of the two

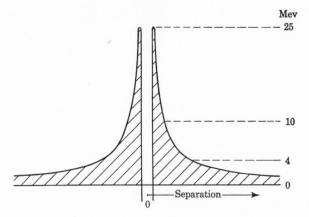

F𝖨𝖦. 12.2. Typical potential barrier between alpha particle and nucleus of an atom near the upper end of the periodic table, such as, for example, Ra^{226}.

parts of the system by Fig. 12.2. At the larger distances of separation this is the same type of potential energy curve as for the Rutherford scattering and also is the same type of nuclear potential energy curve as shown in Fig. 11.3 for a proton-nuclear interaction, except that the potential energy must be larger because of the double charge on the alpha particle. It is the same potential energy curve that would exist in a nuclear reaction if an alpha particle were used as the incident nuclear particle.

Suppose, for example, that Fig. 12.2 is a plot of the potential energy of a system consisting of an alpha particle and the nucleus of a Ra^{226} atom. As the alpha particle approaches along a radial line from considerable distance, the only force that is exerted upon it is the coulomb repulsion of the positive electrostatic charge of the radium nucleus, the same force that produced Rutherford scattering. Because of its repulsive nature, this force, and hence the potential energy of the system, increases with decreasing radial separation of the alpha particle and the nucleus. At that distance of separation at which the very short range attractive force becomes predominant, usually regarded, at least to a first approximation, to be the nuclear radius, the potential energy drops abruptly. If the incident alpha particle can pass either over the top of or through this potential barrier, it can be captured by the target nucleus thereby forming a new and different atom, in our example, Th^{230}. The alpha particle then becomes a part of the new atom. The probability of penetration through the barrier is extremely small, so the experimentally observed threshold energy for a nuclear reaction is the energy of the top of the barrier.

To escape from a nucleus an alpha particle is confronted by the same formidable potential barrier. According to classical theory, an alpha particle that escapes from the nucleus would be expected to have to go over the potential barrier and, after separation to an infinite distance from the nucleus, it would have a kinetic energy equal to, or greater than, the maximum potential energy. However, this is not the case. The top of the barrier is about 25 Mev for nuclei in the region of thorium, but this much energy is neither available for the transition nor are alpha particles experimentally observed to have this much kinetic energy following radioactive decay. The maximum kinetic energy of the alpha particles emitted by radioactive nuclei is about 10 Mev, far below the top of the barrier. The minimum experimentally observed alpha particle kinetic energy is about 4 Mev. On the other hand, the half-lives of the radioactive isotopes emitting these alpha particle radiations extend over a tremendous range, from about 10^{-7} sec to about 10^{10} years. Long before the development of quantum mechanics an empirical relationship between the alpha particle energy and the decay constant was discovered by Geiger and Nuttall, this relationship being:

$$\log_{10} \lambda = c_1 \log_{10} W_{Ka} + c_2, \tag{12.2}$$

in which c_1 and c_2 are constants common to a large number of nuclei, λ is the decay constant, and W_{Ka} is the kinetic energy of the alpha particle. Later Gamow and Condon and Gurney independently explained quantum mechanically both the existence of an alpha particle emission energy less than the energy of the top of the potential barrier and also the tremendous range of half-lives associated with a relatively small range of alpha particle energies. It is alpha particle penetration through the potential barrier as it leaves the parent nucleus that allows the alpha particle to be emitted with an energy lower than that of the top of the barrier. The probability of penetration is still extremely small, just as for nuclear reactions. The extremely small probability of penetration is seen in the long half-lives of some alpha particle emitting radioactive nuclei. In several cases the half-lives are more than a million years. The tremendous increase in half-life with decreasing energy exemplifies the fact that the probability of barrier penetration decreases very rapidly with increasing thickness of the barrier.

The Gamow-Condon-Gurney theory modified the Geiger-Nuttall relationship into the form:

$$\log_{10} \lambda = c_1 - c_2 Z W_{Ka}^{-1/2}. \tag{12.3}$$

To get a better representation of this relationship the transition energy, Q, of the decay is often used in place of the kinetic energy, W_{Ka} (see Problem 3), and the *partial decay constant* for the ground state to ground state transition is used in place of the experimentally measured *total decay constant* (see Problem 6). Also in many cases the half-life is used in place of the decay constant. The relationship between half-life and transition energy is then

$$\log_{10} t_{1/2} = c'_1 + c'_2 Z Q^{-1/2}. \tag{12.4}$$

This relationship for radioactive nuclei containing an even number of neutrons and an even number of protons, so-called even-even nuclei, is plotted in Fig. 12.3.

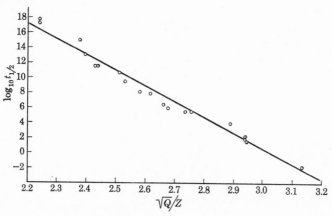

FIG. 12.3. Relationship of half-life and transition energy for alpha particle emitting even-even nuclei, showing the nature of the Gamow-Condon-Gurney theory.

Magnetic analysis of the momenta of alpha particles emitted by radioactive nuclei shows that they are emitted in discrete kinetic energy groups. The results of such a magnetic analysis of the alpha particles from Po^{210}, transformed into an energy spectrum, is shown in Fig. 12.4. It seems rather logical and plausible, in view of the quantum mechanical requirements, that a potential well have discrete energy levels, that alpha particles be emitted with discrete kinetic energies. There is of course a specific amount of energy associated with the ground state of the parent nucleus. During the decay the emitted alpha particle and recoiling daughter nucleus must

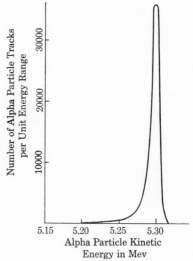

FIG. 12.4. Alpha particle spectrum of Po^{210}. [W. G. Wadey *Phys. Rev.* **74**, 1846 (1948)]

carry away just the correct amount of energy to leave the daughter nucleus in an allowed energy state and still conserve energy and momentum. The probability of alpha particle emission, and hence the half-life of the transition, thus depends on the ability of the alpha particle to penetrate through the barrier at such an energy as to leave the daughter nucleus either in its ground state or in an excited state (see Section 11.8). It is possible, in fact often the case, that there are a number of allowed energy states in the daughter nucleus. There are then a number of possible kinetic energies with which the alpha particle can be emitted and the alpha particle spectrum appears to include several discrete groups. The alpha particles are observed to fall into as many groups as there are possible transitions from the parent nucleus to the daughter nucleus.

12.3 Beta Decay. There are a very large number of radioactive isotopes that decay through emission of a beta particle. Unlike the constituent protons and neutrons of an alpha particle, electrons do not exist in the nucleus of an atom. Therefore the beta particle that is emitted must be formed during the disintegration process. Creation of radiation at the time of emission is not new, though, for the photon emitted when the atom fell from a higher to lower energy state did not exist in the atom prior to its emission. Because it is necessary to conserve electric charge, and since the nucleus consists only of neutrons and protons, the creation of an electron requires that a neutron be transformed into a proton within the nucleus. To conserve energy, the ground state energy of the parent (radioactive) nucleus must exceed the ground state energy of the daughter nucleus by at least the rest energy of the electron.

As in alpha particle decay, it was initially expected that the beta particles emitted by a single radioactive nuclear species would be emitted in discrete monoenergetic groups for which the total (rest plus kinetic) energy would be equal to the energy available for the transition. Just as for alpha particles, the kinetic energy of emitted beta particles has usually been determined by magnetic analysis, which measures momentum, not energy. If the mass of the particle is known, though, the conversion of momentum to kinetic energy is a straight-forward operation. Magnetic analysis of the beta particles emitted by radioactive nuclei did not reveal the expected monoenergetic groups, but rather a continuous distribution of kinetic energies extending from zero to a maximum equal to the expected transition energy. A typical beta particle momentum spectrum is shown in Fig. 12.5, in this case the beta particles emitted by Cu^{64}. It is thus seen that no beta particle carries away the full energy of the transition, indicated by the arrow. Also it can be shown by calorimetric measurements that there is no radiation measurable by

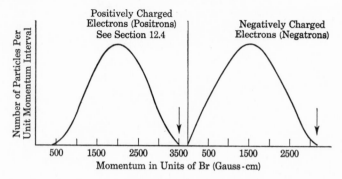

FIG. 12.5. Spectrum of beta particles from Cu^{64} as a function of beta particle momentum.

customary means which takes the remaining energy of the transition from the nucleus. In such calorimetric measurements, a radioactive source decaying by beta particle emission is surrounded by some material of sufficient thickness that all the beta particles are stopped within its confines. The beta particle kinetic energies released in the material appear as heat, giving a rise in temperature in the material. From this rise in temperature can be measured the total energy released when the beta particles lose their kinetic energies. If the total beta particle kinetic energy released during beta decay is divided by the number of beta particles emitted by the source, the average energy per beta particle is found. The average energy per beta particle determined by calorimetric means is the same as the average energy per particle determined from the spectrum using other experimental means, as for example the results of Fig. 12.5.

This evidence implies either that energy is not conserved in the beta decay process or that some of the energy released in this process escapes from the immediate surroundings of the radioactive nucleus in a manner which cannot be detected by available measuring techniques. According to the currently accepted Fermi theory of beta decay, energy is conserved and the undetected energy is carried away by a *neutrino*, a massless particle having no electrical charge. Once the neutrino has been emitted, it interacts with matter only through a reverse beta decay process for which the cross section is extremely small. Such a reverse process has been experimentally observed, thus confirming the existence of the neutrino. There are a number of processes in which one or more neutrinos are apparently emitted. Based on the experimental evidence the spin of the neutrino is $\frac{1}{2}$. A beta particle and a neutrino are apparently emitted simultaneously in the beta disintegration of a radioactive nucleus, and together carry away the total energy available for the transition. As in the case of the photoelectric effect, the nucleus recoils, but because of its extremely large mass compared to the mass of the electron and of the neutrino, its kinetic energy is only a very tiny fraction of the total energy available and is therefore usually ignored in the energy equations describing the process. However, since there are three particles (the beta particle, the neutrino, and the recoiling ion) to share momentum, the beta particle may be emitted at almost any angle relative to the direction of emission of the neutrino. It therefore may carry with it any momentum up to the maximum allowable momentum for the transition. This then explains the continuous spectrum of beta particle momenta observed in Fig. 12.5.

12.4 The Positron. Not all beta-emitting radioactive nuclei decay by the emission of a negatively charged particle. If the electrical charge of the radioactive nucleus is positive relative to its nearest stable isobar (an *isobar* is another nucleus having the same mass number A, but a different charge Z), it is sometimes observed to decay with the emission of a positively charged beta particle. The basic properties of a positively charged beta particle are identical to those of an electron except that it is positively rather than negatively charged. To distinguish between the two types of electrons, the positively charged electron is often called a *positron* and the negatively charged electron a *negatron*. Some radioactive nuclei have two stable neighboring isobars and may decay by either positron or negatron emission. Such a nucleus is Cu^{64}, which may decay either by positron emission to Ni^{64} or by negatron emission to Zn^{64}. Both beta particle spectra are continuous and are illustrated in Fig. 12.5.

The lifetime of a positron is usually quite short, since every positron that is formed sooner or later combines with a negatron and the two particles are annihilated in the interaction. The probability of annihilation is relatively small while the positron is in flight, for it does not spend enough time in the immediate vicinity of any negatron to interact with it. Thus, most annihilation occurs after the positron has come to rest. At this time the only energy available to the process is the rest mass energy of the two electrons, and the energy released is $W = 2m_0c^2 = 1.022$ Mev.

$$hv = m_0 c^2 \qquad hv = m_0 c^2$$

FIG. 12.6. In positron-negatron annihilation, two photons, each with an energy $hv = m_0c^2$, are emitted in opposite directions.

Since the electrons are at rest when they are annihilated, momentum can be conserved only if the total momentum of the system remains zero. To do this two photons, each having an energy $W = hv = m_0c^2 = 0.511$ Mev, are emitted in opposite directions from the point of annihilation, thus conserving both energy and momentum, as indicated in Fig. 12.6.

An adequate explanation of the positron and the phenomena associated with it seems to exist in Dirac's relativistic theory of the electron. This is sometimes called Dirac's "hole" theory of the positron and may be compared qualitatively at least with some of the properties of valence and conduction bands in the theory of solids. Dirac's theory is based upon the knowledge from relativistic mechanics that the total energy W of the electron is, from Eq. 3.19,

$$W = W_K + m_0c^2 = mc^2 = m_0c^2/(1 - v^2/c^2)^{1/2}. \qquad (12.5)$$

Now the momentum of a moving electron is $p = mv = Wv/c^2$, from which $v = pc^2/W$. Substitution of this value for v into Eq. 12.5 and solution for W^2 gives $W^2 = m_0^2c^4 + p^2c^2$. Thus the total energy W of an electron is

$$W = \pm(m_0^2c^4 + p^2c^2)^{1/2}. \qquad (12.6)$$

Not only does this equation state that the electron may have any positive energy equal to or greater than its rest energy, but it also states that the electron may have any energy $W \leq -m_0c^2$. Classically the existence of an electron in a negative energy state has no physical meaning. However, quantum-mechanical theory states that an external field can cause transitions from a positive energy state to a negative energy state, such that, if Dirac's theory is correct, the negative energy states must assume some physical meaning.

It is at this point that the qualitative analogy may be made between the Dirac theory of the electron and solid state theory. Suppose that an electron may exist in any energy state such that $W \leq -m_0c^2$ or $W \geq +m_0c^2$. Suppose also that there exist in the universe slightly more than enough electrons to fill all the negative energy states but not enough to fill all the positive energy states. Since a lowest energy state is always sought, all the negative energy states are customarily filled, thus making

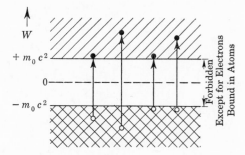

FIG. 12.7. The allowed energy levels for free electrons according to the Dirac theory, illustrating the creation of positrons by the raising of electrons from negative energy levels into positive energy levels.

them equivalent to a filled valence band, and their existence cannot be observed unless an electron is removed to produce a hole in the band, as shown in Fig. 12.7. On the other hand, only part of the states in the positive energy band are filled, with the result that it is equivalent to a conduction band, and all individual electrons in this band may be observed.

If an electron is removed from the continuous sea of electrons in negative energy states, the hole that remains appears to be a positively charged particle, a positron. Since the largest energy which this hole can have is $W = -m_0c^2$, the observed positron appears to have a rest mass just equal to that of the negatron. The positively charged hole moves because it is filled by electrons from neighboring negative energy states. In this way it carries with it kinetic energy and appears to be a particle moving through space.

Neutron-deficient nuclei, which are nuclei that contain more protons than the nearest stable isobar, are often observed to decay by positron emission. Using the Dirac theory as a basis, positron decay of a radioactive nucleus may also be considered to be a case in which a proton captures one of the negative energy state electrons, thereby being transformed into a neutron. The basic criterion for such capture is that the electron be in the immediate vicinity of the neutron-deficient nucleus. This presents no problem in the hole theory of positron decay since electrons in negative energy states exist throughout space. The positively charged hole which appears as a result of electron capture from a negative energy state gives the impression of being a positively charged particle, a positron; and positron decay thus obeys physical laws analogous to those already described for the emission of negatively charged beta particles, including the emission of a neutrino, which is needed to carry away from the nucleus the energy and momentum not taken by the positron.

12.5 Orbital Electron Capture. In undergoing radioactive decay, a neutron-deficient nucleus should conceivably be able to capture an electron from a positive energy state as well as from a negative energy state. However, electrons in positive energy states are not so generally distributed throughout space as those in negative energy states and, furthermore, they are strongly affected by the coulomb forces exerted by positively charged nuclei.

The only electrons which regularly come into the immediate vicinity of the atomic nucleus are those bound electrons having zero orbital angular momentum. These electrons can be captured by neutron-deficient nuclei, and, if they are, the process is known as *orbital electron capture*.

When an electron is captured from a positive energy state, no measurable nuclear radiation is evolved, since the neutrino is the only emitted particle. However, as a result of the electron being captured from one of the atomic shells, there is radiation emitted when another electron falls into the vacated shell. Thus the only measurable radiation emitted during orbital electron capture usually consists of one or more x-rays or Auger electrons. Because electrons in the innermost (K) shell spend a larger percentage of time in the immediate vicinity of the nucleus than do the electrons from outer shells $(L, M, N, \text{etc.})$, there is a larger probability for capture of a K-shell electron than for capture of electrons from the other shells. Because of this greater amount of capture from the K-shell the process is sometimes called K-capture.

It should be noted that radioactive decay by orbital electron capture depends on the availability of electrons to be captured. Unlike beta decay, which would occur spontaneously, even for a bare nucleus, the probability of decay, and hence the half-life for a nucleus that decays by orbital electron capture, may be changed in accordance with the amount of time that electrons spend in the vicinity of the radioactive nucleus. Experiments using different chemical compounds involving different molecular electronic structures have shown differences in the measured half-life of Be^7, for example, because of changes in the availability of orbital electrons for capture.

12.6 Energy Requirements for Beta Decay. In nuclear transitions it is customary to consider energy levels in terms of atomic rather than nuclear masses, since it is the mass of the atom that can be measured in mass spectrometers. If a negatively charged beta particle is emitted by the nucleus, the charge of the nucleus increases in magnitude by $q = +e$ and, for the atom to remain neutral, one additional electron must be added to the atomic shells. In this case, when the atom as a whole is considered, the total energy difference between the initial and final states is the sum of the electron kinetic energy and the neutrino energy.

During positron emission the minimum energy that can be carried away from the nucleus is the rest energy of the positron (m_0c^2). To maintain neutral atomic charge following the emission of a positron, an electron must also be lost by one of the outer shells of the atom. The atom as a whole therefore loses a minimum energy equal to twice the rest energy of the electron, and, since it is customary to draw energy level diagrams in terms of the whole atom, the minimum energy change required for positron emission is $2m_0c^2$.

During orbital electron capture the nucleus loses a single positive charge merely by taking an electron from one of its own atomic shells. The only energy loss by the atom as a whole during this process is the energy that is emitted as x-radiation during rearrangement of the atomic shells following nuclear capture and the energy carried away by the neutrino.

Although the frequency of occurrence is small, it is distinctly possible for capture to take place from a shell having very small binding energy. In this case almost no energy is available for release during the rearrangement of the atomic electrons. In the limit, therefore, electron capture without the release of appreciable radiant energy is possible.

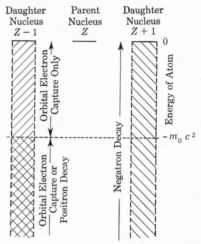

Fig. 12.8.   Illustration of the energy regions for which negatron emission, positron emission, and orbital electron capture are energetically possible.

In Fig. 12.8 the energy requirements for beta decay and for orbital electron capture are shown. It can be seen that, unless the nuclear ground state energy levels of two neighboring isobars are exactly equal, one should in due course decay to the other by beta emission or by orbital electron capture. Thus no adjacent stable isobars should exist in nature. A few such isobars do exist but, in each case, such as Sb[123] and Te[123], it is believed that one of the adjacent isobars is radioactive with a half-life of several billions of years, or more. Unless a nucleus can decay by the simultaneous emission of two beta particles — such double beta decay has not been experimentally verified — isobars differing by $\Delta Z = 2$ may exist. An example of this is the isobars Ni[64] and Zn[64]. The radioactive nucleus Cu[64], which is between these two, may thus decay either by negatron or positron emission or by orbital electron capture.

12.7 Gamma-Ray Emission.   The third type of radiation experimentally observed to be associated with radioactive decay, gamma radiation, has been analyzed to consist simply of photons emitted by the nucleus. Just as nuclear reactions may end in excited energy states (see Section 11.8), radioactive nuclei may also decay by alpha particle or beta particle emission or by orbital electron capture to excited states of the daughter nucleus, as well as to the ground state. Regardless of how it arrives there, a nucleus in an excited state usually is de-excited through the emission of electromagnetic radiation. This is analogous to the release of a quantum of electromagnetic energy at the time an atom undergoes a transition from a higher to lower energy state. However, nuclear energy levels are usually separated by larger energy differences than are atomic energy levels, with the result that photons emitted by the nucleus usually have comparable or higher energies than the x-radiation originating from transitions between the atomic shells.

The name "gamma ray" simply designates photons of nuclear origin. A gamma ray is identical in every way to an x-ray of the same energy, the only difference being the manner of origin. Since it arises from nuclear transitions between discrete energy states, gamma radiation is mono-energetic. The energy of most gamma radiation is too large for easy wavelength measurements. Even using crystals as the diffracting medium, the angle of the first order diffraction is so small that direct measurements of the wavelength of gamma radiation are extremely difficult. With such extremely small angles required for a measurable separation of the diffracted gamma-ray lines, such measurements are possible only if the detector is several meters from the diffracting crystal, and, with these dimensions, relatively intense sources are required, thereby limiting the general usage of this type of wavelength measuring apparatus.

The methods more customarily used for detecting and measuring gamma radiation are the interactions already discussed in the study of atomic structure, the Compton effect and the photoelectric effect, and one additional process, known as pair production, which is discussed in the following section. The energies of the gamma radiation are determined from analysis of the distribution of the kinetic energies of the electrons produced by these interactions.

On energy level diagrams, gamma-ray transitions are illustrated in much the same manner as photon transitions between atomic energy levels, as vertical lines drawn between an excited energy state and the ground state or a lower excited energy state.

12.8 Pair Production. The term "pair production" refers to a process during which a negatron-positron pair is created, or, according to the Dirac theory, an electron is raised from a negative energy state to a positive energy state, thereby creating what appears to be two particles. It is a complete process — the gamma ray completely disappears, and all its energy is transferred to the particles resulting from the interaction. Because two electrons must be created, the threshold energy for the process is the rest energy of the two particles $(2m_0c^2)$, but the process becomes much more probable for higher energy gamma rays. Incident gamma-ray energy in excess of the threshold energy appears as kinetic energy in the negatron-positron pair.

Energy and momentum cannot both be conserved by a single direct interaction between only the gamma ray and the negatron-positron pair. The process always occurs in matter in the immediate vicinity of an atom; in this way the atom absorbs sufficient momentum for the conservation laws to be valid. As in the photoelectric process, a small amount of kinetic energy is also absorbed by the atom but, because of its much larger mass, the kinetic energy of the atom is insignificantly small compared to the kinetic energy carried by the pair of electrons.

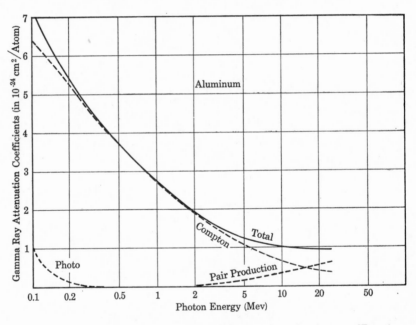

FIG. 12.9. Gamma-ray attenuation coefficients for aluminum. [Based on tabular information in G. W. Grodstein, *X-ray Attenuation Coefficients from 10 kev to 100 Mev, NBS Circular 583* (U. S. Government Printing Office, Washington, 1957)]

The relative cross sections as a function of energy for the Compton, photoelectric, and pair production processes for aluminum and lead are shown in Figs. 12.9 and 12.10.

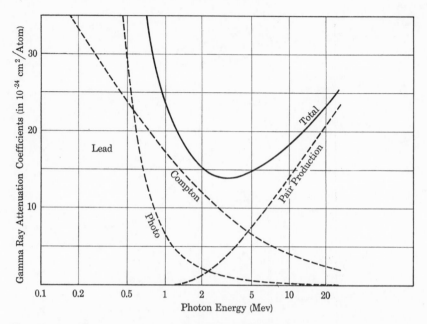

Fig. 12.10. Gamma-ray attenuation coefficients for lead. (From same source as Fig. 12.9)

12.9 Internal Conversion. The energy from a transition between nuclear energy levels in a single isotope not only can be released in the form of a gamma ray, but also may be carried away by a radiationless transition. This radiationless type of transition is known as *internal conversion*, an appropriately descriptive title because the energy from the nucleus is transferred internally within the atom to one of the atomic electrons. The internally converted electron is ejected from the atom with a kinetic energy equal to the transition energy minus the binding energy of the electron. Thus, if a *K*-shell electron is internally converted, the electron kinetic energy is less than the energy of the corresponding gamma ray by an amount equal to the *K*-shell binding energy. Electrons from outer shells, if converted, are bound to the atom by a smaller energy, and therefore are ejected with kinetic energies much closer to the photon energy of the nuclear transition. The principles of the internal conversion process are similar for nuclear transitions to the radiationless emission of energy known as the Auger effect for atomic transitions.

If the energy of the nuclear transition is transferred to one of the inner shell electrons in the internal conversion process, the shell that is vacated by that electron must subsequently be filled by an electron from one of the outer shells of the atom. Such transitions produce x-rays

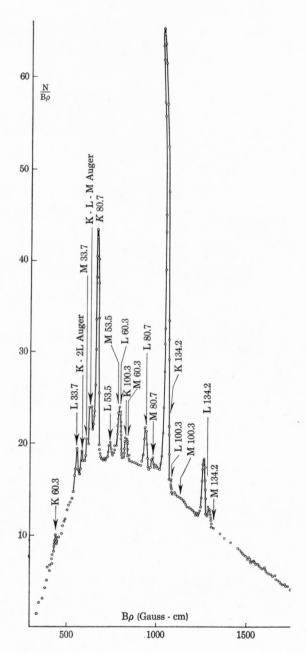

Fig. 12.11.　Electron emission spectrum of Ce[144] showing monoenergetic internal conversion electron peaks superposed on continuous beta spectrum. [F. T. Porter and C. S. Cook, *Phys. Rev.* **87**, 464 (1952)]

characteristic of the element in which the conversion takes place, so both the ejected electron and characteristic x-rays are observed during the internal conversion process. Internal conversion electrons appear as monoenergetic groups and may appear superposed on the continuous electron spectrum from beta emission, as shown in Fig. 12.11 for the decay of Ce^{144} (these transitions actually occur between levels of Pr^{144} following the beta-decay of Ce^{144}).

12.10 Energy Released by Fission. As the number of nucleons composing a stable nucleus is increased, the ratio of neutrons to protons also increases. Hence, when a uranium atom fissions, the product atoms have an excess of neutrons compared to the nearest stable isobar, with the result that they are radioactive and decay by negatron emission. Since the nucleon binding energy is much greater in nuclei near the middle of the periodic table than in nuclei at the upper end of the periodic table, a considerable amount of energy must be released during the fission process. Some of the energy released is delayed, though, and appears during the radioactive decay of the fission products. Suppose, for example, that neutron induced fission of U^{235} results in the light and heavy fragments Sr^{94} and Xe^{140}, as in the example in Section 12.10. In this reaction

$$n + U^{235} \rightarrow U^{236} \rightarrow Xe^{140} + Sr^{94} + 2n \tag{12.7}$$

Both Xe^{140} and Sr^{94} decay by successive beta-ray emission through the chains (where the time interval under each arrow is the half-life of the decaying radioactive isotope)

$$Xe^{140} \underset{16s}{\rightarrow} Cs^{140} \underset{66s}{\rightarrow} Ba^{140} \underset{12.8d}{\rightarrow} La^{140} \underset{40 \text{ hr}}{\rightarrow} Ce^{140}$$

and

$$Sr^{94} \underset{1.3m}{\rightarrow} Y^{94} \underset{20m}{\rightarrow} Zr^{94}.$$

The total energy released by fission can be determined from the difference between the masses of the initial nuclei (U^{235} and n) and the stable product nuclei (Zr^{94}, Ce^{140}, and $2n$). The mass of U^{235} is 235.116600 AMU, of Zr^{94} is 93.935800 AMU, of Ce^{140} is 139.949760 AMU, and of the neutron is 1.008982 AMU. Thus the total mass in the Zr^{94} and Ce^{140} atoms and two neutrons is 235.903524 AMU, 0.222058 AMU less than the mass of the U^{235} atom and one neutron, which, when converted into electron volts (1 AMU = 931.2 Mev) is 206.8 Mev. This is a tremendous amount of energy when compared with the energy released by the previously discussed exoergic nuclear reactions or by a radioactive nucleus. The energy release is so great that the fission process has been developed into a practical source of energy in power reactors.

Most of the energy of the fission process is released immediately and appears as kinetic energy of the nuclear fragments and the prompt neutrons. The kinetic energy of the fragments has been observed and its distribution is shown in Fig. 12.12 for the thermal neutron fission of U^{235}. Since these particles must conserve momentum, the lower energy peak is

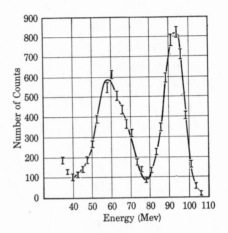

FIG. 12.12.   Distribution of the kinetic energies of the fission fragments from thermal neutron fissioning of U^{235}. [D. C. Brunton and G. C. Hanna, *Can. J. Research* **28A**, 190 (1950)]

produced by the heavy fragments and higher energy peak by the light fragments. The total kinetic energy observed in the two fragments differs quite markedly from one fission to another. From the fission of a single nucleus this sum may be as low as 120 Mev or as high as about 180 Mev. This rather wide range is attributed to variations in the number and energies of the prompt neutrons or to the primary charge distributions.

A much smaller, but still appreciable, energy is released in the decay of the radioactive isotopes that are formed as a result of the fission process. In the radioactive chains that result, as for example the mass 94 and mass 140 chains illustrated previously, there is usually an energy release of several Mev following any single fission.

Not all neutrons released following fission are prompt neutrons. Some are released as long as several seconds after the fission process. These are known as *delayed neutrons* and have been shown to follow the decay of certain of the radioactive fission products. For example, the radioactive fission product Br^{87} decays by beta emission to Kr^{87} following the decay scheme of Fig. 12.13. In about 2 percent of the disintegrations the beta decay goes to an excited level of Kr^{87} that exceeds the ground state

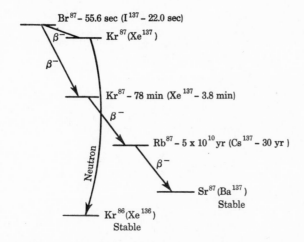

Fig. 12.13. Energy level diagram for the decay of Br^{87} showing how delayed neutron emission occurs. In parentheses are indicated corresponding levels and half-lives in the decay of I^{137} during which delayed neutrons are also emitted.

energy of Kr^{86} by an amount greater than the binding energy of one neutron. The emission of a neutron then becomes the most probable process and appears to be radiation following the decay of Br^{87}. A similar process occurs in the decay of I^{137} to Xe^{137}, except that in this case 6 percent of the decays go to the excited state, as also shown in Fig. 12.13. The total yield of delayed neutrons following fission is very small. Less than 1 percent of the total neutron yield from fission can be associated with radioactive nuclei having half-lives in excess of 0.05 sec.

The basic difference between these neutrons and the prompt neutrons is that these cannot be released until after the decay of some of the fission products, whereas the prompt neutrons are released from the pair of fission product nuclei almost immediately after the fissioning of the uranium or other fissionable nucleus.

References

Most of those references listed at the end of Chapter 11 are equally applicable to Chapter 12. In addition are the following:

R. E. Lapp and H. L. Andrews, *Nuclear Radiation Physics* (Prentice-Hall, Inc., Englewood Cliffs, N. J., 2nd Ed., 1954).

K. Siegbahn, *Beta and Gamma Ray Spectroscopy* (North-Holland Publishing Co., Amsterdam, 1955).

G. E. M. Jauncey "Early Years of Radioactivity," *Am. J. Phys.* 14, 226 (1946).

P. Morrison, "The Neutrino," *Scientific American* 194, No. 1, 58 (1956).

J. S. Allen, *The Neutrino* (Princeton University Press, Princeton, N. J., 1958).

E. Segre, *Experimental Nuclear Physics*, Vol. III (John Wiley and Sons, Inc., New York, 1959).

H. Primakoff and S. P. Rosen, "Double Beta Decay," *Reports on Progress in Physics* **22**, 121 (1959).

G. R. Keepin, "Interpretation of Delayed Neutron Phenomena," *Journal of Nuclear Energy* **7**, 13 (1958).

C. S. Cook and G. E. Owen, "The Allowed Beta Spectrum," *Am. J. Phys.* **7**, 453 (1950).

Problems

1. The half-life of Na^{24} is 15.0 hours. What is the decay constant for this source? Suppose a counter which subtends a solid angle 0.1 steradian with respect to the Na^{24} source counts one disintegration per second. How many radioactive nuclei are in the source?

2. The half-life of Al^{28} is 2.3 minutes, that of Mn^{56} is 2.56 hours, and that of Na^{24} is given in Problem 1. Suppose a radioactive source initially contains equal quantities of Na^{24}, Al^{28}, and Mn^{56}. What is the ratio of the rates of decay of these three isotopes at that time? What is the ratio of the rates of decay and the relative abundance of the three radioactive isotopes after 1 minute? 10 minutes? 1 hour? 5 hours? 25 hours?

3. The energy between the ground state of a radon atom (Rn^{222}) and a radium A atom (Po^{218}), to which it decays by alpha particle emission, is 5.59 Mev. Suppose a free radon atom in gaseous form decays by alpha particle emission; what are the kinetic energies and momenta of the emitted alpha particle and of the recoil daughter atom? Note that both energy and momentum must be conserved in the process.

4. The radioactive isotope Ra^{224} emits alpha particles with kinetic energies of 5.45 Mev and 5.68 Mev. If these alpha particles are to be analyzed magnetically, what magnetic flux density must be applied to bend them through a radius of curvature of 1 meter?

5. Because the neutron mass is greater than the proton mass, it will, if it is not captured by a nucleus, undergo radioactive decay by beta emission. Calculate the maximum energy of the beta particle emitted in the process.

6. The term "partial half-life" has been developed to express the half-life of a single transition when there is more than one level in the daughter nucleus to which the parent nucleus can decay. For example, in the decay of Zn^{65} (half-life 245 days), 56 percent of the transitions go to the ground state of Cu^{65} and 44 percent to a level 1.11 Mev above the ground state. The experimentally measured decay constant λ, being the probability of decay, is the sum of the decay constants of the individual transitions. The measured transition intensities are proportional to the probability that the transition occurs. Calculate the partial half-lives of each of the Zn^{65} beta transitions.

7. DuMond has measured gamma-ray wavelengths by means of the Bragg reflections from the (310) planes of quartz, $d = 1177.637$ x.u. At what angle would the maximum of the first order diffraction pattern occur for a 50 kev photon? For a 100 kev photon? For the annihilation radiation?

8. If the detector in Problem 7 is 2 meters from the crystal, how far apart are the first order maxima for the 50 kev, the 100 kev, and the annihilation photons?

9. A negative electron is emitted at right angles to a neutrino from radioactive Cu^{64}. Using only the laws for the conservation of energy and momentum, calculate the kinetic energy of the electron.

10. If double beta decay were possible, would Ni^{64} or would Zn^{64} be radioactive? What would be the transition energy in this case? Would particle emission then be possible? Attempts have been made to look for double beta decay in Sn^{124}. To what would Sn^{124} decay and what would be the expected beta particle energies?

11. A gamma ray with an energy $h\nu = 6m_0c^2$ produces a positron-negatron pair. The positron and negatron leave the interaction at an angle of 60° with respect to each other and each at 30° with respect to the extension of the gamma-ray path beyond the point of the interaction. What is the kinetic energy and the momentum of each electron? How much momentum must be carried away by an atom in the vicinity of the interaction, and in which direction must this atom move? What fraction of the kinetic energy will be taken by the recoiling atom if the atom is aluminum? If the atom is beryllium? If the atom is gold?

12. Show that energy and momentum cannot be conserved in an interaction in which a positron-negatron pair are produced directly from the destruction of a gamma ray.

13. The most intense photon transition in Pr^{144} following the decay of Ce^{144} is a 0.134 Mev gamma ray (see Fig. 12.11). At what energies does one expect to find K-, L-, and M-shell internal conversion electrons? At what energies would one expect to find photoelectrons produced by this gamma ray in lead?

14. Calculate the energy release when an excited U^{236} nucleus, formed from neutron capture by U^{235}, fissions into nuclei of mass number 80 and 154 and two neutrons. What clue does this calculated energy release give as to the reason that nuclear fission of U^{236} is more apt to produce the isotopes of mass 140 and 94, plus 2 neutrons, used as an example in the text in Section 12.10, than isotopes of mass 80 and 154, plus two neutrons? The mass excess of Se^{80} is -0.058020 AMU, of Sm^{154} is -0.029480 AMU, and of U^{235} is 0.117496 AMU.

15. Calculate the energy release when the excited U^{236} nucleus of Problem 14 fissions into two nuclei each with a mass number 117, plus two neutrons. Is this indicative that the double hump of the fission yield curve is a function of energy release? The mass excess of Sn^{117} is -0.059800 AMU.

16. A set of nuclear reactions that appear to possess future practical significance are the thermonuclear, or fusion, processes. One such process would release energy through the series of two nuclear reactions $H^2 + H^2 \rightarrow H^3 + H^1$ and $H^2 + H^3 \rightarrow He^4 + n$. Calculate the energy in Mev released by this series of reactions.

17. The efficiency of the fission and fusion processes is determined by the ratio of the energy released to the rest energy of the initial material. In the fusion process described in Problem 16, the initial material is three atoms of deuterium. Compare the efficiency of this process with the efficiency of the fissioning of U^{235} in the manner described by Eq. 12.7.

Chapter XIII

NUCLEAR STRUCTURE

13.1 Interpretation of Nuclear Data. In the last two chapters several experimentally observable nuclear phenomena have been discussed. Such an accumulation of experimental information is of importance primarily because of the assistance it gives in formulating a description of the structure of the nucleus. In an analogous manner the unique description of the structure of the electron shells of the atoms has been based upon observations of optical spectra, x-ray spectra, spins and magnetic moments, and many other experimentally determined phenomena. As yet, no single nuclear model has been formulated by means of which all experimental observations can be explained. Although many nuclear models have been proposed, most of them can be categorized into two general groupings, the strong interaction models, of which the liquid drop model serves as the primary example in this chapter, and the independent particle models, of which the shell model serves here as the primary example. According to the *strong interaction models* the individual nucleons are closely coupled because of their strong, short-range forces, whereas in the *independent particle models* the nucleons are considered to move nearly independently in a common nuclear potential well. Apparently neither model is entirely correct. The *unified model*, which attempts to combine some of the features of both the other models, is also discussed, but it, too, is not able to present a wholly consistent picture. Several other models incorporating variations and refinements of the concepts presented here have also been proposed.

13.2 The Liquid Drop Model. Many experimental observations can be explained by assuming that individual nucleons are tightly packed into the nucleus in much the same manner as molecules are packed into a liquid drop. Because of the strong, short-range nuclear forces, individual nucleons interact only with their nearest neighbors, just as individual molecules interact only with their nearest neighbors in a solid or in a liquid. Individual nucleons are then limited in their motion to a mean free path that is small compared to the nuclear diameter. Because of this close packing and strong interaction with individual neighbors, energy added at any part of the drop is quickly distributed statistically among all the constituent particles. The effective nuclear temperature is then uniform throughout the nuclear volume, just as the temperature of a liquid drop is uniform throughout its volume.

From such analogies as can be made between a liquid drop and the nucleus, von Weizsacker derived a theoretical formula for the nuclear binding energies, in which, however, the constants had to be determined empirically. The primary contributor to this formula is a volume energy produced by the effects of the bonds between individual neighboring nucleons. Because the volume of the nuclear droplet is $4\pi R^3/3 = 4\pi R_0^3 A/3$, in which R_0 is the radius of an individual nucleon, this energy is directly proportional to the number of nucleons, A, in the nucleus (see Section 11.6). The volume energy is then $-c_1 A$, where c_1 is a constant. The negative sign is used because the force that produces this energy is attractive. Theoretically in a liquid of infinite extent this would be the only energy; but for a drop of finite extent at least one bond is missing from each of the surface atoms, or nucleons. These missing surface bonds produce what is customarily called the surface energy, which is proportional to the surface area of the drop, $4\pi R^2 = 4\pi R_0^2 A^{2/3} = c_2 A^{2/3}$. The nature of the surface energy is such as to reduce the absolute magnitude of the total energy and hence must be positive.

Since all nuclei except hydrogen contain several protons, a long-range coulomb repulsive force is exerted on each individual proton by all the other protons in the nucleus. The electrostatic energy of a charge q that is distributed uniformly throughout a sphere of radius R is $3q^2/5R$. In a nucleus the charge is Ze, and the coulomb energy is $3Z^2 e^2/5R_0 A^{1/3} = c_3 Z^2/A^{1/3}$. Because the force is repulsive, the energy is positive and again reduces the absolute magnitude of the volume energy.

Besides these terms there are in the von Weizsacker formula two terms not arising from liquid drop considerations. These are discussed in Section 13.8, following some additional discussion of the liquid drop model of the nucleus.

13.3 Liquid Drop Model Explanation of Nuclear Fission. One success of the liquid drop model has been an explanation of the general characteristics of the fissioning of elements at the upper end of the periodic table. This explanation has been based on the observation that addition of energy to a liquid drop can set the drop into vibration. During elongation the volume of the drop remains approximately constant, but the total surface area increases; thus the volume energy does not change appreciably, but the surface energy increases. Also during elongation the mean distance of separation between nucleons increases, so that the electrostatic energy produced by the charge distribution decreases. For small deformation the surface energy increase is greater than the electrostatic energy decrease; hence there is an increase in the total potential energy of the system, as seen in Fig. 13.1. There is, though, a limit to the increase in the surface energy for, with increased elongation, the drop forms a dumbbell shape, after which further separation of the two halves does not greatly increase the surface area. However, as the two parts of the dumbbell expand, the electrostatic energy continues to decrease. This results in a net reduction in the potential energy of the system as the distance of separation increases. With continued expansion the connecting arm between the two halves of the dumbbell eventually breaks, producing two fission product nuclei that can no longer be held together by either the volume energy or the surface energy: the distance of separation has become greater than the range of the short-range nuclear forces. Still effective, though, is the electrostatic

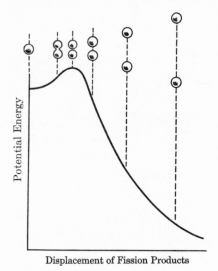

Displacement of Fission Products

FIG. 13.1. The potential energy for a nuclear system undergoing fission, plotted as a function of the distance of separation between the centers of masses of the two fission components. At the top of the figure is an illustration of the mechanical characteristics of the fissioning nucleus according to the liquid drop model.

repulsive force. Potential energy continues to be transformed into kinetic energy as the distance of separation between the two fission products increases, as is illustrated in Fig. 13.1.

The potential barrier that prevents the spontaneous fissioning of a nucleus, then, is produced by the surface energy term. For the nuclei at the upper end of the periodic table this barrier is about 5 Mev, sometimes a little more or less, depending on the exact details of the nuclear structure. In several cases this barrier is less than the energy that is released when a thermal neutron is captured. Following neutron capture it is not necessary that the excess energy be radiated, although an (n,γ) type reaction is never completely forbidden. If the excess energy sets the nucleus into vibration, the formation of two fission products is possible. A number of examples of this process have been found. Immediately after the addition of a thermal neutron to U^{235} the U^{236} nucleus has an excess energy, because of neutron binding, of 6.4 Mev. The fission barrier for U^{236} is only 5.25 Mev, with the result that fission is very probable. A similar situation occurs with the addition of a neutron to Pu^{239}, or to U^{233}. However, the addition of a thermal neutron to U^{238} does not leave the resultant nucleus with enough energy to pass over the fission potential barrier, for the binding energy of the neutron is only 5.4 Mev, and the energy required for fission is 5.9 Mev.

Because of the extremely rapid reduction in energy on the right side of the potential barrier of Fig. 13.1, the barrier width is sufficiently small that barrier penetration is possible. The situation may be likened to that of field emission (see Section 10.3). Barrier penetration in the form of spontaneous fission does occur and has been found experimentally, for example, in U^{238}, which at its ground state energy level has a decay constant of about 2.7×10^{-24} sec^{-1}. This decay constant, though, is extremely small compared to the decay constant for fission that occurs above the top of the potential barrier, such as the fissioning of U^{235} by neutron capture. Energy states above the fission barrier have been found to decay with a speed characterized by a decay constant $\lambda \approx 10^{14}$ sec^{-1}. This change in λ through approximately 38 orders of magnitude is relatively abrupt because the top of the barrier is not sharply peaked but is reasonably broad. The result is that the probability of barrier penetration quickly changes as a function of energy from a high value to a very small, though measurable, value near the top of the barrier, which acts as a rather well-defined threshold for the fission process. The large decay constant for nuclei in energy states above the top of the potential barrier also indicates that the vibrational states necessary for fission are formed very quickly.

The height of the fission potential barrier can be found experimentally relatively easily by the photofission process. For example, the photofission threshold energy for U^{235} (not to be confused with the fission potential barrier of U^{236}, which is produced through the capture of a thermal neutron by U^{235}) is 5.75 Mev, for U^{238} is 5.85 Mev, and for Pu^{239} is 5.5 Mev.

13.4 Charge Distribution in the Nucleus. Since electrons cannot interact with nuclei through nuclear type forces, the strongest forces between nucleons and electrons are the electromagnetic forces of the electric charges. If an electron can be accelerated to a sufficiently large energy so that its wavelength (and hence size) becomes much smaller than the size of the nucleus, it can be used as a probe to determine the distribution of charge within the nucleus. This has been done at Stanford University, using an electron linear accelerator as the source of high energy electrons.

The results of the exploration of the distribution of nuclear charge has led to the conclusions that, except for the very light elements, the charge density is very nearly constant throughout the interior of any single

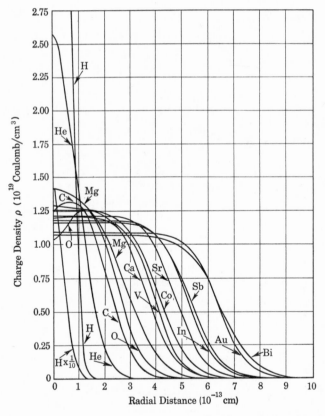

FIG. 13.2. Nuclear charge distribution as a function of distance from the center of the nucleus, as determined by electron-scattering experiments. [From R. Hofstadter, "Nuclear and Nucleon Scattering of Electrons," *Annual Review of Nuclear Science* Vol. 7, pp 231-316 (Annual Reviews, Inc., Palo Alto, Calif., 1957)]

nucleus and this density does not change very much for nuclei in different parts of the periodic table. This is illustrated for a number of elements in Fig. 13.2. At the surface of a nucleus the charge density drops
from its maximum to zero in a distance of about 4×10^{-13} cm. The
general uniformity of charge distribution throughout the nucleus is
again a feature characteristic of a liquid drop. In some cases a slight
tendency for protons to have a greater density near the periphery of the
nucleus, expected because of the coulomb repulsion between protons, has
been found, but there is certainly no generally prevalent trend in this
direction.

13.5 Characteristics of Nuclear Reactions. Many of the features
of nuclear reactions can be explained by a model related to the liquid

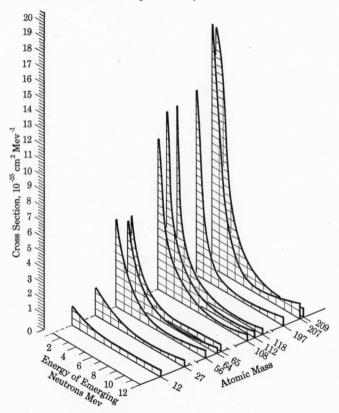

FIG. 13.3. Neutron emission cross section as a function of energy of emitted
neutrons for elements bombarded by 14 Mev neutrons. [From Cranberg *et al.*,
"Techniques for Measuring Elastic and Non-Elastic Neutron Cross Sections,"
Progress in Nuclear Energy (*Physics and Mathematics*), Vol. 1, pp 107–160
(Pergamon Press, Inc., New York, 1956)]

drop model and called the *statistical model.* The basic assumption for this model of a nuclear reaction is that, if an incident nuclear particle enters a nucleus, it rapidly shares its incoming energy with the other constituent nucleons. The decay of the compound nucleus is then a separate process, independent of the method of formation, resulting from the statistical concentration of sufficient energy and momentum for a single nucleon to escape.

In a statistical process of this type it is expected that most of the evaporating nuclei would barely have enough kinetic energy to escape. The anticipated rapidly decreasing probability of emission as a function of energy has been found experimentally, as shown in Fig. 13.3, from a series of experiments in which observations have been made of the

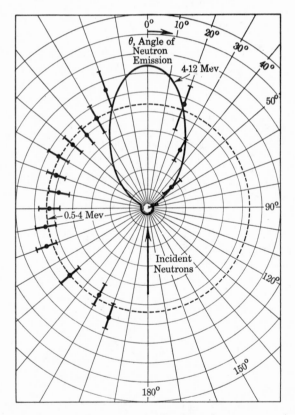

FIG. 13.4. Polar graphs of angular distribution of neutrons emitted from a bismuth target that is being bombarded by monoenergetic neutrons (14 Mev kinetic energy) from the direction indicated by the arrow. The dashed line is the distribution for neutrons with kinetic energies from 0.5 Mev to 4.0 Mev and the solid line for neutrons with kinetic energies from 4 Mev to 12 Mev. [Based on L. Rosen and L. Stewart, *Phys. Rev.* **99**, 1052 (1955)]

neutrons emitted by compound nuclei that have been formed as a result of bombardment by neutrons with incident kinetic energies of 14 Mev. A very rapid decrease in neutron intensity with increasing energy is apparent among the low energy emergent neutrons. However, there are still more high energy neutrons emitted than would be expected from a purely statistical process. Studies of emission direction show that the slow neutrons are emitted isotropically, as expected from the statistical model, but that the faster neutrons are emitted primarily in a forward direction, that is in the direction in which the incident neutron was traveling. For example, Fig. 13.4 shows the relative rate of neutron emission from a bismuth target as a function of angle for two different energy intervals. There is a nearly isotropic emission of neutrons below 4 Mev but a predominantly forward emission of neutrons above 4 Mev. These results lead to the conclusion that neither the liquid drop nuclear model nor a single particle nuclear model can by itself explain the nuclear reaction process. Apparently the energy of the incident nucleon is sometimes absorbed by the target nucleus in such a way that it gets distributed among the constituent nucleons much as would be expected in the liquid drop. On the other hand, some incident nuclei apparently react with individual particles in the target nucleus and either are themselves scattered or transfer their energy to an individual target nucleon followed by its subsequent emission from the nucleus.

The discussion above has been limited to neutrons, since the shape of their potential wells is controlled only by the nuclear forces. Proton emission encounters a coulombic superstructure on the potential well which requires that the proton have much higher energies than a neutron inside the nucleus before it can escape. The result is that proton emission obeys more closely the individual particle expectations.

13.6 Nonclassical Terms of the von Weizsacker Formula.
There are finally two additional terms which contribute to the semi-theoretical, semiempirical von Weizsacker formulation of the binding energy of the nucleus. These two terms, known as the *symmetry term* and the *pairing term*, have no analogy in the description of the energy of a liquid drop, or in any other part of classical physics.

Derived from nuclear force considerations, the symmetry term is based on the premise that nuclei are most stable if they have equal numbers of protons and neutrons. This assumption is verified experimentally in the lower end of the periodic table. In the upper end of the periodic table, though, the large coulombic repulsive forces between the protons shift stability in favor of an excess of neutrons. The loss of binding energy, because of this departure from symmetry, is reflected in the von Weizsacker formula through a term dependent on the neutron excess, $A - 2Z$. This term $c_4(A - 2Z)^2/A$ again reduces the energy of the system, and is hence positive.

A final contributor to the von Weizsacker binding energy formula, the pairing term, states that even numbers of like nucleons are more tightly bound together than odd numbers. This applies to both protons and neutrons. This means that nuclei with an even number of neutrons and an even number of protons (so-called *even-even* nuclei) are much more stable than *odd-odd* nuclei, and that nuclei with odd numbers of nucleons lie somewhere between these two extremes. This is seen in the periodic table of elements by the almost complete absence of stable odd-odd nuclei. The only stable odd-odd nuclei are H^2, Li^6, B^{10}, and N^{14}, all of which have equal numbers of neutrons and protons, hence a strong symmetry term. The pairing energy term is $c_5 A^{-\epsilon} \delta$, in which ϵ is a constant, currently determined empirically to be about $\frac{3}{4}$, and δ is $+1$ for odd-odd nuclei, 0 for odd-even nuclei, and -1 for even-even nuclei. This term is again positive.

The complete von Weizsacker formula for the binding energy of the nucleus is:

$$W_B = -c_1 A + c_2 A^{2/3} + c_3 Z^2/A^{1/3} + c_4(A - 2Z)^2/A + c_5 A^{-\epsilon}\delta. \quad (13.1)$$

The best currently available empirically determined values for the constants in this equation are: $c_1 = 15.75$ Mev, $c_2 = 17.8$ Mev, $c_3 = 0.710$ Mev, $c_4 = 23.7$ Mev, and $c_5 = 34$ Mev.

That the binding energy of the last neutron in even-even nuclei is much greater then in odd-even nuclei has made its appearance in the fission process. A thermal neutron, for example, can initiate fission when added to U^{235} or Pu^{239} to form even-even nuclei, but not when added to U^{238} to form an odd-even nucleus. Additional energy of about 1 Mev is required for the neutron to produce fission in the product nucleus after a reaction with U^{238}.

The effects of the last two terms of the von Weizsacker formula can also be seen in a plot of the atomic mass (total energy) of any set of adjacent isobars. The symmetry term indicates that within any single set of isobars only one should have minimum energy, and hence be stable. This condition is illustrated in a plot of the atomic mass as a function of nuclear charge for $A = 61$, shown in Fig. 13.5(a). Note that these are all odd-even nuclei, with either odd Z or odd N. Under these circumstances $\delta = 0$ in the pairing term of the von Weizsacker formula and the only nonclassical effect is contributed by the symmetry term. There is a single lowest mass isobar on a curve that is parabolic in shape. Because the spacing of isobars on the parabolic curve is quantized, the isobar of lowest mass seldom is exactly at the lowest point on the parabolic curve. Lower Z nuclei decay by negatron emission to the single

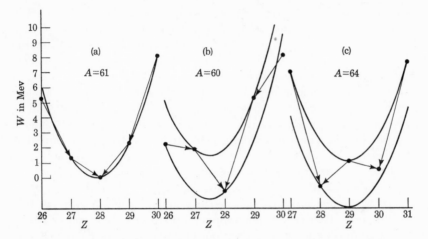

FIG. 13.5. Parabolic energy surfaces for three sets of adjacent isobars at (a) $A = 61$; (b) $A = 60$; and (c) $A = 64$. Solid circles are experimentally observed positions of individual isotopes and arrows indicate direction of radioactive transitions.

stable nucleus, while those of higher Z decay by either positron emission or orbital electron capture.

Nuclei with even A must be either odd-odd or even-even. In either case the pairing term of the von Weizsacker formula is not zero. For odd-odd nuclei $\delta = +1$ and energy is increased, but for even-even nuclei $\delta = -1$ and energy is decreased. Thus, for each even A series of isobars there are two parabolic curves, one above the other. Most groups of even A isobars have two stable nuclei on or near the lower, even-even nucleus, parabola, as for $A = 64$ in Fig. 13.5(c), but occasionally there is only one, as for $A = 60$ in Fig. 13.5(b), or three, as for $A = 124$.

13.7 The Nuclear Shell Model. Just as the symmetry and pairing terms of the von Weizsacker formula cannot be explained in terms of a classical liquid drop, there are also numerous other nuclear characteristics that cannot be explained simply by analogy with a liquid drop. There are, for example, many experimentally observable properties which indicate that the atomic nucleus possesses an individual particle structure resembling the structure of the electron shells of the atom.

One type of evidence of the individual particle structure is the large binding energy of nucleons in selected nuclei, such as in the helium nucleus (the alpha particle). This extreme stability is comparable to the high ionization potential of atoms having closed electron shells, such as helium, neon, argon, etc., and certainly makes it appear that the helium nucleus forms some sort of closed shell.

Further study indicates that the nuclear shells form independently for protons and neutrons. The helium nucleus has a doubly closed shell at $Z = N = 2$, each of which can be compared to the closed $1s$ electron shell in the helium atom. Using a form of the vector model, but now applying it to the individual particles of the nucleus, one finds that each of these closed shells can be considered to consist of two like nuclear particles with oppositely directed spins, forming a resultant spin 0. Other very stable nuclear systems occur at Z (and N) = 8, 20, 50, and 82, and for $N = 126$, but these closed shells are not nearly so pronounced as the shells at $Z = N = 2$.

Theoretical descriptions of nuclear shell structure now consider the nucleons outside a closed shell as essentially independent particles interacting with a spherically symmetric potential well, formed by the nuclear core. To a very rough approximation the nuclear core might be compared to the core of electrons that form closed shells in atomic structure, such as the $2p$ electron core that influences the actions of the $3s$ valence electron in the sodium atom. However, the characteristics of the potential well formed by the nuclear core must be determined by the nature of the forces holding the nuclear particles together. Even though a detailed description of these forces is still lacking, it is known that they are extremely strong and extremely short range, and apparently do not form a central force field in the nucleus, since individual nucleons are influenced only by nearest neighbors, as discussed in connection with the liquid drop model.

Experimental evidence indicates that the nuclear potential well has steep sides and finite depth. It appears to be spherically symmetric around the center of the nucleus and can, at least to a first approximation, be represented by the equation:

$$V(r) = V_0\{1 + \exp\left[(r - R)/a\right]\}^{-1}, \tag{13.2}$$

in which $V_0 \approx -50$ Mev is the potential energy at the center of the nucleus, $R = 1.33 \ A^{1/3} \times 10^{-13}$ cm is the radius of the nucleus, and $a \approx 0.5 \times 10^{-13}$ cm. Because of the spherical symmetry of the nuclear potential well, the Schroedinger equation must be the same as for the hydrogen atom, Eq. 7.1a in Appendix 7.1, except for a different form of the potential function, $V(r)$. The solution of the wave equation is then*
$\psi(r, \theta, \phi) = \Re(r)\Theta(\theta)\Phi(\phi)$ as for the hydrogen atom. The functions Θ and Φ are the same as for the hydrogen atom since they do not depend on the potential energy V. The function $\Re$ is the same as the equivalent function for the hydrogen atom, Eq. 7.14 in Appendix 7.1, except for the substitution of the correct potential energy term for the term $Ze^2/\epsilon r$.

---

*In atomic physics the radial function of the Schroedinger equation was designated by R. However, the letter R is here used to represent the nuclear radius so the letter $\Re$ has been used for the radial function of the Schroedinger equation.

The Schroedinger equation is not easily solved using the potential energy of Eq. 13.2. However, this potential energy equation is intermediate between the potential energy for a three-dimensional harmonic oscillator, $V = \frac{1}{2}kr^2$, and a spherically symmetric rectangular well for which $V = -V_0$ if $r < R$, and $V = 0$ if $r > R$. For both of these potential wells the Schroedinger equation can be solved without too much difficulty. In the case of the harmonic oscillator potential well the solution is of the same general form but differing in detail from the solutions for the hydrogen atom (Appendix 7.1) and for the one-dimensional harmonic oscillator (Section 6.6). It is $\Re = Cr^l F(r) \exp\left(-\frac{1}{2}r^2\right)$, in which $F(r) = \sum_{\kappa=0}^{\infty} a_\kappa r^{2\kappa}$ and κ is an integer. The solution to the Schroedinger equation for the three-dimensional harmonic oscillator gives energy levels, $W = (N + \frac{3}{2})h\nu$, in which N is any integer including 0. Even though the lowest energy state of a three-dimensional harmonic oscillator is $\frac{3}{2}h\nu$, this term is generally omitted in descriptions of nuclear shell

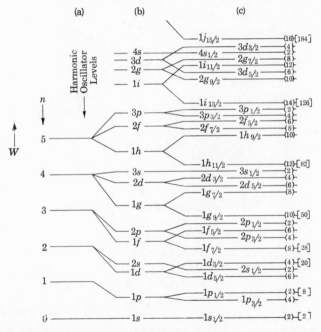

FIG. 13.6. Schematic diagram of the energy levels of (a) a three-dimensional isotropic harmonic oscillator modified (b) to have much steeper, more rectangular walls on its potential well, and further modified to include (c) strong spin-orbit coupling of the individual nucleons. Positions of energy levels are only relative in each part of the diagram and are not to scale. [Based on Figs. IV.1 and IV.3 of M. G. Mayer and J. H. D. Jensen, *Elementary Theory of Nuclear Shell Structure* (John Wiley and Sons, Inc., New York, 1955)]

structure, since nuclear energy levels are usually referenced to some arbitrarily predetermined level. The energy levels of the three-dimensional harmonic oscillator are shown on the left hand side of Fig. 13.6.

The solution of the Schroedinger equation for the rectangular potential well gives a larger number of possible energy levels than are found for the three-dimensional harmonic oscillator. However, the degeneracy of each state is generally smaller for the rectangular well than for the harmonic oscillator well. The smaller degeneracy results from a limitation by the Pauli Exclusion Principle. This principle limits the number of nucleons in each state of the rectangular well more than the number in each state of the harmonic oscillator well. If the shape of the real nuclear potential well is intermediate between these two idealized wells, energy levels for the real well should exist intermediate between the energy levels of the two examples. In the shell model it is assumed that, as the harmonic oscillator potential well is modified to approach more closely a rectangular well, the energy levels both split and move to approach the energy levels of a rectangular well, as indicated in the middle portion of Fig. 13.6. The number and letter associated with each level give the appropriate nl state. The quantum number l appears in the radial portion of the Schroedinger equation and is the orbital angular momentum quantum number for the nuclear particle, just as it was for the electron in the mathematical description of the hydrogen atom. The quantum number n does not appear in the radial portion of the Schroedinger equation, Eq. 7.14; hence it may and does have a different significance in nuclear structure than it does in atomic structure. In the nuclear shell model the quantum number n simply designates the nth time that an energy level having an orbital quantum number l appears in the sequence of energy levels.

Since each nucleon has a spin, $s = \frac{1}{2}$, each of the levels, with the exception of the $l = 0$ levels, further splits into two levels with total quantum numbers $j = l + \frac{1}{2}$ and $j = l - \frac{1}{2}$, as indicated in the right-hand part of Fig. 13.6. Furthermore, there are $2j + 1$ possible magnetic quantum numbers m_j associated with each level. Based on these considerations, the number of nucleons expected to occupy each subshell is indicated in the round brackets, and the cumulative total of nucleons from all lower levels in the square brackets. With this method of splitting energy levels, closed shells at N (and Z) = 2, 8, 20, 28, 50, 82, 126, and 184 are expected, in agreement with experimental observations. Note that this scheme of shell structure requires a strong spin-orbit coupling for individual nucleons, resulting in a j-j coupling rather than the l-s coupling that is prevalent in most atomic energy level schemes.

Experimental measurements of the spins of odd A nuclei show excellent consistency with this scheme of shell structure. The ground states of all even-even nuclei have spin zero, because of the pairing of like nuclear particles. The measured spin (I) of odd A nuclei is then determined by the quantum number j of the added particle, or by the vector addition of the j's for a group of particles beyond a closed shell or subshell. Note that what is measured as nuclear spin (I) is really the result of the combination of individual particle interactions, and that the nuclear spin quantum number corresponds to the total quantum number (J) of the atom.

Based on the information available it must be concluded that there is in the nucleus a well-defined shell structure which must be worked into any scheme for explaining nuclear phenomena. In addition to the evidence already presented there are also other experimentally observable nuclear characteristics that indicate this. These include: (1) the larger relative abundance of isotopes that have a closed shell; (2) higher energy first excited states near closed shells; and (3) smaller neutron capture cross sections for closed shell nuclei.

13.8 Intermediate Models. It is evident that some of the observable nuclear properties can be explained by each of the quite different liquid drop and shell models. Therefore, to give a complete nuclear theory, one hopes that some intermediate model may be developed and that it may incorporate features from both these extreme models. The unified model adds to the shell model in that it provides for a collective motion of the nucleus, brought about by the distortion of the nuclear core into a spheroidal shape from the influence of the nucleons in the unfilled subshell. Based upon the possible motions of a spheroidally shaped nucleus, the unified model provides for both vibrational and rotational nuclear energy states, thereby picking up some of the features of the liquid drop model as well as those of the shell model. Selected nuclear properties can now be compared to similar characteristics already observed in molecules and in solids. The rotational and vibrational states are apparently similar to molecules, but, instead of two or more individual atoms moving as a group that are tied together by the electrostatic forces of the valence electrons, portions of a single nucleus now move under the influence of the strong force binding between nucleons.

The existence of rotational states in nuclei has been experimentally demonstrated, especially in the regions $155 < A < 185$ and $A > 225$. Rotational energy levels have been identified primarily by their characteristic spin sequence and energy ratios, just as for the molecular rotational levels. This then leads to the same type of energy relationship between rotational levels as for molecules; a rotational level belonging to a band with a ground state spin I_0 has an energy, relative to the ground state given by:

$$W_I = (h^2/2\mathfrak{J})[I(I + 1) - I_0(I_0 + 1)], \tag{13.3}$$

where $\mathfrak{J}$ is the moment of inertia of the system. For the lowest rotational bands in even-even nuclei, $I_0 = 0$, and the spin sequence is 0, 2, 4, etc., with odd values of I being forbidden. The energies above the ground state energy for the different rotational states of these nuclei are then expected to be: $W_4/W_2 = 10/3$, $W_6/W_2 = 7$, and $W_8/W_2 = 12$ where the subscript gives the spin I of the level. The experimental ratios for the energies of the higher excited states relative to the first excited state (spin $I = 2$) for a number of nuclei in the region above $A = 150$ are shown in Fig. 13.7. In the region relatively far from closed shells the

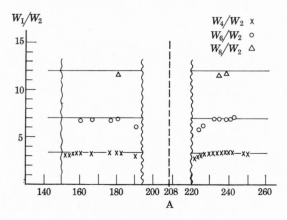

FIG. 13.7. Energy ratios of rotational excited states in even-even nuclei. [K. Alder *et al.*, *Rev. Mod. Phys.* **28**, 432 (1956)]

energy level ratios fit very well the expected ratios for rotational levels; thus it would appear that the nucleus can have rotational states on a collective motion basis. There also exist numerous cases in which the value of I is an odd integer or a half-integer, in which case the magnitude of ΔI between successive rotational energy levels is $\Delta I = 1$, as for molecular rotational states.

Vibrational energy states are also expected in the unified model of the nucleus. As for molecular vibrational levels, equal spacing between nuclear vibrational energy levels is anticipated. Thus, relative to the ground state energy level, the ratio of the energy of the second excited level to the energy of the first excited level is expected to be $W_2/W_1 = 2$, and similarly $W_3/W_1 = 3$, $W_4/W_1 = 4$, etc., where the subscript is the level number. The energy spacing between vibrational energy levels is expected to be larger than the spacing between rotational levels. Thus, if there is permanent deformation of the nucleus, such that rotational states are easily possible, the first few excited levels are expected to be rotational states. But if only a few nucleons are in or missing from unfilled shells, there may be interactions between the nucleons without permanent deformation, and vibrational levels may be possible without rotational levels. Because of the higher energy intervals between vibrational energy states, the first excited state for those even-even isotopes that have no ground state rotational levels is expected to be at a considerably higher energy than the first excited state for those isotopes that do have ground state rotational levels.

The isotope Pb^{208} ($Z = 82$, $N = 126$) like He^4, has a doubly closed shell. Hence there should be no permanent deformation of its nucleus in its ground state, with the result that it and those isotopes near it should not exhibit rotational energy states. This is the reason for the gap in Fig. 13.7 between $A = 185$ and $A = 225$. Consequently the first excited level with a spin $I = 2$ in even-even isotopes near Pb^{208} should be a vibrational level and should be at a considerably higher energy above the ground state energy than the first excited level of those isotopes farther from the doubly closed shell. This type of characteristic energy interval is seen in Fig. 13.8, in which the energy of the first $I = 2$ level is plotted both as a function of neutron number N and as a function of proton

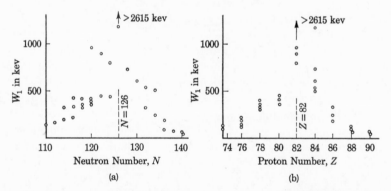

Fig. 13.8.   Energy of the first excited state in even-even nuclei, plotted (a) as a function of neutron number N and (b) as a function of proton number Z, for nuclei with mass numbers near $A = 208$. The vertical dashed lines indicate the positions on the plot of the magic number closed shell at $N = 126$ and $Z = 82$.

number Z for even-even isotopes near Pb^{208}. In another way a similar result can be seen if the ratio of the energy of the second excited state to the energy of the first excited state is plotted as a function of the energy of the first excited state. This is done in Fig. 13.9 for even-even nuclei for which the first excited state has a spin $I = 2$ and the second excited state

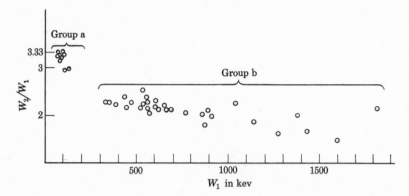

FIG. 13.9. Energy ratios of rotational and vibrational states in even-even nuclei as a function of energy of the first excited state for nuclei in the range $36 \leq N \leq 108$. [G. Scharff-Goldhaber and J. Weneser, *Phys. Rev.* **98**, 212 (1955)]

has a spin $I = 0$, 2, or 4, and for which $36 \leq N \leq 108$. There are two distinctly different ratios for W_2/W_1, one of which is near 2, corresponding to vibrational states, and the other near 3.3, corresponding to rotational states. It should be noted that the rotational energies are always much smaller than the vibrational energies, as expected.

13.9 Summary. The nature of nuclear forces cannot be explained in terms of a force that can be observed in our macroscopic world. Neither can the basic structure of the nucleus be described by an analogy with some system that can be seen in our macroscopic world. Any discussion of nuclear forces and nuclear structure is made more complex by the existence in the nucleus of two types of particles, the proton and the neutron. Even though many nuclear properties can be theoretically explained, nuclear structure as a whole is simply not as well understood as atomic structure, and must be subject to much more investigation before a completely satisfactory explanation of all its properties can be given.

References

J. M. Blatt and V. F. Weisskopf, *Theoretical Nuclear Physics* (John Wiley and Sons, Inc., New York, 1952).

P. M. Endt and M. Demeur, *Nuclear Reactions*, Vol. 1 (North Holland Publishing Co., Amsterdam, 1959).

L. Eisenbud and E. P. Wigner, *Nuclear Structure* (Princeton University Press, Princeton, N. J., 1958).

S. Flügge, *Handbuch der Physik*, Vol. XXXIX, *Structure of Atomic Nuclei* (Springer-Verlag, Berlin, 1957).

H. J. Lipkin, *Proceedings of the Rehovoth Conference on Nuclear Structure* (North-Holland Publishing Co., Amsterdam, 1958).

M. G. Mayer and J. H. D. Jensen, *Elementary Theory of Nuclear Shell Structure* (John Wiley and Sons, Inc., New York, 1955).

E. Feenberg, *Shell Theory of the Nucleus* (Princeton University Press, Princeton, N. J., 1955).

R. E. Marshak, "The Nuclear Force", *Scientific American* **202**, No. 3, 99 (1960).

R. van Wageningen, "Nuclear Models," *Am. J. Phys.* **28**, 423 (1960).

Problems

1. Assume that the nuclear radius is $R = R_0 A^{1/3}$ and that two fission products separate when their distance between centers is $a_1 + a_2$, where a_1 and a_2 are the radii of the fission products. Calculate the potential barrier against fission if a U^{236} nucleus is split into components $A = 81$ and $A = 155$. Compare with the actual energy release calculated in Problem 14, Chapter 12.

2. Using the top of the potential barrier as the threshold energy, calculate the photofission and neutron fission threshold for U^{238}.

3. Based upon the decay constant of 2.7×10^{-24} sec^{-1}, as given in Section 13.3, what is the mean time interval between spontaneous fissions in one gram of U^{238}?

4. Using the von Weizsacker formula, calculate which isobar of mass number $A = 61$ should have minimum energy. Does this agree with the experimentally observed information in Fig. 13.5?

5. Electrons with kinetic energies of about 600 Mev have been used for probing the nucleus to study its charge distribution. What is the wavelength of an electron with this kinetic energy? Compare this wavelength with the diameter of a gold nucleus.

6. In Pu^{238}, an even-even nucleus, the first two rotational excited states are 44.0 kev and 146.2 kev, respectively, above the ground state. Calculate the moment of inertia of the Pu^{238} nucleus and compare it with the moment of inertia of the HCl molecule found in Problem 14, Chapter 8.

7. The odd A nucleus Th^{229} has a ground state for which $I = 5/2$. The first two rotational states above the ground state are at 43.2 kev and 100.0 kev above the ground state. Calculate the moment of inertia of the Th^{229} nucleus. At what energy levels above the ground state would the rotational states for which $I = 11/2$, $I = 13/2$, and $I = 15/2$ be expected?

8. Because of the short range of the nuclear forces the nuclear potential well should appear graphically to have about the same shape as the distribution of nuclear particles. Plot the potential well represented by Eq. 13.2 for cobalt and for gold and compare the radial distribution of this potential well with the radial distribution of nuclear particles as obtained from Fig. 13.2.

9. For the case $I_0 = \frac{1}{2}$, Eq. 13.3 is no longer valid and should be replaced by:

$$W_I = (h^2/2\mathfrak{F})[I(I + 1) + a(-1)^{I+1/2}(I + \tfrac{1}{2})] \tag{13.4}$$

The ground state of Tm^{169} has a spin $I = \frac{1}{2}$ and the rotational levels above the ground state are at 8.4 kev, 118.2 kev, and 140.0 kev. Calculate the constant a and the moment of inertia $\mathfrak{F}$.

Chapter XIV

ELEMENTARY PARTICLES

14.1 Definition of Elementary Particles. An elementary particle has unique, characteristic properties that distinguish it from other particles. Each is elementary because it cannot be subdivided. Within atoms there are three types of elementary particles, the negatively charged electron (or negatron), the proton, and the neutron; but atoms and atomic nuclei, except the hydrogen nucleus, are not elementary particles themselves, since they can be subdivided into constituent parts. For example, an alpha particle, or helium nucleus, consists of two protons and two neutrons held together as a single nucleus by nuclear forces. Even though electrons, protons, and neutrons are all elementary, only two, the electron and the proton, exist alone in stable form. It has already been seen that the neutron, if left alone long enough, undergoes radioactive decay.

Other elementary particles that have been discussed in earlier chapters are the photon, the neutrino, and the positron (or antielectron). All these technically are stable particles, for in a perfect vacuum they last forever. However, when any one of them interacts with matter, there is a finite, though in some cases extremely small, probability that the particle will be destroyed. In such an interaction the photon, neutrino, or positron transfers all its energy, including its rest energy, to some other type of particle. For example, in intergalactic space a photon may exist for many millions of years, as exemplified by the light which comes to the earth from some of the more distant galaxies. But in a region as densely populated by atoms as the earth, a photon quickly finds an atom with which to interact, and it is destroyed or modified. Because of the extremely low cross section, the neutrino passes through much matter before an interaction occurs.

In addition to these, there are several other fundamental particles, the characteristics of which are tabulated in this chapter.

14.2 The Antiproton. Prior to considering the antiproton, it is perhaps best to recall (from Section 12.4) the Dirac relativistic theory of the electron, which states that a positron is the hole left in a continuous sea of negative electron energy states when an electron is lifted into a positive energy state. This process creates a negatron-positron pair and requires the expenditure of at least $2m_0c^2$ (1.022 Mev) of energy. To conserve momentum, the process can occur only in the vicinity of an atom. A similar theory predicts that antiprotons should be created as holes left in space by the removal of protons from negative energy states. An antiproton should have the same apparent properties as the proton except for a negative charge and a magnetic moment oppositely directed to that of the proton. Such a particle has been produced, and the predicted mass and charge have been verified.

When a proton-antiproton pair is produced, both energy and momentum must be conserved, just as in the production of a negatron-positron pair. The energies and masses of all particles participating in the process are so great, though, that there exists no particle, such as the atom in negatron-positron pair production, that is capable of carrying away appreciable momentum from the reaction without having to be considered in the energy balance for the process. If the proton-antiproton pair is to be produced with the expenditure of a minimum amount of energy, all particles in the system must be at rest at the conclusion of the process. Thus the initial momentum of the system must be zero. Such a process can occur if the interaction results from two like nuclear particles approaching each other at equal rates of speed (center of mass collision), as indicated graphically in Fig. 14.1. If the two approaching particles are

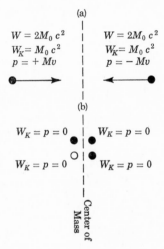

(a)

$W = 2M_0\,c^2$ $W = 2M_0\,c^2$
$W_K = M_0\,c^2$ $W_K = M_0\,c^2$
$p = +\,Mv$ $p = -\,Mv$

(b)

$W_K = p = 0$ $W_K = p = 0$

$W_K = p = 0$ $W_K = p = 0$

Center of Mass

FIG. 14.1. If two protons (a) approach each other with kinetic energies equal to their rest energies, it is possible (b) to create a proton-antiproton pair and conserve both energy and momentum.

protons, each particle has a rest energy M_0c^2 and each must have a minimum kinetic energy M_0c^2 if a new proton-antiproton pair is to be produced. The end result is four nuclear particles (three protons and one antiproton) at rest. The total energy of the system is still $4M_0c^2$, but now entirely in the form of rest energy.

In the laboratory, though, the problem is usually encountered that one of the initial nuclei (the target nucleus) is at rest and the other nucleus is accelerated by some means to high energy. Thus, at the instant of collision, the system has a finite momentum. Since this momentum must be conserved, the system of four particles that results from the encounter must have the same momentum after the interaction as was carried by the single nucleon prior to collision. If all four resultant nucleons are at rest in the center of mass system immediately after the interaction, they must travel as a group in the laboratory system of coordinates. Thus the four have equal kinetic energies and equal momenta. The equations expressing these conditions for the conservation of energy and momentum are:

$$M_0c^2 + M_0c^2/(1 - \beta_1{}^2)^{1/2} = 4M_0c^2/(1 - \beta_2{}^2)^{1/2} \qquad (14.1)$$

and

$$M_0\beta_1c/(1 - \beta_1{}^2)^{1/2} = 4M_0\beta_2c/(1 - \beta_2{}^2)^{1/2}, \qquad (14.2)$$

where $\beta_1 = v_1/c$ for the incident proton and $\beta_2 = v_2/c$ for each of the resultant particles. If the substitutions $(1 - \beta_1{}^2)^{1/2} = \gamma_1$ and $(1 - \beta_2{}^2)^{1/2} = \gamma_2$ are made, it is seen that $(1 + \gamma_1)/\gamma_1 = 4/\gamma_2$ and $(1 - \gamma_1{}^2)^{1/2}/\gamma_1 = 4(1 - \gamma_2{}^2)^{1/2}/\gamma_2$. The solution of these two simultaneous equations is $\gamma_1 = 1/7$; hence the total energy of the incident proton must have a minimum magnitude of $7M_0c^2$, and the kinetic energy must be at least $6M_0c^2$ (5.6 Bev).

If the target is a multiparticle nucleus, such as copper, rather than a single proton, the minimum energy required for proton-antiproton pair production is less than 5.6 Bev. This lowering of the threshold energy arises because the individual nucleons in compound nuclei are in motion. Because of the randomness of their motion, some of the constituent nuclear particles in the target nucleus are certain to be approaching the incident proton at the time of collision; hence the total momentum of the system of individual colliding nucleons is reduced. For example, using copper targets, the threshold proton kinetic energy required to produce proton-antiproton pairs at the University of California bevatron is 4.4 Bev.

Because of the large energy available, the number of modes for annihilation of a proton-antiproton pair is much greater than for the annihilation of a positron-negatron pair. A total energy of $2M_0c^2$, 1876.4 Mev, is available, extremely large compared to the $2m_0c^2$, 1.022 Mev, released during positron-negatron annihilation. Often the products of this annihilation process are fundamental particles other than photons, the basic requirement being that all conservation laws are obeyed.

14.3 Mesons. The name *meson* was initially given to three groups of particles, μ-mesons (*muons*), π-mesons (*pions*), and K-mesons, all of which have masses intermediate between the mass of the electron and the mass of the proton. More recently though the trend is to exclude the muons from this group because of the difference in their physical properties, as will be discussed below.

The muon has a mass of 206.9 $\pm$ 0.1 m_0 (electron masses) and may be either positively or negatively charged. Except for mass, its properties are similar to those of an electron. It possesses no nuclear force properties; hence it may move through the nucleus in the same manner as the electron, without interacting with any property of the nucleus other than charge distribution and magnetic moment. In this sense this particle is not a meson but a lepton. The term *lepton* distinguishes a special group of particles not possessing nuclear force properties. This group includes the electrons and neutrinos and their antiparticles. Leptons are produced during those weak interactions (see Section 14.5) characterized by the emission of neutrinos. Each lepton has a spin quantum number $\frac{1}{2}$.

Experimental evidence indicates the existence of both positively and negatively charged muons, as predicted by the Dirac relativistic theory of the electron, which states that the μ^+ particle is the antiparticle of the μ^- particle. The muon decays into an electron and two neutrinos with a mean life* of $(2.22 \pm 0.02) \times 10^{-6}$ sec.

The pions are either neutral or carry a charge of $\pm e$. The mass of the neutral π-meson (π^0) is slightly less than that of charged mesons (π^- or π^+). The masses and other physical properties of each type are summarized in Table 14.1. The π-mesons do interact with nuclei, and are almost certainly responsible for the strong nuclear forces which hold individual nuclear particles together. There are a number of modes of decay ($\mu^\pm + \nu$, $e^\pm + \nu$ for $\pi^\pm$ and $\gamma + \gamma$, $e^+ + e^- + \gamma$ and $2e^+ + 2e^-$ for π^0).

The K-mesons are also either neutral or carry a charge of $\pm e$, but are much more massive than either the μ- or π-mesons. They, too, may interact with nuclei. Their properties are summarized in Table 14.1. For the K-mesons, too, there are a large number of modes of decay (see Table 14.1).

*In many decay processes and interactions it is customary to measure the lifetime of the process in terms of mean life rather than half-life. In radioactive decay, for example, the mean life is defined as the sum of the lifetimes of all radioactive nuclei divided by the number of nuclei initially available. Based on the reasoning that led to Eq. 12.1, the number of nuclei that decay in the interval between t and $t + dt$ is $dN = \lambda N dt$ and the total lifetime of these dN nuclei is

$$dL = tdN = \lambda N t dt = \lambda N_0 \exp(-\lambda t) t dt.$$

The summed lifetime of all initially available nuclei is then

$$L = \int_0^\infty \lambda N_0 \exp(-\lambda t) t dt = N_0/\lambda,$$

from which it is seen that the mean life is $\tau = L/N_0 = 1/\lambda$. The half-life and the mean life are related by the equation $t_{1/2} = 0.693\tau$. The mean life is the time required for N_0 radioactive nuclei to be reduced to $N = N_0 \exp(-1)$ such nuclei.

TABLE 14.1. CHARACTERISTICS OF ELEMENTARY PARTICLES

Type	Particle*	Mass, in Mev‡	Mean Life, in Sec	Spin	T	T_z	⚲
Photon	γ	0	Stable	1			
Leptons	ν	0	Stable	$\frac{1}{2}$			
	e^-	0.511	Stable	$\frac{1}{2}$			
	μ^-	105.70	2.22×10^{-6}	$\frac{1}{2}$			
Mesons	π^+	139.63	2.56×10^{-8}	0	1	$+1$	0
	π^0	135.04	$<4 \times 10^{-16}$	0	1	0	0
	K^+	494.0	1.22×10^{-8}	0	$\frac{1}{2}$	$+\frac{1}{2}$	$+1$
	K^0	497.9	K_1†1.05×10^{-10} K_2†6.1×10^{-8}	0	$\frac{1}{2}$	$-\frac{1}{2}$	$+1$
Baryons	p	938.213	Stable	$\frac{1}{2}$	$\frac{1}{2}$	$+\frac{1}{2}$	0
	n	939.506	$1.01 \times 10^{+3}$	$\frac{1}{2}$	$\frac{1}{2}$	$-\frac{1}{2}$	0
	Λ	1115.2	2.51×10^{-10}	$\frac{1}{2}$	0	0	-1
	Σ^+	1189.5	0.83×10^{-10}	$\frac{1}{2}$	1	$+1$	-1
	Σ^0	1191.9	$<0.1 \times 10^{-10}$	$\frac{1}{2}$	1	0	-1
	Σ^-	1196.4	1.59×10^{-10}	$\frac{1}{2}$	1	-1	-1
	Ξ^-	1319.1	1.9×10^{-10}	?	$\frac{1}{2}$	$-\frac{1}{2}$	-2
	Ξ^0	1311	?	?	$\frac{1}{2}$	$+\frac{1}{2}$	-2

*Only the particles are given here. Except for π^0 there are equivalent antiparticles for which both T_z and the charge have a reversal of sign.

†K_1 decay is to $\pi^+ + \pi^-$ or $\pi^0 + \pi^0$. K_2 decay is to $e\pm + \pi^\mp + \nu$, $\mu\pm + \pi^\mp + \nu$, $\pi^+ + \pi^- + \pi^0$ or $3\pi^0$.

‡The masses of the elementary particles are commonly expressed in units of equivalent rest mass energy (M_0c^2), such as Mev.

14.4 Hyperons and Baryons. A group of elementary particles having mass greater than the neutron and possessing the same nuclear forces as nucleons have also been discovered. These particles are called *hyperons*. There appear to be three distinct groups of hyperons, the Λ particles, the Σ particles, and the Ξ particles.

To explain adequately certain observed properties, hyperons must be grouped together with the nucleons into a class of particles known as *baryons*. This group obeys a baryon conservation law which states that the difference between the number of baryons and the number of anti-baryons in the Universe must remain constant. If a baryonic number is defined as $+1$ for each baryon, -1 for each antibaryon, and 0 for all other particles, then the law of the conservation of baryons states that, for the entire Universe the total baryonic number, $\mathfrak{N} = \mathfrak{N}_+ - \mathfrak{N}_-$, must remain constant.

The basic properties of the baryons are listed in Table 14.1. For the hyperons, as well as the K-mesons, there is still considerable uncertainty in the values quoted for the mean life in Table 14.1. The values so quoted are what appear to be the best available at the time of preparation of the text.

14.5 Interactions Between Elementary Particles. Interactions between elementary particles can be placed into three categories, commonly called the *strong interactions*, the *electromagnetic interactions*, and the *weak interactions*. The strong interactions are those directly involving the nuclear forces, such as the baryon and meson reactions and collisions. By means of the electromagnetic interactions, photons are coupled to all charged particles and to any particles having electric and/or magnetic moments. It is through the electromagnetic interaction that a photon is emitted or absorbed by a charged particle. The weak interactions are characterized by the nonelectromagnetic decay processes. Typical is beta decay, during which there must be formed a lepton-antilepton pair, one of which is a beta particle and the other a neutrino or antineutrino. Muon decay (see Problem 4) is similar to beta decay. Other weak interactions are considered in Section 14.8.

The strength of a strong interaction is about 1000 times greater than that of an electromagnetic interaction, and many orders of magnitude (about 10^{14} times) greater than the weak interactions. The strength of these interactions is manifested in the time required for each of them to take place. The basic reaction times, exclusive of factors which have a slowing influence, are about 10^{-22}, 10^{-18}, and 10^{-8} sec, respectively, for the strong, electromagnetic and weak interactions. The slowing influence of selection rules of various types often increase the reaction time of electromagnetic interactions (the metastable states of the atom and nucleus) and weak interactions (such as in β decay) to quite long, easily measurable times.

14.6 Isotopic Spin. The discussions of the properties and interactions of nuclei and elementary particles have here been made as simple as possible consistent with an adequate explanation of the necessary basic concepts. In this basic explanation there have been omitted a number of concepts and formalisms that categorize and clarify many observed physical properties. The first such formalism to be discussed here is the *isotopic spin* quantum number, a development arising from the idea that the proton and the neutron may be considered to be the same type of particle, even though the proton has an electrostatic charge and the neutron does not. The concept of isotopic spin has now been extended to express the charge independence of the forces holding together all strongly interacting particles (baryons and mesons). The name is somewhat of a misnomer, for neither is it "isotopic" nor is it "spin." Some authors have attempted to correct the term "isotopic" by use of the name *isobaric* spin. The term "spin" will probably always remain because the formalism of the system is patterned after the formalism of the spin quantum numbers introduced in Chapter 7. Based upon the experimental observation that the nuclear forces between neutron-neutron, proton-neutron, and proton-proton pairs appear to be very nearly identical, the concept of isotopic spin appears to have merit. The primary differences in the overall forces between these pairs are the coulomb forces introduced by the existence of charge on the proton.

In the isotopic spin formalism, an isotopic spin quantum number T, corresponding to the spin quantum number s (or S) is introduced. The observed isotopic spin in any physical system is then the oriented z-component, T_z, corresponding to the magnetic quantum number m_s, which could just as easily have been called s_z in the spin angular momentum concept. The observed component of isotopic spin in any system of nucleons is $T_z = \frac{1}{2}(Z - N)$. Analogous to the spin and orbital angular momentum quantum states, the multiplicity of any isotopic spin state is $2T + 1$, with the components T_z of the multiplet ranging in magnitude from $+T$ to $-T$ with all intermediate values allowed for which $\Delta T_z = 1$. A unit change in the magnitude of T_z ($\Delta T_z = 1$) represents a change in magnitude of the charge on the particles of the multiplet by an amount $\pm e$.

In the isotopic spin formalism, the proton and the neutron form a doublet for which $T = \frac{1}{2}$. The doublet has two components, $T_z = +\frac{1}{2}$, a proton, and $T_z = -\frac{1}{2}$, a neutron. For a system consisting of more than one nuclear particle, the vector model used in Chapter 7 for the addition of spin and orbital angular momentum quantum numbers can be used in a parallel manner to determine the appropriate isotopic spin quantum numbers. For example, consider a system consisting of two nuclear particles. Vector addition of the single particle isotopic spin quantum numbers gives quantum numbers for the two particle system of $T = 1$ and $T = 0$. The $T = 1$ part of the system is a triplet state since $2T + 1 = 3$, and the $T = 0$ part is a singlet state. Associated with the triplet state are the three components of isotopic spin $T_z = +1$, corresponding to a two proton system; $T_z = 0$, corresponding to a system consisting of one proton and one neutron; and $T_z = -1$, corresponding to a two neutron system. The singlet $T = 0$ state can arise only from a one proton, one neutron system. The singlet state is quantum mechanically associated with what is known as an antisymmetric isotopic spin function, and the triplet state with a symmetric isotopic spin function. For isotopic spin, no simple analogy can be made between a physically picturable system and the symmetric and antisymmetric functions, as was done for the spin angular momentum vector system, in which parallel orientation of the spins formed the symmetric wave function and antiparallel orientation of the spins formed the antisymmetric wave function. Quantum mechanically, the formalism is the same, though. The isotopic spin formalism exists for all possible nuclear angular momentum states.

Since there are four possible spin angular momentum wave functions for a two nucleon system (three symmetric and one antisymmetric), there is a set of sixteen possible combinations of spin angular momentum functions and isotopic spin functions for a two nucleon system.

The isotopic spin concept is applicable not only to the proton-neutron system but also to all other systems of particles and antiparticles possessing nuclear force properties, such as hyperons, mesons, and their corresponding antiparticles. If all such particles and antiparticles are plotted, as in Fig. 14.2, the isotopic spin quantum number for all known

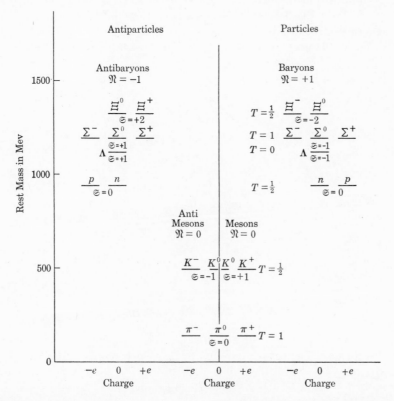

FIG. 14.2. Plot showing the rest energy, charge, isotopic spin (T), strangeness quantum number $(\mathfrak{S})$, and baryonic number $(\mathfrak{N})$ of the mesons and baryons. Ordinate is in units of Mev, the energy equivalent of rest mass $(M_0 c^2)$; see Table 14.1.

systems of elementary particles is either $T = 0$, $T = \frac{1}{2}$, or $T = 1$, depending on whether the system is a singlet, doublet, or triplet system. The components of isotopic spin, T_z, are plotted in Fig. 14.2 with the positive component on the right. It is seen that for the antineutron

$T_z = +\frac{1}{2}$ and for the antiproton $T_z = -\frac{1}{2}$. Similarly the K-meson and the Ξ particle appear to form isotopic spin doublets, the π-meson and the Σ particle appear to form isotopic spin triplets and only the Λ particle appears to form an isotopic spin singlet. The isotopic spin component T_z of each antiparticle is in magnitude the same as the isotopic spin component of the particle, but has a reversal of sign.

Only for strong interactions is there conservation of isotopic spin ($\Delta T = 0$). However, there appears to be a requirement for conservation of T_z in both strong and electromagnetic interactions but not in weak interactions. This is one of the selection rules, mentioned in Section 14.5, that increases the length of the mean reaction time for some electromagnetic and weak interactions. For example, consider the isobars O^{14}, N^{14}, and C^{14} (Fig. 14.3). The ground states of O^{14} and C^{14} and the first

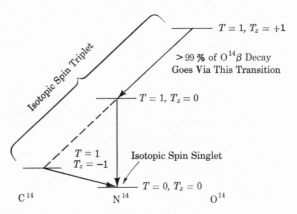

FIG. 14.3.   Energy levels and decay processes for C^{14}, N^{14}, and O^{14}.

excited state of N^{14} appear to form an isotopic spin triplet for which $T = 1$. An isotopic spin triplet would be expected to have the same energy except for the effects of nuclear charge, which produces the lowering of the energy levels of the triplet in going from O^{14} to C^{14}. The ground state of N^{14} is apparently an isotopic spin singlet. As a result, decay of either O^{14} or C^{14} to the ground state of N^{14} requires a transformation in isotopic spin for which both T and T_z must change by one unit. On the other hand, decay of O^{14} to the first excited state of N^{14} is a transformation for which $\Delta T = 0$. These conditions are manifested in the relatively short half-life (72 sec) for the decay of O^{14}, primarily to the first excited state of N^{14}, and the extremely long half-life (5500 yr) for the decay of C^{14}. Note also that, although the electromagnetic transition from the first excited state of N^{14} to the ground state requires a change of T by one unit, there is no change in T_z.

14.7 Parity. Another concept that arises in more detailed discussions of atomic and nuclear structure is that of the spatial symmetry of a system, known as the *parity* of the system. Any energy state in the system is said to have either even or odd parity, depending on the sign of the wave function of this state after a reversal of sign of the spatial coordinates. For example, consider the wave function of the linear harmonic oscillator of Section 6.6. Since any number of terms of Eq. 6.21 is a solution to Eq. 6.20, any number of wave functions $\psi_n = Au_n$ exp $(-\alpha x^2/2)$, where n is an integer, are solutions for the Schroedinger equation for the linear harmonic oscillator. It will be noted, though, that with a reversal in sign of the spatial coordinate x, the wave function reverses sign if n is odd, $\psi_n(x) = -\psi_n(-x)$, but does not reverse sign if n is even, $\psi_n(x) = \psi_n(-x)$. Those states for which there is a reversal of sign of the wave function are said to have *odd parity*, sometimes designated simply with a $(-)$ sign, whereas those states for which there is no reversal of sign of the wave function are said to have *even parity*, sometimes designated simply with a $(+)$ sign.

All fundamental particles and all energy states in atomic and nuclear systems have either even $(+)$ or odd $(-)$ parity. For example, each atomic energy state considered in the discussions of atomic energy levels in Chapter 7 has odd parity if its orbital angular momentum quantum number l is odd, and even parity if its orbital angular momentum quantum number is even. The intrinsic parity of the photon is odd, so to conserve parity, which must be done in both strong and electromagnetic interactions, the emission of a photon must change the parity of the state. This was the basis for the requirement that allowed transitions between atomic energy levels can occur only if the orbital angular momentum quantum number of the system change by one unit either from odd l (or L) to even l (or L) or vice versa.

Parity is conserved in both strong and electromagnetic interactions but not in weak interactions.

14.8 Strangeness Quantum Number. The final concept to be considered here is relatively new, the strangeness quantum number, a quantum number that was introduced because the decay of K-mesons into π-mesons occurred at an extremely slow rate compared to that expected for a strong interaction. It had been expected initially that the decay would be a strong interaction since both K- and π-mesons possess nuclear force properties and there are no leptons involved in the decay. Some other explanation had to be found for the long decay lifetime of the K-meson.

Prior to the discovery of the K-mesons and the hyperons — the so-called *strange particles* — the charge, isotopic spin, and baryonic number for the proton, neutron, and the pions could be related by the simple formula:

$$Q = T_z + \tfrac{1}{2}\mathfrak{N}, \tag{14.3}$$

in which Q is the charge in units of electron charge. For antiparticles, all quantities are reversed in sign. As indicated in Fig. 14.2, Eq. 14.3 simply is no longer valid for the K-meson and other strange particles. It appears, though, that the charge, isotopic spin, and baryonic number can be related if a new quantum number, called the strangeness quantum number and designated here by the letter $\mathfrak{S}$,* is introduced in such a way that Eq. 14.3 becomes:

$$Q = T_z + \tfrac{1}{2}\mathfrak{N} + \tfrac{1}{2}\mathfrak{S}. \tag{14.4}$$

The introduction of the strangeness quantum number brought considerable order and understanding to the previous chaotic state for the elementary particles. The apparently large number of different elementary particles could be systematized. Assuming, based upon actual experimental observation, that there are no multiply charged elementary particles, there are now a limited number of possible elementary particles If $\mathfrak{S} = 0$ the same nucleon and pion states are obtained from Eq. 14.4 as from Eq. 14.3. If $\mathfrak{S} = +1$, then the combination of $\mathfrak{N} = 0$ and $T = \tfrac{1}{2}$ gives $Q = -1$ or 0 corresponding to the K^-- and K^0-mesons. If $\mathfrak{S} = -1$, then $\mathfrak{N} = 0$ and $T = \tfrac{1}{2}$ gives $Q = 0$ or $+1$ corresponding to the antiparticles K^0 and K^+. For $\mathfrak{S} = -1$, $\mathfrak{N} = 1$, and $T = 0$, there is but a single $Q = 0$ state corresponding to the neutral Λ particle. For a reversal in sign of the strangeness quantum number and baryon number, $\mathfrak{S} = +1$ $\mathfrak{N} = -1$, and $T = 0$, no particle has been experimentally found but it is assumed that it is the Λ antiparticle, indicated in Fig. 14.2. By appropriate use of Eq. 14.4 it can also be shown that the Σ hyperons have a strangeness quantum number $\mathfrak{S} = \pm 1$, and the Ξ hyperons a strangeness quantum number $\mathfrak{S} = \pm 2$.

If it is assumed that for strong interactions the strangeness quantum number must be conserved, as were T_z and $\mathfrak{N}$, then the observed products of strange particle decay indicate these processes are not strong interactions, but rather that they are apparently weak interactions belonging to the nonelectromagnetic decay processes. Further evidence for the strange particle decay belonging to the weak interaction group has been indicated by an apparent nonconservation of parity in the processes. If these decays belong to the weak interaction group, it is expected that the mean life of strange particle decay would be much longer than predicted by strong interaction theory.

*In most sources the strangeness quantum number is represented by the letter S. However, this letter has already been used to represent an $l = 0$ state and to represent the spin quantum number, so it is felt that some other letter must be used, such as the equivalent German letter $\mathfrak{S}$ that is used here.

References

H. A. Bethe and P. Morrison, *Elementary Nuclear Theory* (John Wiley and Sons, Inc., New York, 2nd Ed., 1956).

R. B. Leighton, *Principles of Modern Physics* (McGraw-Hill Book Co., Inc., New York, 1959); see especially Chapter 20.

E. Segre, "Antinucleons," *Am. J. Phys.* **25**, 363 (1957), and *Ann. Rev. Nuclear Sci.* **8**, 127 (1958).

G. Burbidge and F. Hoyle, "Antimatter," *Scientific American* **198**, No. 4, 34 (1958).

P. M. S. Blackett "The Elementary Particles of Nature," *British Journal of Radiology* **31**, 1 (1958).

M. Gell-Mann and A. H. Rosenfeld, "Hyperons and Heavy Mesons," *Ann. Rev. of Nuclear Sci.* **7**, 407 (1957).

J. D. Jackson, *The Physics of Elementary Particles* (Princeton University Press, Princeton, N. J., 1958).

J. P. Davidson, "Isotopic Spin," *Am. J. Phys.* **27**, 457 (1959).

P. Morrison, "The Overthrow of Parity," *Scientific American* **196**, No 4, 45 (1957).

E. O. Okonov, "Decay Properties of Heavy Mesons and Hyperons," *Soviet Phys. — Uspekhi*, **67(2)**, 119 (1959).

L. Okun, "Strange Particles: Decays," *Ann. Rev. Nuclear Sci.* **9**, 61 (1959).

R. E. Marshak "Elementary Particles of Modern Physics," *Science* **132**, 269 (1960).

Problems

1. It was stated in Section 14.2 that the threshold proton kinetic energy incident on a copper target required for the production of a proton-antiproton pair is 4.4 Bev. Assume that the pair is produced following an interaction between the incident proton and a proton in the copper nucleus that collides head-on with the incident proton. At what speed must the proton within the nucleus be moving for there to be conservation of both energy and momentum among the individual nucleons involved in the interaction? Is the kinetic energy of this proton of reasonable magnitude?

2. Assume that an incident proton interacts with a Cu^{63} nucleus at rest and that, following the interaction, the copper nucleus carries away momentum and energy as if it were a single particle. What would have to be the minimum energy of the incident proton in this case to produce a proton-antiproton pair?

3. Suppose an antiproton at rest is annihilated by a proton at rest and that five π-mesons are produced in the process. How much energy must be released as kinetic energy? Suppose this kinetic energy is shared by the five mesons and two protons. Draw a possible set of directions, with momenta and energies indicated, for the emission of these particles from the point of annihilation. Such a group of emission particles observed experimentally is called a star.

4. Muon decay is another weak interaction, similar to beta decay, in which the muon replaces the electron as the decay product. For example a π^--meson may decay either by muon decay or by beta decay. Compare the kinetic energies and momenta of the decay products if a π-meson decays into a muon and a neutrino with the kinetic energies and momenta of the decay products if it decays into an electron and a neutrino.

5. Calculate the kinetic energies and momenta of the decay products if a K^--meson decays into a μ^- and a neutrino.

6. Suppose a K^--meson at rest decays into a π^--meson and two π^0-mesons. Calculate the maximum momentum that the π^--meson can have in this decay process.

7. Show that charge, isotopic spin, the z-component of isotope spin, and the strangeness quantum number are conserved in the reaction $\pi^- + p \rightarrow K^0 + \Lambda$, if K^0 is a particle, but that the strangeness quantum number would not be conserved if K^0 were an antiparticle. Therefore only the reaction in which K^0 is a particle can take place.

8. In a manner similar to Problem 7 show that the reaction $K^- + p \rightarrow K^0 + n$ can take place only if K^0 is an antiparticle.

Appendices

Appendix 1.1 Physical Constants

These physical constants are given only to four significant figures, all that are needed to solve the problems in this book.

If more precise values of these constants are desired, there are numerous reviews of the subject, as, for example, J. W. M. DuMond and E. R. Cohen, "Fundamental Constants of Atomic Physics," in Condon and Odishaw's *Handbook of Physics* (McGraw-Hill Book Co., Inc., New York, 1959), pp. **7**-143 to **7**-173.

Electron charge	$e = 4.803 \times 10^{-10}$ statcoulomb
Rest mass of electron	$m_0 = 9.108 \times 10^{-28}$ gram
Avogadro's number	$N_0 = 6.025 \times 10^{23}$ (gram-mole)$^{-1}$
Speed of light in vacuo	$c = 2.998 \times 10^{10}$ cm sec^{-1}
Planck's constant	$h = 6.625 \times 10^{-27}$ erg sec
Boltzmann constant	$k = 1.380 \times 10^{-16}$ erg deg^{-1}
Ratio of proton to electron rest mass	1836.13
Ratio of physical to chemical scale of atomic masses	1.000275
Universal gas constant	$R = 8.317 \times 10^7$ erg gram-mole^{-1} deg^{-1}
Atomic mass unit (physical)	1 AMU $= 1.660 \times 10^{-24}$ gram
Proton rest mass	$M_p = 1.672 \times 10^{-24}$ gram
Neutron rest mass	$M_n = 1.675 \times 10^{-24}$ gram
Ratio of charge to mass of electron	$e/m = 5.273 \times 10^{17}$ statcoulombs gram^{-1}
Bohr magneton	$\mu_0 = he/4\pi mc = 0.9273 \times 10^{-20}$ erg gauss^{-1}
Nuclear magneton	$\mu = he/4\pi M_p c = 0.5050 \times 10^{-23}$ erg gauss^{-1}
Magnetic moment of electron	$\mu_e = 0.9284 \times 10^{-20}$ erg gauss^{-1}

Appendix 1.2 List of Elements

The nuclear charge (Z) and chemical atomic weight of each element are given. After the name of each element the abbreviation for that element is given in parentheses.

	Z	Atomic Wt.		Z	Atomic Wt.
Actinium (Ac)	89	*	Berkelium (Bk)	97	*
Aluminum (Al)†	13	26.98	Beryllium (Be)	4	9.013
Americium (Am)	95	*	Bismuth (Bi)	83	209.00
Antimony (Sb)	51	121.76	Boron (B)	5	10.82
Argon (A)	18	39.944	Bromine (Br)	35	79.916
Arsenic (As)	33	74.91	Cadmium (Cd)	48	112.41
Astatine (At)	85	*	Calcium (Ca)	20	40.08
Barium (Ba)	56	137.36	Californium (Cf)	98	*

273

	Z	*Atomic Wt.*		Z	*Atomic Wt.*
Carbon (C)	6	12.011	Nobelium (No)	102	*
Cerium (Ce)	58	140.13	Osmium (Os)	76	190.2
Cesium (Cs)	55	132.91	Oxygen (O)	8	16.0000
Chlorine (Cl)	17	35.457	Palladium (Pd)	46	106.7
Chromium (Cr)	24	52.01	Phosphorus (P)	15	30.975
Cobalt (Co)	27	58.94	Platinum (Pt)	78	195.23
Copper (Cu)	29	63.54	Plutonium (Pu)	94	*
Curium (Cm)	96	*	Polonium (Po)	84	*
Dysprosium (Dy)	66	162.46	Potassium (K)	19	39.100
Einsteinium (E)	99	*	Praseodymium (Pr)	59	140.92
Erbium (Er)	68	167.2	Prometheum (Pm)	61	*
Europium (Eu)	63	152.0	Protactinium (Pa)	91	*
Fermium (Fm)	100	*	Radium (Ra)	88	*
Fluorine (F)	9	19.00	Radon (Rn)	86	*
Francium (Fr)	87	*	Rhenium (Re)	75	186.31
Gadolinium (Gd)	64	156.9	Rhodium (Rh)	45	102.91
Gallium (Ga)	31	69.72	Rubidium (Rb)	37	85.48
Germanium (Ge)	32	72.60	Ruthenium (Ru)	44	101.1
Gold (Au)	79	197.0	Samarium (Sm)	62	150.43
Hafnium (Hf)	72	178.6	Scandium (Sc)	21	44.96
Helium (He)	2	4.003	Selenium (Se)	34	78.96
Holmium (Ho)	67	164.94	Silicon (Si)	14	28.09
Hydrogen (H)	1	1.0080	Silver (Ag)	47	107.880
Indium (In)	49	114.76	Sodium (Na)	11	22.991
Iodine (I)	53	126.91	Strontium (Sr)	38	87.63
Iridium (Ir)	77	192.2	Sulfur (S)	16	32.066
Iron (Fe)	26	55.85	Tantalum (Ta)	73	180.95
Krypton (Kr)	36	83.80	Technetium (Tc)	43	*
Lanthanum (La)	57	138.92	Tellurium (Te)	52	127.61
Lead (Pb)	82	207.21	Terbium (Tb)	65	158.93
Lithium (Li)	3	6.940	Thallium (Tl)	81	204.39
Lutetium (Lu)	71	174.99	Thorium (Th)	90	*
Magnesium (Mg)	12	24.32	Thulium (Tm)	69	168.94
Manganese (Mn)	25	54.94	Tin (Sn)	50	118.70
Mendelevium (Mv)	101	*	Titanium (Ti)	22	47.90
Mercury (Hg)	80	200.61	Wolfram (W)§	74	183.92
Molybdenum (Mo)	42	95.95	Uranium (U)	92	*
Neodymium (Nd)	60	144.27	Vanadium (V)	23	50.95
Neon (Ne)	10	20.183	Xenon (Xe)	54	131.3
Neptunium (Np)	93	*	Ytterbium (Yb)	70	173.04
Nickel (Ni)	28	58.69	Yttrium (Y)	39	88.92
Niobium (Nb)‡	41	92.91	Zinc (Zn)	30	65.38
Nitrogen (N)	7	14.008	Zirconium (Zr)	40	91.22

*There are no stable atoms of these elements, all are radioactive — see Chapter 12.

†In much of the world this element is called aluminium.

‡Known by metallurgists in the United States as Columbium (Cb).

§By international agreement this element is now called wolfram, but was formerly called tungsten in the United States, and is still called tungsten in most industrial uses in the United States.

Appendix 1.3   Units and Dimensions

The real value of physics, applied science, and engineering exists in the use that can be made of the principles in solving problems. The first step in the solution of any problem involves the transformation of the physical situation into a mathematical equation in which each symbol represents some physical quantity such as force or energy. In all problems of mechanics each physical quantity can be dimensionally represented by three basic dimensional quantities — length, mass, and time. During the course of history three different systems of unit magnitudes of length, mass, and time have become accepted standards. They are the English or foot-pound-second (fps) system, the centimeter-gram-second (cgs) system, and the meter-kilogram-second (MKS) system.

Just as the basic units of any one system may be related to other units of the same type in the same system — for example, 12 inches = 1 foot or 3 feet = 1 yard — there is also a factor of proportionality between corresponding units in the different systems. When solving a problem all quantities should be transformed to the basic units of the system of units to be used in the attempted solution of a problem. If this is properly done, the numerical answer will also be in the basic units of the system used in the solution.

A list of some common physical quantities, their dimensions in terms of length [meters (M) or centimeters (c)], mass [kilograms (K) or grams (g)] and time [second (S) or (s)] are given in Table 1.1.

TABLE 1.1. UNITS AND DIMENSIONS (IN PARENTHESES) FOR MECHANICAL QUANTITIES

Physical Quantity	MKS Units		cgs Units
Length	1 meter (M)	=	10^2 centimeters (c)
Mass	1 kilogram (K)	=	10^3 grams (g)
Time	1 second (S)	=	1 second (s)
Force	1 newton (MKS^{-2})	=	10^5 dynes (cgs^{-2})
Energy	1 joule (M^{2}KS^{-2})	=	10^7 ergs (c^{2}gs^{-2})

The units and dimensions for electric and magnetic quantities and the transformations between different systems of units usually seem to be less well understood than the simple mechanical transformations of Table 1.1. The difficulties in understanding have generally originated from the rationalization of units and from the use of a fourth-dimensional quantity.

To understand the so-called rationalization of units, consider the electric flux density, D, resulting from a point charge q_1. The flux density is the flux traversing a unit cross sectional area; and at a distance r from the point charge q_1, the flux density is $D = \Phi/4\pi r^2$, where Φ is the total flux originating at the charge q_1, and $4\pi r^2$ is the area of the spherical shell surrounding the charge at a distance r. Rationalization involves the definition of unit flux. In a rationalized system one unit of flux originates at a unit charge, but in the unrationalized system of electrostatics there is one unit of flux for each unit solid angle surrounding a unit charge, in which case there are 4π units of flux originating at a unit charge.

Now the force exerted upon a charge q_2 by an electrostatic field E is $F = q_2 E = q_2 D/\epsilon$, where ϵ is the electric permittivity of the medium in which the force is being measured. Thus the force upon a charge q_2 by a charge q_1 separated from q_2 by a distance r is q_2 times the field produced by q_1 at q_2, which is $F = q_1 q_2/ 4\pi\epsilon r^2$ in the rationalized system, and $F = q_1 q_2/\epsilon r^2$ in the unrationalized system.

Obviously the force exerted upon one charge by another charge a distance r away must be the same regardless of any mathematical manipulation used in the expression for this force. Therefore, because of rationalization, the permittivity ϵ of any given medium must differ in the two equations of force by a factor 4π.

An analogous situation arises in the rationalization of the magnetic flux density B, for the magnetic permeability μ which must be used to relate the magnetic flux density B with the magnetic field H, $B = \mu H$, differs by a factor 4π between the rationalized and unrationalized system.

Because the cgs system is the basic system of units used in this book, and because the general practice is to use unrationalized units in the cgs system, equations, such as Eq. 1.18, are expressed in the unrationalized formalism.

The need for a fourth-dimensional quantity can be seen in the equation $F = q_1 q_2 / \epsilon r^2$. Two new physical quantities, charge and permittivity, are introduced in this equation. If both are assumed to have dimensions of some sort, it is impossible to define either in terms of only the dimensional quantities of mass, length, and time. Therefore one must be defined in terms of the other and the three basic dimensions. If it is decided to use the permittivity as the basic dimension (ϵ_{dim}), the dimensions of charge (Q) are $Q = K^{1/2}M^{3/2}S^{-1}\epsilon_{dim}^{1/2}$; or, if charge is used as the basic dimension, the dimensions of permittivity are $\epsilon_{dim} = K^{-1}M^{-3}S^2Q^2$. Both the charge Q and the electric current I are in relatively common use in the MKS system of units as the fourth-dimensional quantity. By definition an electric current is the rate of flow of charge through a surface, $I = dQ/dt$. Thus dimensionally charge and current are related by the equation $I = QS^{-1}$. The reason for current being used as the fourth-dimensional quantity in many systems comes from a fundamental definition of current in terms of the force between two wires, each carrying an electric current. This is related to the magnetic flux produced at one wire as a result of the current in the other wire, and hence is known as an electromagnetic system. Actually two systems of electric and magnetic units are commonly accepted in the cgs system; therefore further discussion of the two definitions of current is postponed for a few paragraphs until the discussion of the cgs system of units.

A few examples can perhaps assist in clarifying the use of K, M, S, and Q in dimensional analysis. For example, the electrostatic field strength, E, defined previously by the equation $F = QE$, is dimensionally $E_{dim} = KMS^{-2}Q^{-1}$. Its units in the cgs system are statvolts/cm, or in the MKS system, volts/meter. Electrostatic potential, volts or statvolts, therefore dimensionally is $V_{dim} = KM^2S^{-2}Q^{-1}$. An electrostatic flux density, $D = \epsilon E$, dimensionally is $D_{dim} = M^{-2}Q$.

As stated above, within the cgs system two systems of units have been developed for electric and magnetic quantities. The cgs *electrostatic units* (esu) have been developed on the basis of the force between two charges, or the electrostatic field produced by an electric charge. The cgs *electromagnetic units* (emu) have been developed on the basis of the magnetic field produced by the flow of charge, a current, in a wire. In the cgs esu system the electric permittivity is assumed to be unity and dimensionless in vacuo, and the unit of charge is defined such that a unit charge produces in an evacuated region at a distance of one centimeter a force of one dyne on another unit charge. A unit of electric current is then defined in this system as the flow of one unit charge per second through some cross sectional area, such as, for example, the cross sectional area of a conducting wire, or the cross sectional area of a region in an evacuated volume through which a beam of electrons is passing. In the cgs emu system one unit of electric current is defined as that amount of current which must be flowing in a wire one centimeter in length in order that there be a force of one dyne exerted upon the wire when there is a unit normal component of magnetic flux density at the wire. Thus the force on a straight length of wire of length L, in a region in which the perpendicular component of magnetic flux density is B, is $F = iLB$, where i is the magnitude of the current flowing in the wire. The cgs emu system further assumes that the magnetic permeability of vacuum is unity and dimensionless, so that in vacuo this equation also defines the magnetic field.

Since unit current in each of these two systems is defined in an entirely different way, to have equal unit currents in the two systems would be completely unexpected. In the cgs esu system the unit of current is called the statampere, and in the cgs emu system the unit of current is called the abampere. By a series of experiments and appropriate calculations it can be shown that 1 abampere $= c$ (1 statampere), where c is numerically equal to the velocity of light in the cgs system. The transformation from one system to the other involves the relative magnitudes of the magnetic permeability and the electric permittivity in the two systems. It is found that the dimensions of the product $\epsilon\mu$ are those of the inverse square of a velocity, and in magnitude $(\epsilon_0\mu_0)^{-1/2} = c$, where the subscript zero means the magnitude of the appropriate quantity in vacuum. The dimensions of magnetic permeability are then c^2s^{-2} in cgs esu and the dimensions of electric permittivity are c^2s^{-2} in cgs emu.

In many scientific writings it has been customary to use the *Gaussian system*, which utilizes cgs esu units for electric quantities and cgs emu units for magnetic quantities. This has the advantage that both the electric permittivity and the magnetic permeability are unity in vacuum. In an equation in which both types of units appear there must be a factor of proportionality which leads to correct dimensional analysis [see, for example, G. L. Trigg, *Am. J. Phys.* **25**, 117 (1957); **27**, 515 (1959)] for the result. The most common example found in this text where this situation occurs is that of a force exerted on an electric current, or a moving charge, by a magnetic field. This force is $F = iLB$ or $F = qvB$. If i and q are expressed in cgs esu and B in cgs emu, either i and q or B must be converted to the other type of unit, the proportionality factor for which is $1/c$. It is for this reason that the equation for the force exerted by a magnetic field on a moving charge is often found written in the form $F = qvB/c$.

The quantities defined by the cgs esu and the cgs emu systems were found in many cases to be either too small or too large to be of practical importance. To overcome this, a practical system of units was developed for electric and magnetic quantities. To set the pattern for the practical system of units, an ampere was defined as a unit of current which is one-tenth the magnitude of the abampere. The MKS system of units has utilized the practical system of electric and magnetic quantities. The transformations between systems for several of these quantities are listed in Table 1.2.

Any formula applicable in one system of units must be just as applicable in any other consistent system. The unit of charge in the cgs esu system is defined as that amount of charge necessary to produce at a distance of one centimeter a force of one dyne on an equal charge. But the unit of charge in the MKS system is the coulomb and the unit of distance is the meter; therefore the force which one coulomb of charge exerts in vacuum at a distance of one meter on another charge of equal magnitude is

$$(3 \times 10^9 \text{ statcoulombs})^2/(10^2 \text{ cm})^2 = 9 \times 10^{14} \text{ dynes.}$$

The unit of force in the MKS system is the newton, which is 10^5 dynes; so to have an equation which is consistent in the MKS system of units requires that the

TABLE 1.2. UNITS AND DIMENSIONS (IN PARENTHESES) OF ELECTRIC AND MAGNETIC QUANTITIES

Physical Quantity	MKS	cgs esu	cgs emu
Charge	1 coulomb (Q)	= 3 × 10⁹ statcoulombs ($g^{1/2}c^{3/2}s^{-1}$)	= 10^{-1} abcoulomb ($g^{1/2}c^{1/2}$)
Potential	1 volt ($M^2KS^{-2}Q^{-1}$)	= (1/300) statvolt ($g^{1/2}c^{1/2}s^{-1}$)	= 10^8 abvolts ($g^{1/2}c^{3/2}s^{-2}$)
Electric field intensity	1 volt/meter ($MKS^{-2}Q^{-1}$)	= $(10^{-4}/3)$ statvolt/cm ($g^{1/2}c^{-1/2}s^{-1}$)	= 10^6 abvolts/cm ($g^{1/2}c^{1/2}s^{-2}$)
Current	1 ampere ($S^{-1}Q$)	= 3 × 10⁹ statamperes ($g^{1/2}c^{3/2}s^{-2}$)	= 10^{-1} abamperes ($g^{1/2}c^{1/2}s^{-1}$)
Magnetic flux density	1 weber/meter² ($MS^{-1}Q^{-1}$)	= $10^{-6}/3$ statvolt sec/cm² ($g^{1/2}c^{-3/2}$)	= 10^4 gauss ($g^{1/2}c^{-1/2}s^{-1}$)

electric permittivity in vacuum be $10^{-9}/9$ in unrationalized units, or $10^{-9}/36\pi$ in rationalized units. From the knowledge that the product $\epsilon_0\mu_0 = 1/c^2$, which is $1/[9 \times 10^{16} \text{ (meters/sec)}^2]$ in the MKS system of units, it can be calculated that the magnetic permeability in vacuum is 10^{-7} in unrationalized units and $4\pi \times 10^{-7}$ in rationalized units. The dimensions of permittivity have already been expressed, and the dimensions of permeability are MKQ^{-2}. The names of the units used in the MKS system for these quantities are related to the units for capacitance and inductance, neither of which are treated in this book, so they will not be discussed in this appendix.

Appendix 1.4   Rutherford Scattering

The purpose of this appendix is the derivation of Eq. 1.18, which describes, in terms of parameters given in Fig. 1.6, the angle of scatter of a positively charged particle by a much heavier positively charged particle. If the alpha particle, with charge $2e$ and mass m, approaches the general vicinity of a much more massive nucleus, with charge Ze, the alpha particle is forced to change its direction of motion by a radial coulomb repulsive force, $F = 2Ze^2/\epsilon r^2$. By appropriate use of vector analysis, it can be shown [see, for example, E. U. Condon and H. Odishaw's *Handbook of Physics* (McGraw-Hill Book Co., Inc. 1958) p. 2-4] that the radial acceleration of a moving particle under the influence of a radial force is $d^2r/dt^2 - r(d\theta/dt)^2$, such that, for the alpha particle moving in the force field of the heavier nucleus,

$$d^2r/dt^2 - r(d\theta/dt)^2 = F/m = 2Ze^2/\epsilon mr^2. \tag{1.31}$$

The angular momentum of the system [see Condon and Odishaw, *op. cit.* pp. 2-13 and 2-30], $L = mr^2(d\theta/dt)$, must be conserved. When the distance separating the incident alpha particle from the target nucleus is very large, the angular momentum of the system is mvb, where v is the velocity of the alpha particle prior to moving into the field of influence of the scattering nucleus. Thus

$$mr^2d\theta/dt = mvb \quad \text{and} \quad d\theta/dt = vb/r^2.$$

The $d\theta/dt$ term of the radial acceleration is then a function of r, so that

$$d^2r/dt^2 - v^2b^2/r^3 - 2Ze^2/\epsilon mr^2 = 0. \tag{1.32}$$

The solution of this equation is much more easily determined if there is a substitution $r = 1/u$ for the variable r. Under these conditions $dr/dt = -(du/dt)/u^2$, and $d^2r/dt^2 = -(d^2u/dt^2)/u^2 + 2(du/dt)^2/u^3$.

Experimental measurements of the time required for the alpha particle to scatter from a silver nucleus are not possible, but measurements of the angle through which the alpha particle scatters can be made. For a solution that can be compared to experimental measurements, there is a need to transform the variable of time into a variable of angle. The appropriate transformation equation, $d\theta/dt = vb/r^2$, has already been determined. Thus

$$du/dt = (du/d\theta)(d\theta/dt) = vbu^2(du/d\theta)$$

and

$$d^2u/dt^2 = (d\theta/dt)[(d/d\theta)(du/dt)]$$

$$= (vbu^2)[vbu^2(d^2u/d\theta^2) + 2vbu(du/d\theta)^2].$$

The differential equation (1.32) now becomes:

$$-vb[vbu^2(d^2u/d\theta^2) + 2vbu(du/d\theta)^2] - 2v^2b^2u(du/d\theta)^2 - v^2b^2u^3 - 2Ze^2u^2/\epsilon m = 0$$

which reduces to:

$$d^2u/d\theta^2 + u = -2Ze^2/\epsilon mv^2b^2. \tag{1.33}$$

If the right side of this equation were zero, its solution would be $u = A \sin \theta + B \cos \theta$, where A and B are constants. Since the right side of the equation is a constant for the scattering of any single particle, the solution of Eq. 1.33 is

$$u = A \sin \theta + B \cos \theta - 2Ze^2/\epsilon mv^2b^2. \tag{1.34}$$

The constants A and B can be determined from the boundary conditions of the problem. First, under the initial conditions, as the alpha particle approaches from a large distance, $r \rightarrow \infty$ ($u = 0$), and $\theta = 0$, so $B = 2Ze^2/\epsilon mv^2b^2$. Also under these initial conditions $dr/dt = v$, and, since $dr/dt = -(du/dt)/u^2 = -vb$ $du/d\theta$, $A = 1/b$ when $\theta = 0$, so the solution of Eq. 1.33 is

$$u = 1/r = \sin \theta/b + (2Ze^2/\epsilon mv^2b^2)(\cos \theta - 1). \tag{1.35}$$

Now at the angle of scatter, $\phi = \pi - \theta$, the radial distance r again approaches infinite magnitude, $u = 0$, and for these special conditions

$$(1 - \cos \theta)/\sin \theta = \tan (\theta/2) = \cot (\theta/2) = \epsilon mv^2b/2Ze^2. \tag{1.18}$$

Appendix 4.1   The Rayleigh-Jeans Radiation Law

In developing the theoretical spectral distributions for black-body radiation, it must be remembered that at the time (1900-1910) Rayleigh, Jeans, and Planck were in heated debate in the scientific literature regarding the theoretical basis for the nature of the spectral characteristics of radiation in an enclosure and for the structure of the atom, the nature of particles having atomic dimensions were not understood in the same way that they are now. The electron had been observed but its charge had not yet been determined accurately by Millikan nor had Rutherford's nuclear model of the atom been accepted as yet. Maxwell's theory of electromagnetic radiation had been developed, though, so the treatment of electromagnetic radiation as a wave phenomenon was quite acceptable.

What is *black-body*, or cavity (*hohlraum*) *radiation?* It is simply the radiation inside a cavity or furnace that has been heated to some arbitrarily chosen temperature and has been allowed to reach an equilibrium condition. The spectral characteristics of the radiation are experimentally observed to be a function only of wall temperature. As long as all the walls of the enclosure remain in equilibrium, the amount of radiation in the enclosure remains constant — there is just as much radiation radiated at the walls as is absorbed. Since there is a constancy of radiation in the enclosure, both in intensity and in spectral characteristics, any radiation absorbed at a wall must be reradiated. This is equivalent to having all the radiation incident on a wall reflected from that wall. Rayleigh and Jeans assumed that the radiation that strikes a surface sets an oscillator into motion in the wall, without necessarily specifying the exact nature of the oscillator. Under equilibrium conditions, assuming that each oscillator has its own characteristic frequency, standing waves are established between oscillators of the same frequency in the walls of the furnace, and the oscillators then function continuously. By considering long wavelengths, in which only a small number of complete waves can exist in the distance between the walls, it is seen that, if an oscillator does not function at a frequency capable of producing standing waves, it would be quickly damped. This can perhaps be understood most easily by considering the one-dimensional case. To maintain continuous operation of the oscillator, an electromagnetic wave must, on returning to its starting point, be in phase with the wall oscillator. In any enclosure of measurable dimensions, though, oscillators developing radiations in the visible and near visible parts of the spectrum need shift their frequency by only an extremely small amount to reach another frequency which is also capable of producing standing waves within the enclosure. These frequency intervals are so small that the resulting distribution of radiation as a function of wavelength appears continuous.

A transverse wave, such as the electric field vector of electromagnetic radiation, moving in the direction of the x-coordinate axis, may be described by the cosine function $Y = A \cos \beta(x - vt)$, in which A is the amplitude of the wave, β is for the moment a constant, and v is the velocity with which the wave moves in the x-direction. At any single instant of time the distance between two successive maxima in the wave is one full wavelength, λ. The magnitude of Y must be the same at these two points one full wavelength apart, so $\cos \beta(x + \lambda - vt) = \cos$

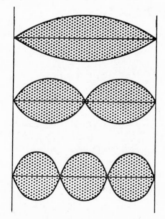

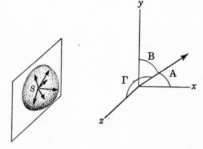

FIG. A.1.   Illustration of one-dimensional standing waves.

FIG. A.2.   From a plane surface radiation is emitted throughout a 2π solid angle. Any single part of this radiation is emitted at angles A, B, and Γ relative to the x-, y-, and z-coordinate directions.

$\beta(x - vt)$, from which it is seen that $\beta\lambda = 2\pi$ and $\beta = 2\pi/\lambda$. Standing waves are established in an enclosure if the distance between reflecting surfaces is an integral number of half wavelengths, such that nodes are established in the wave pattern at the walls and incident and reflected waves reenforce each other at intervals one-half wavelength apart. This is illustrated in Fig. A.1 for the one-dimensional case for which standing waves are established if $a = n\lambda/2$, where a is the distance separating the walls and n is an integer.

In a three-dimensional enclosure radiation is emitted from a wall in any direction in the hemisphere defined by the interior of the enclosure, as illustrated in Fig. A.2. If the x-, y-, and z-coordinate axes are set parallel to the walls of the enclosure, the direction of propagation, k, of radiation is defined by the angles A, B, and Γ it makes with the walls. It can be shown (see Problem 21, Chapter 4) by the geometry of this situation that $\cos^2 A + \cos^2 B + \cos^2 \Gamma = 1$. To establish standing waves in the enclosure, nodes must exist in the wave pattern at all walls.

The three-dimensional standing wave problem is somewhat difficult to visualize. As a result it is probably easiest to discuss the two-dimensional standing wave pattern of Fig. A.3, and draw conclusions regarding the three-

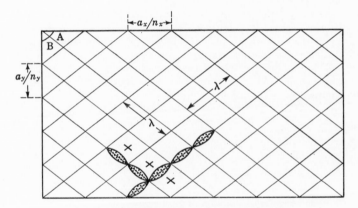

Fig. A.3.   Illustration of two-dimensional standing waves.

dimensional case by analogy with the two-dimensional solution. Note that the standing wave pattern of Fig. A.3 results when the direction of propagation of the radiation makes an angle A with respect to the x-coordinate and an angle B with respect to the y-coordinate. Loops and nodes of the standing waves are separated at intervals $\lambda/2$ apart along the direction of propagation, just as in the one-dimensional case. Lines projected through the nodes between successive loops intersect the walls at separation distances of a/n, where a is the length of the wall and n is the number of intervals along the wall. The interval lengths are related to the wavelength of the radiation by the relations $\cos A = (\lambda/2)/(a_x/n_x)$ and $\cos B = (\lambda/2)/(a_y/n_y)$. For the three-dimensional enclosure the third relationship would be $\cos \Gamma = (\lambda/2)/(a_z/n_z)$.

The shape and size of the enclosure should have negligible effect on the type of radiation existing within an enclosure that is large compared to the wavelength of the radiation. Hence an enclosure with three equal sides, each of length a, should give as valid results as does any other type of enclosure. In this case,

$$\cos^2 A + \cos^2 B + \cos^2 \Gamma = 1 = (n_x{}^2 + n_y{}^2 + n_z{}^2)(\lambda/2)^2/a^2$$

and

$$n_x{}^2 + n_y{}^2 + n_z{}^2 = 4a^2/\lambda^2 = 4a^2\nu^2/c^2.$$

Each possible set of n_x, n_y, and n_z represents one possible standing wave within the enclosure. To determine the number of possible standing waves within the enclosure and the wavelength of each, a space can be constructed in which the three mutually orthogonal n integers are the coordinates. The distance from the origin of any set of n_x, n_y, and n_z is $(n_x{}^2 + n_y{}^2 + n_z{}^2)^{1/2} = 2a\nu/c$. Since the distance from the origin in this space is proportional to the frequency of the radiation, such a space is called a *frequency space*. A sphere in this space, with the origin at its center, encloses all possible radiation frequencies less than a frequency ν, which in magnitude is proportional to the radius of the sphere. Because such a space cannot be physically realized in the macroscopic world of our existence, it is often difficult for us to realize how such a space can exist, or to picture the physical meaning of such a space. A similar type of reasoning was used in the discussion of the Maxwell distribution of speeds, for which we constructed a velocity space in which a length represented a velocity magnitude. In frequency space distance is directly proportional to the magnitude of frequency. Thus, in frequency space, within a sphere of radius $2a\nu/c$ exist all possible frequencies less than ν. All possible combinations of n are given in the positive octant of the sphere, so that the number of different standing waves that can occur can be calculated from the volume of the positive octant of this frequency space, which is (since one set of n's occurs in each unit volume of this space)

$$S(\nu) = (1/8)(4\pi/3)(2a\nu/c)^3 = (4\pi a^3/3c^3)\nu^3. \tag{4.9}$$

The distribution of frequency combinations in the range between ν and $\nu + d\nu$ is given by the differential of the above expression for S and is

$$dS(\nu) = (4\pi a^3/c^3)\nu^2 \, d\nu, \tag{4.10}$$

provided S is a continuous function of ν. The extremely small size of the wavelength of the radiation under consideration makes S sufficiently close to a continuous function of ν so that differentiation is legitimate.

The mean kinetic energy of the oscillators in the walls is $\frac{1}{2}kT$ (see Section 1.3), and, assuming simple harmonic motion for the oscillators, there is also a mean potential energy $\frac{1}{2}kT$, thus the mean energy of the oscillators from which the radiation is derived is kT. Polarization of the oscillators parallel to the surface of the wall of the enclosure must be described by two coordinates. Thus, associated with each possible oscillator, from which radiations may be distributed into the enclosure, is a mean energy $2kT$. Thus the energy in the frequency interval $d\nu$ that is placed into the enclosure by the oscillators is $I_T(\nu)d\nu = (8\pi a^3\nu^2 kT/c^3)d\nu$, and since the volume of the enclosure is a^3, the energy density of the radiation in the enclosure as a function of radiation frequency is

$$I(\nu)d\nu = (8\pi\nu^2 kT/c^3)d\nu. \tag{4.11}$$

This is the *Rayleigh-Jeans law* describing the theoretically calculated energy density as a function of the spectral distribution of black-body radiation.

Appendix 4.2 The Planck Radiation Law

As indicated in the text, the Rayleigh-Jeans radiation distribution law does not correspond to what is actually observed, but agrees with experimental observations only at the longer wavelengths. However, Planck was able to use the Rayleigh-Jeans reasoning and, with an assumption that appeared quite radical at the time (1901), was able to prepare a formulation that agrees very well with experimental observations. His assumption was that the energy of an oscillator in the walls of the enclosure cannot have any value, but can have only the value $nh\nu$, where n is an integer and h is a constant which will henceforth be called *Planck's constant.* This assumption for simple harmonic oscillators can be derived from quantum mechanics, with the slight variation that $W = (n + \frac{1}{2})h\nu$ rather than $nh\nu$ (see Section 6.6), but quantum mechanics was yet several years away. Even though Planck's hypothesis seemed quite arbitrary, it did make theory agree with experimental observations.

Suppose there are N oscillators in the lowest (zero) energy state. Then, by Boltzmann's distribution, Eq. 1.10, there must be $N_1 = N \exp(-h\nu/kT)$ oscillators in the first excited state, $N_2 = N \exp(-2h\nu/kT)$ oscillators in the second excited state, etc., according to Planck's assumptions. The total number of possible states is then

$$\Sigma N = N[1 + \exp(-h\nu/kT) + \exp(-2h\nu/kT) + \dots]$$
$$= 1/[1 - \exp(-h\nu/kT)]. \quad (4.12)$$

The total energy in the system of oscillators is

$$\Sigma W = N[0 + h\nu \exp(-h\nu/kT) + 2h\nu \exp(-2h\nu/kT) + \dots]$$
$$= Nh\nu \exp(-h\nu/kT)/[1 - \exp(-h\nu/kT)]^2, \quad (4.13)$$

and the mean energy per oscillator, $\Sigma W / \Sigma N$, is

$$\Sigma W/\Sigma N = \{Nh\nu \exp(-h\nu/kT)/$$
$$[1 - \exp(-h\nu/kT)]\}/\{N/[1 - \exp(-h\nu/kT)]\}$$
$$= [h\nu \exp(-h\nu/kT)]/[1 - \exp(-h\nu/kT)]$$
$$= h\nu/[\exp(h\nu/kT) - 1] \quad (4.14)$$

If this new mean energy is substituted for kT in the Rayleigh-Jeans equation for the distribution of energy density in the enclosure, the result is

$$I(\nu)d\nu = (8\pi\nu^2/c^3)\{h\nu/[\exp(h\nu/kT) - 1]\}d\nu, \quad (4.15)$$

which is the Planck equation for the radiation density as a function of radiation frequency for black-body radiation, at a temperature T. This agrees, within measurement error, with the experimentally observed distribution. When measured in terms of wavelength, this distribution is, since $|d\nu| = |d(c/\lambda)| = cd\lambda/\lambda^2$,

$$I(\lambda, T)d\lambda = (8\pi d\lambda/\lambda^4)\{h\nu/[\exp(h\nu/kT) - 1]\} \quad (4.1)$$
$$= (8\pi cd\lambda/\lambda^5)\{h/[\exp(hc/kT\lambda) - 1]\}.$$

Appendix 6.1 The Imaginary Exponential

It is sometimes convenient to use a form of the imaginary exponential:

$$C \exp i\theta = C(\cos\theta + i\sin\theta), \quad (6.25)$$

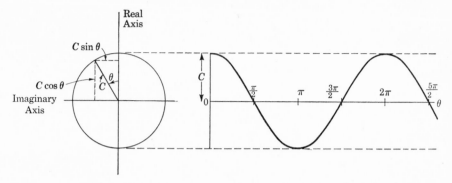

Fɪɢ. A.4.   Illustration of the rotating vector in the real-imaginary plane and the sinusoidal type function produced by the projection of this vector on the real axis.

in expressing mathematically some of the wave properties of physical phenomena. If a plot is made, as in Fig. A.4, in which the real axis is in the y-direction and the imaginary axis in the x-direction, the imaginary exponential simply describes a vector of magnitude C with a directional angle, θ, relative to the y-axis. If the magnitude of θ changes, the direction of the vector changes, but not its magnitude. For constant rate of change of θ, the vector moves with uniform angular velocity, $\omega = d\theta/dt =$ a constant. The projection of the end of the vector on the real axis moves in simple harmonic motion, and a plot of the motion of this projection as a function of time results in a sinusoidal type of wave motion, seen in Fig. A.4.

Now if $\theta = \beta(x - vt) = (2\pi/\lambda)(x - vt) = \beta x - \omega t$, it is the motion of the projection of the vector on its real axis that may be given physical interpretation. The motion of the vector itself may be considered a generating function from which results the sinusoidal motion of the projection as a function either of spatial position or of time. The physical picture of a wave can then be represented mathematically as

$$y = C\{\text{real part of exp } i[\beta(x - vt)]\}$$

$$= C \cos [\beta(x - vt)]. \tag{6.26}$$

For many physical situations concerned with wave motion the imaginary exponential is in common use, since many mathematical manipulations are simpler if exponential functions can be used. Because of this usage, it has become quite customary to omit the expression "real part of" and merely to write $y = C \exp i[\beta(x - vt)]$ as the representation of a wave.

It is important to remember that the imaginary exponential is nothing more than a mathematical expediency, which is useful in obtaining the correct physical interpretation with a minimum of effort. The vector picture of wave phenomena is not physically important in itself, since only its real part can be used to give a physical picture of the wave.

The solution of the time-dependent wave equation, Eq. 6.4, contains both a spatial part, $\exp i\beta x$, and a temporal part, $\exp (\pm i\omega t)$. Since the temporal part is common to all terms of the equation, it has been cancelled from Eq. 6.11, 6.12, and 6.13. If it is assumed that, as in Eq. 6.15, the temporal portion carries the negative sign, then in Eq. 6.13 the first part of the equation represents a wave for which x increases as t increases, a right going wave, and the second part represents a wave for which x decreases as t increases, a left going wave.

The absolute magnitude of the imaginary exponential, Eq. 6.25, is

$$|C \exp i\theta| = C(\cos^2 \theta + \sin^2 \theta)^{1/2} \tag{6.27}$$

so $|y|^2 = C^2(\cos^2 \theta + \sin^2 \theta) = C^2$. This gives the same result as the product yy^*, where y^* is the complex conjugate of y, $y^* = C(\cos \theta - i \sin \theta)$. Because of the physical interpretation that must be made on the results, it has become customary to determine the energy density of an atomic system by using the relationship $|\psi|^2 = \psi\psi^*$.

Appendix 6.2   Solution of the Equations for a Potential Barrier

The probability $|F|^2/|A|^2$ that an electron, or other atomic particle, can penetrate a potential barrier is found from the solution of Eq. 6.14. Multiply Eq. 6.14a by $i\alpha$ and add to Eq. 6.14b; then

$$2i\alpha A \exp (i\alpha a) = C(\beta + i\alpha) \exp (\beta a) - D(\beta - i\alpha) \exp (-\beta a). \tag{6.28}$$

Multiply Eq. 6.14c by β and add to Eq. 6.14d; then

$$2\beta C \exp (\beta b) = F(\beta + i\alpha) \exp (i\alpha b). \tag{6.29}$$

Multiply Eq. 6.14c by β and subtract from Eq. 6.14d; then

$$-2\beta D \exp (-\beta b) = -F(\beta - i\alpha) \exp (i\alpha b). \tag{6.30}$$

From Eqs. 6.18 and 6.19,

$$C = F(\beta + i\alpha) \exp (i\alpha b) \exp (-\beta b)/2\beta, \tag{6.31a}$$

$$D = F(\beta - i\alpha) \exp (i\alpha b) \exp (\beta b)/2\beta. \tag{6.31b}$$

Substituting these results into Eq. 6.17 gives

$$\frac{F}{A} = \frac{4i\alpha\beta \exp [-i\alpha(b - a)]}{(\beta + i\alpha)^2 \exp [-\beta(b - a)] - (\beta - i\alpha)^2 \exp [\beta(b - a)]}$$

$$= \frac{4i\alpha\beta \exp [i\alpha(b - a)]}{(\beta^2 - \alpha^2)\{\exp [-\beta(b - a)] - \exp [\beta(b - a)]\} + 2i\alpha\beta\{\exp [-\beta(b - a)] + \exp [\beta(b - a)]\}}$$

$$= \frac{2i\alpha\beta \exp [i\alpha(b - a)]}{-(\beta^2 - \alpha^2) \sinh [\beta(b - a)] + 2i\alpha\beta \cosh [\beta(b - a)]}$$

To obtain the absolute magnitude of the square of a term containing an imaginary part, multiplication is made with its complex conjugate, so:

$$\frac{|F|^2}{|A|^2} = \frac{4\alpha^2\beta^2}{(\beta^2 - \alpha^2)^2 \sinh^2[\beta(b - a)] + 4\alpha^2\beta^2 \cosh^2 [\beta(b - a)]}.$$

Since $\cosh^2 [\ ] = 1 + \sinh^2 [\ ]$,

$$\frac{|F|^2}{|A|^2} = \frac{1}{1 + \dfrac{(\alpha^2 + \beta^2)^2 \sinh^2 [\beta(b - a)]}{4\alpha^2\beta^2}},$$

which, upon substitution of the magnitude of α and β as given following Eqs. 6.6 and 6.7, leads to Eq. 6.15.

Appendix 7.1 Solution of the Schroedinger Equation for a Hydrogen-like Atom

Because an unperturbed atom is spherically symmetric about its nucleus, the spherical coordinate representation of the Schroedinger equation (as developed in Problems 14 and 15, Chapter 6) is well suited to use in solving for the energy states of a hydrogen-like atom. This equation is then

$$\frac{1}{r^2}\frac{\partial}{\partial r}\left(r^2\frac{\partial\psi}{\partial r}\right) + \frac{1}{r^2\sin\theta}\frac{\partial}{\partial\theta}\left(\sin\theta\frac{\partial\psi}{\partial\theta}\right)$$
$$+ \frac{1}{r^2\sin^2\theta}\frac{\partial^2\psi}{\partial\phi^2} + \frac{8\pi^2 m}{h^2}(W - V)\psi = 0. \quad (7.1a)$$

If the atomic nucleus is considered to be infinitely massive, the electron is all that is in motion in the system; hence it is the electron that assumes the various possible energy states, and the mass m of the equation is the mass of the electron. The potential energy of a system consisting of an electron and an infinitely massive nucleus having charge $+Ze$ is $V = -Ze^2/\epsilon r$.

A solution of Eq. 7.1 can be found if the wave function ψ is assumed to be the product of three separate functions, $\psi(r,\theta,\phi) = R(r)\Theta(\theta)\Phi(\phi)$, in which each of the separate functions depends on only a single independent variable. If Eq. 7.1 is multiplied by $r^2\sin^2\theta/R\Theta\Phi$, and if appropriate substitution of the independent functions R, Θ, and Φ is made, the equation becomes

$$\frac{\sin^2\theta}{R}\frac{d}{dr}\left(r^2\frac{dR}{dr}\right) + \frac{\sin\theta}{\Theta}\frac{d}{d\theta}\left(\sin\theta\frac{d\Theta}{d\theta}\right)$$
$$+ \frac{1}{\Phi}\frac{d^2\Phi}{d\phi^2} + \frac{8\pi^2 mr^2\sin^2\theta}{h^2}\left(W + \frac{Ze^2}{\epsilon r}\right) = 0. \quad (7.11)$$

The third term of Eq. 7.11 is a function of ϕ only and the remainder of the equation is a function of r and θ only. If the term in which ϕ is the independent variable is transposed to the right side of the equation, the two equal sides are composed of functions for which the independent variables are entirely different. The only way this can be true is for each side of the equation to be constant. If this constant is called $-m_l^2$, then*

$$(d^2\Phi/d\phi^2)/\Phi = -m_l^2 \quad \text{and} \quad (d^2\Phi/d\phi^2) + m_l^2\Phi = 0, \quad (7.12)$$

the solution of which is a sinusoidal function of $m_l\phi$, customarily taken as $\Phi = A\exp(im_l\phi)$, where A is a constant. Note that the derivatives in Eqs. 7.11 and 7.12 are total derivatives rather than partial derivatives, since the function now has only a single independent variable. If the value obtained from this solution for $(d^2\Phi/d\phi^2)/\Phi$ is resubstituted into Eq. 7.11 and the whole equation divided by $\sin^2\theta$, it becomes

$$\frac{1}{R}\frac{d}{dR}\left(r^2\frac{dR}{dr}\right) + \frac{8\pi^2 mr^2}{h^2}\left(W + \frac{Ze^2}{\epsilon r}\right) = \frac{m_l^2}{\sin^2\theta} - \frac{1}{\Theta\sin\theta}\frac{d}{d\theta}\left(\sin\theta\frac{d\Theta}{d\theta}\right). \quad (7.13)$$

Now the left side of the equation is a function only of r and the right side a function only of θ, and, since they are equal, each side of the equation must be

*The constant m_l is written in many books simply as m and, in such cases, must not be confused with the electron mass, m, which also appears in the Schroedinger equation for the hydrogen-like atom. Unfortunately general usage has made the letter m the standard symbol for both these quantities.

constant. If this constant is called $l(l+1)$, the two sides of Eq. 7.12 may be written as independent equations which are:

$$\frac{d}{dr}\left(r^2\frac{dR}{dr}\right) + \left[\frac{8\pi^2 mr^2}{h^2}\left(W + \frac{Ze^2}{\epsilon r}\right) - l(l+1)\right]R = 0, \qquad (7.14)$$

$$\frac{1}{\sin\theta}\frac{d}{d\theta}\left(\sin\theta\frac{d\Theta}{d\theta}\right) + \left[l(l+1) - \frac{m_l^2}{\sin^2\theta}\right]\Theta = 0. \qquad (7.15)$$

Both Eqs. 7.14 and 7.15 have the same general form as Eq. 6.20, suggesting that the solution of each of them may very well be some sort of polynomial.

To transform Eq. 7.14 into a form more nearly like Eq. 6.20, a new function, $u = rR$, is defined, such that $dR/dr = d(u/r)/dr = (ru' - u)/r$, and $d(r^2 dR/dr)/dr = ru'' + u' - u' = ru''$. Equation 7.14 then becomes

$$u'' + [(8\pi^2 mW/h^2) + (8\pi^2 mZe^2/\epsilon h^2 r) - l(l+1)/r^2]u = 0. \qquad (7.16)$$

This equation is not exactly like Eq. 6.20 and simply to substitute $u = \sum\limits_{k=0}^{\infty} a_k r^k$, as was done for the most general solution of Eq. 6.20, does not lead to a satisfactory solution. There are, however, in the solution certain multiplicative factors which are dependent on the boundary conditions for r and which can be determined by appropriate reasoning.

To determine the first of these multiplicative factors consider the case that $r \to \infty$, which means that the hydrogen-like atom approaches a condition of ionization ($W \to 0$). In this case Eq. 7.16 becomes $u'' + (8\pi^2 mW/h^2)u = 0$. If $W > 0$, corresponding to the continuum of free energy states, u is a sinusoidal function, commonly expressed as $u = C \exp(i[8\pi^2 mW/h^2]^{1/2}r)$, where C is an arbitrary constant. For the present, though, there is more interest in the case $W < 0$, corresponding for this simpler equation to bound states having energies close to the ionization energy. The solution then is $u = C \exp(\pm[8\pi^2 mW/h^2]^{1/2}r)$. For physically interpretable wave functions (see Section 6.3) only a negatively valued exponent may be retained, for only under these conditions does the exponential function remain finite as $r \to \infty$. Because W is negative for bound states, the positive sign must be retained in the exponent of this equation. If it is assumed that the energies W of the bound electrons correspond to the experimentally observed Bohr levels for a hydrogen-like atom, $W = -2\pi^2 me^4 Z^2/\epsilon^2 n^2 h^2$, the solution of the modified radial function is

$$u = C \exp(-4\pi^2 me^2 Zr/\epsilon nh^2) = C \exp(-\rho),$$

in which $\rho = Zr/na$, and $a = \epsilon h^2/4\pi^2 me^2 = 5.2917 \times 10^{-9}$ cm, the radius of the first Bohr orbit of the hydrogen atom. Thus u contains a factor $\exp(-\rho)$.

If r is now made very small, the term $l(l+1)/r^2$ becomes very large compared to the other terms in the brackets of Eq. 7.16, and this equation becomes $u'' - l(l+1)u/r^2 = 0$, the solutions for which are $u = r^{-l}$ and $u = r^{l+1}$. If l is finite, $r^{-l} \to \infty$ and $r^{l+1} \to 0$ as $r \to 0$, so to be physically interpretable u contains r^{l+1} as a factor, but cannot contain r^{-l}. Thus, since $R = u/r$, the function R contains a factor r^l or ρ^l.

Inclusion in the solution for Eq. 7.14 of these two physically interpretable factors found for the limiting conditions $r \to \infty$ and $r \to 0$, suggests as a solution the radial function $R = C\rho^l L(\rho) \exp(-\rho)$, where $L(\rho)$ is as yet an unspecified function of ρ. Substitution of this expression for R into Eq. 7.14 gives (see Problem 3, Chapter 7):

$$\rho \frac{d^2 L}{d\rho^2} + 2[(l + 1) - \rho] \frac{dL}{d\rho} + 2(n - l - 1)L = 0. \tag{7.17}$$

If the series $L(\rho) = \sum\limits_{k=0}^{\infty} a_k \rho^k$ is substituted into Eq. 7.17, that equation becomes the power series:

$$\sum\limits_{k=0}^{\infty} \rho^k \{a_{k+1}[2(l + 1)(k + 1) + k(k + 1)] + 2a_k(n - l - k - 1)\} = 0, \tag{7.18}$$

from which is obtained the recursion formula:

$$a_{k+1}/a_k = 2(k - n + l + 1)/(k + 2l + 2)(k + 1). \tag{7.19}$$

Just as in the solution of Eq. 6.20, this recursion formula determines a relationship between the coefficients a_{k+1} and a_k in each term of the power series, and results in a factor $(n - l - k - 1)$ in each term. For each term to have a magnitude zero, the quantities in this factor must be related such that $n = l + k + 1$. Because k can be equal only to zero or an integer, $n = l +$ an integer, with the relationship between n and l being such that $n \geq l + 1$.

The solution of Eq. 7.15 found by mathematicians (see, for example, F. S. Woods, *Advanced Calculus*, Ginn and Co., Boston, 2nd Ed., 1934, pp. 268-272) is the associated Legendre polynomial

$$\Theta = BP_l{}^{m_l}(\cos \theta) = B \frac{(\sin \theta)^{|m_l|}}{2^l l!} \left[\frac{d}{d(\cos \theta)} \right]^{l+|m_l|} (\cos^2 \theta - 1)^l \tag{7.20}$$

in which B is a constant. If $|m_l| > l$, $P_l{}^{m_l}(\cos \theta) = 0$, which means that, for a physically interpretable solution, it is necessary that $|m_l| \leq l$.

Thus the wave equation ψ for a hydrogen-like atom is

$$\psi = KR_{nl}(r)P_l{}^{m_l}(\cos \theta) \exp(im_l\phi) \tag{7.1a}$$

in which K is a constant that incorporates the constants of the individual expressions for Θ and Φ.

The solution for Φ has an arbitrary constant A, the solution for Θ a constant B, and the solution for R a constant a_0C. It is customary to normalize these constants, that is, to choose constants such that $\int |\psi|^2 dv = 1$. For the function R normalization means that the constant a_0C must be chosen such that $\int_0^{\infty} |R|^2 r^2 dr = 1$. The magnitude of a_0C for a hydrogen-like atom is then $a_0C = 2(n - l - 1)!^{1/2}Z^{3/2}/(n + l)!^{3/2}n^2$, such that for hydrogen $(Z = 1)$, the radial portion of the wave function, in which r is expressed in units of the Bohr radius, a, is

$$R_{10} = 2 \exp(-r)$$

$$R_{20} = (2)^{-1/2}(1 - r/2) \exp(-r/2)$$

$$R_{21} = (1/2\sqrt{6})r \exp(-r/2)$$

$$R_{30} = (2/3\sqrt{3})(1 - 2r/3 + 2r^2/27) \exp(-r/3)$$

$$R_{31} = (8/27\sqrt{6})r(1 - r/6) \exp(-r/3)$$

$$R_{32} = (4/81\sqrt{30})r^2 \exp(-r/3).$$

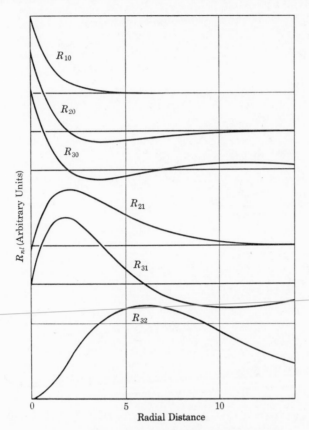

FIG. A.5.   Plots of the radial wave function R_{nl} for selected values of n and l. Radial distances are in units of Bohr radii, defined in caption for Fig. 7.3.

These wave functions are plotted in Fig. A.5 and their normalized probability density distributions $r^2|R|^2$ in Fig. 7.3.

It is usually customary to express the functions Θ and Φ as the normalized spherical harmonic $Y_{lm} = \Theta\Phi$, (note that m of Y_{lm} is really m_l) and in this case normalization covers a unit sphere, so

$$\int_0^\pi \int_0^{2\pi} |Y_{lm}|^2 \sin\theta d\theta d\phi = \int_0^{2\pi} |\Phi|^2 d\phi \int_0^\pi |\Theta|^2 \sin\theta d\theta = 1,$$

and the normalized constants are $A = (2\pi)^{-1/2}$ and $B = [(2l+1)(l-|m_l|)!/2(l+|m_l|)!]^{1/2}$ so the first few spherical harmonics are:

$Y_{00} = (4\pi)^{-1/2}$ 　　　　　　　$Y_{20} = (5/4\pi)^{1/2}(3\cos^2\theta/2 - \tfrac{1}{2})$

$Y_{10} = (3/4\pi)^{1/2}\cos\theta$ 　　　　$Y_{21} = (15/8\pi)^{1/2}\sin\theta\cos\theta\exp(i\phi)$

$Y_{11} = (3/8\pi)^{1/2}\sin\theta\exp(i\phi)$ 　$Y_{22} = (15/32\pi)^{1/2}\sin^2\theta\exp(2i\phi)$

These are used for the plots of the probability density distributions in the $r\theta$ plane of Figs. 7.4 and 7.5.

INDEX